Artificial Intelligence

and the

Human Mind

D1453198

Artificial Intelligence and the Human Mind

A Radical ~~New~~ Old Science of the Human Mind

Part I

B. K.

Baldur Press
First Edition
For additional information and
updated bibliography & endnotes,
visit: www.AiAndHumanMind.org

An urgent call to action for human minds

Artificial Intelligence

and the

Human Mind

Contents

Artificial Intelligence

and the

Human Mind

There are more things in Heauen and Earth, Horatio,
Then are dream't of in our Philosophy.

William Shakespeare,
Hamlet (First Folio)

Foreword

The field of artificial intelligence is experiencing dazzling growth, and AI is poised to become one of the most consequential technologies humanity has ever developed. Because AI can demonstrate intelligent behavior, it is entering the domain where human beings reigned supreme until recently. Humanity is reacting with a mix of enthusiasm and fear. AI promises seem boundless, but its anticipated dangers are frightening. The big question is whether our human intelligence can contain and align AI so that it can be beneficial for humanity. A great riddle, also an immense opportunity, are hidden in this question. We know very little about the human intelligence and mind. Our modern worldview, deeply rooted in the scientific way of thinking, does not yet provide many insights regarding the nature of human intelligence, or the nature of the human mind.

Reasoning mind vs. raw intelligence

The human mind is much more than raw intelligence, it has the capacity to reason. Scientifically speaking, we don't exactly know what either intelligence or reason is, and where or how they originate. However, every healthy human being easily recognizes a reasoning mind, and we refer to our sophisticated reasoning faculty — unmatched by anything we know in nature or technology — by using the humble term "common sense." Reasoning human minds can demonstrate rational behavior, the results of which we see in the greatness of human culture and civilization. However, many disciplines warn us that we humans are also driven by powerful irrational forces hiding in our minds, which are destructive and make the lives of many in human society miserable: we are told that human "reason is no match for passion" (Hume), that the human self is "not even master in its own home" (Freud) and also that "out of the crooked timber of humanity no straight thing was ever made" (Kant).

It is universally acknowledged that effective global cooperation is necessary to tame dangerous aspects of AI, but this necessity is proving to be a bar set too high for present-day humanity. Ideas presented in this book acknowledge such a perspective and argue that — if no progress is made toward a deeper understanding of what the individual human mind is, and of its ability to willingly harness its irrational forces of raw self-interest — AI technology will enable a dangerous tempest humanity may not be able to contain. The constellation of irrational forces in human beings is such that, on the whole, humans are way too selfish, glaringly unwilling to cooperate on a global scale, and utterly unprepared for impending global challenges. Furthermore, AI is not the only explosive danger taking shape on the horizon of history whose overcoming requires global cooperation. The ongoing climate transformation, propelled by human irrational behaviors, is starting to decimate ecosystems, and is already making some parts of the planet uninhabitable. In addition to this, rampant societal inequalities, societal polarizations, and the rise of anti-democratic nationalism worldwide are all threatening the institutions of civilized society. Taken together, these dangers are poised to cause an unprecedented setback to human civilization commencing in the lifetimes of many of us.

If we assume that this is indeed the case and that the possibility for effective global cooperation depends on it, we will likely want to ponder what does it actually mean "to make progress in the deeper understanding of the individual human mind and its ability to willingly harness its irrational forces?" This work argues that human minds should not be viewed statically, but rather as very potent developing entities, yearning to learn and grow. Human minds can develop reason that can be match for their "passions," that can indeed be the sovereign "in its own home," and that can enable them to realize the hidden unifying links with the rest of humankind. This kind of understanding and such development of individual human minds may sound like a tall order and a radical transformation. However, humanity has a solid head start in this endeavor, thousands of years in fact. But, before this endeavor can be reinvigorated and its potency realized, several important obstacles must be cleared.

Modern worldview based on science

Starting with the Renaissance and the Age of Reason (Age of Enlightenment), humanity has embarked on an unprecedented transformative journey and created a modern worldview based on reason. This worldview has endowed us with modern science, advanced technology, and new impulses in art and philosophy. These advancements have brought about significant liberation and enhanced the dignity of many individual human beings. If we wanted to capture the essence of this worldview in one word, we would likely choose the word science. Even if the first roots of science could arguably be traced to the birth of philosophy and increased levels of trust in free human thought more than two millennia ago, it was in the 16th and 17th centuries that science took the form we recognize today. Scientific facts, obtained by following the scientific method, represent today the trusted beacons humanity uses as guidance in almost all matters. Science has also been the main instrument used to purge many irrational beliefs and harmful traditions. However, some irrationality survived the purge, evident from the destructive human behavior. Most of it disguised itself in new kinds of beliefs, and some of our most resilient irrational beliefs are the ones that dress in science's clothing. They are also among the most damaging because we trust in them unreservedly, being deceived that they are scientific facts. Our pursuit of a deeper understanding of the human mind, which would enable us to harness better the irrational forces we harbor, requires that we expose and dissolve several beliefs of this kind. Such a pursuit also requires that we remain loyal to reason and the scientific method. This process will not be easy, as these beliefs have found their place inside many of today's scientific establishments. They seem to have thus metamorphosed into almost imperceptible habits of thinking, and any questioning thoughts about their validity stand the risk of being self-censored. We all cling to our beliefs and deep-seated habits. These beliefs are entrenched in a similar way any religious dogma is. Still, our pursuit of a deeper understanding of the human mind inevitably leads through the gate that must expose some of our beliefs as irrational and misleading. Three irrational beliefs, which all took shape in the last 150 years or so, are of particular concern here, and all three are related to the idea of *human agency* or *human self*, which has been a battleground of philosophy for millennia, and which is currently unjustifiably closeted away and eliminated from most of our scientific considerations.

Three pernicious beliefs dressed in the science's clothing

The first belief concerning us here posits that human beings are purposeless deterministic mechanisms of sorts (the terms "robots" and "survival machines" have also been used). Each of us is seen as only a group of physical particles swirling around in an organized manner somehow. It is also believed that the human mind (with its capacities for objective thinking, feeling, intentional will, and consciousness) is somehow instantiated when these particles, driven by certain deterministic forces, move in the tissues of the human brain. Many scientists today indeed consider human beings to be, in principle, as deterministic as thermostats, without any authentic agency, intentions, and purposes. Our direct and ever-present experiences, which are a powerful testament to the contrary, are assumed to be some sort of (yet unexplained) illusion. Free will is also considered to be some kind of an illusion. This model of our reality (and of what human beings are) can be regarded as mainstream in science today. Instead of humbly accepting the limits of what we know scientifically, and not superimposing our beliefs onto reality, we impatiently chose to put together a scientific model of sorts and zealously believe in it as if it were some sort of a scientific fact, akin to an infant trying to touch the moon.

After it was scientifically established that living beings, including humans, have been developing by means of evolution, another belief was enshrined, putting forward an assumption that evolution occurs solely through purposeless random-chance mutations and the selection of our genes. This belief spawned two harmful prejudices, that of evolution being ruthless "survival of the fittest" (by Spencer) and that of "selfish gene" (by Dawkins) in which it is proclaimed that human beings are "robots", "survival machines," and that "pure, disinterested altruism … has no place in nature" (truth be told, Dawkins states that he would be open to "discuss ways of deliberately cultivating and nurturing pure, disinterested altruism.") These prejudices have dominated the discourse about human evolution since their inception. The belief that purposeless random-chance mutations and selection are the only drivers of human evolution reigns supreme in our scientific establishments as if a spell was put on them. (As can be seen in his *On The Origin of Species*, even Darwin himself felt that he needed to leave the door open for other alternatives, as he famously characterized his proposal of natural selection as "not exclusive means of modification" in the evolutionary process.) It didn't help that as far back as 1986, Karl Popper, who is regarded as one of the greatest philosophers of science of the 20th century, tried to dissolve such belief by openly calling for "a new interpretation of Darwinism" and for recognition "that living organisms are active agents."

One possible way to dispel this belief is to simply examine the findings of science over the last several decades. Even if we seem unwilling to talk much about it, we have gathered an overwhelming amount of evidence to counter this belief, most notably through experiments in developmental bioelectricity and epigenetics. For example, among other things packed into this belief, it is also assumed that genes represent the only mechanism for the inheritance of traits. However, the experiments in developmental bioelectricity challenge the assumption that genes alone specify the complex features of bodily anatomy and how it unfolds from a single cell into a whole organism. Experiments demonstrate that these capabilities actually rely on the superimposed bioelectrical pattern through which the anatomical features are affected, and through which we can observe the "agential" behavior, with "autonomy" and "agenda." There are many mere assumptions, prejudices really, packed into the belief in evolution without agency, and very little (and only indirect, like in evo-devo research) scientific evidence to back it up. There is some progress in dissolving this belief, but scientific establishments and science textbooks are very slow (with noteworthy exceptions!) to accept new facts. Therefore, the public narrative remains backward, still powerfully dominated by the prejudice of non-agentive interpretations of evolution. This topic will weigh heavily in our discussions. Despite our own everyday experiences of it, something about intentional agency simply seems to scare many scientists; at least one (rather candid) Nobel laureate even stated that it is too "spooky" to talk about agency in science, whatever that means. But it is a hard fact — and it should be considered an important scientific data point — that every healthy human being experiences themselves as an active agent, as a self, with will, purposes, and intentions, every waking hour of every day.

Because we can't easily explain it, we indeed seem to be frightened at the thought that human agency is real and that our minds are expressions of our inherent agentive selves. Therefore, many scientists and philosophers of science feverishly seek to close off and eliminate such thoughts at any cost, without any regard to the scientific method. Hence the third belief, that the human self itself is an "illusion" or "hallucination" of sorts (of course, we have no idea how that could possibly work.) The narrative of this "eliminative materialism" also seems entrenched in many scientific establishments, even if it, too, is a mere assumption not grounded in any scientific fact.

Any notion of concepts like self, mind, consciousness, or agency naturally invokes the age-old concept of mind-body dualism. This work does not propose any immediate solution to it, but it deems it necessary to expose the irrational positions of the modern physicalist philosophy of science, which seeks to eliminate the fundamentally important concept of mind by wishfully thinking it into a derivative or "emergent property" of what is referred to as the physical body. Neither reason nor science nor our direct experiences point in that direction. These three beliefs cannot even be fought on scientific grounds as we didn't arrive at them via scientific experiments or via any other aspect of the scientific method, they are mere assumptions, reflections of a certain (physicalist) belief system.

In reality, humans cannot be considered deterministic mechanisms, developing solely via random-chance mutations and selection, whose selves are only illusions. The human mind must be considered fundamental if we are to make any further progress as human beings. We do have notable examples of trailblazing scientists who remained committed to the path that the scientific method opened in front of them, and who indeed courageously knocked on the door they arrived at. For example, the three founders of modern physics said the following about the mind and consciousness:

> "I regard consciousness as fundamental ... I regard matter as derivative from consciousness. We cannot get behind consciousness. Everything that we talk about, everything that we regard as existing, postulates consciousness" and: "the individual self ... [is] a whole world, embracing all our emotional life, our will, and our thought."
>
> Max Planck

"I regard consciousness and matter as different aspects of one and the same thing."

Louis de Broglie

"The material universe and consciousness are made out of the same stuff" and "from all we have learnt about the structure of living matter, we must be prepared to find it working in a manner that cannot be reduced to the ordinary laws of physics. ... The unfolding of events in the life cycle of an organism exhibits an admirable regularity and orderliness, unrivalled by anything we meet with in inanimate matter. ... We must be prepared to find a new type of physical law prevailing in it. Or are we to term it a non-physical, not to say a super-physical, law?"

Erwin Schrödinger

These notions are explored further in the material in this book.

We need the 21st-century Humanist Renaissance accomplished by human reason

If we manage to dispose of these "crude materialistic" beliefs (as Nobel laureate Francis Crick called them, even if he accepted them) that human beings are agentless deterministic mechanisms, that are randomly developed and selected, and whose essential selves are illusions of sorts, we can finally move on with our quest for methods and disciplines appropriate for the scientific research in the domains of the mind. We are in need of deeper insights into the nature of our minds, and we also need methods for effective mind cultivation and development. This paradigm must open if we are to move from the dangerous position we brought ourselves into while harboring powerful irrational forces in our minds. Threatening dangers are approaching humanity and it is already evident that existential despair is on the rise among human beings. We need to wake up and usher in a new era of humanism, we indeed need a new 21st-century Renaissance if we are to continue as a civilized society.

It was mentioned earlier that humanity has a solid head start in this endeavor, thousands of years in fact, and that we can choose to reinvigorate it. From time immemorial, various disciplines for the cultivation of the human mind have been in existence. Such disciplines view the reality of the mind as foundational and provide insights into the intimate inner aspects of human nature and methods for their cultivation and transformation. Their history has been quiet and somewhat veiled. At the onset of the Age of Reason, these disciplines retreated into the background. In many ways, it was Galileo who helped pave the way for this process by leaving the phenomena of the mind outside of the domain of "natural philosophy" (natural science), thus reducing it solely to phenomena that could be captured "in the language of mathematics" (a.k.a. natural or physical phenomena). This enabled the rise of the philosophy of empiricism that recognizes only those experiences that enter our reasoning minds via the portal of our physical senses. Such development opened the doors for the creation of natural science (even if it had to be positivist and reductionist) as an objective discipline that can be universally understood. Human reason flourished, even if its domain of inquiry was significantly reduced. However, neglecting the phenomena of the mind — through which all meanings and purposes manifest — could only be a temporary detour before the existential dread started to enter the human experience. The signs are now palpable that we might be ready to open our minds again for the more direct experiences of mental nature (we never entirely relinquished this capacity, it was always there to a certain degree in our abstract thinking, for example in mathematics and philosophy). In the meantime, during the liberating Age of Reason detour, our reasoning minds have strengthened, and our objective thinking can now be trusted with comprehending complex phenomena, unimaginable to us beforehand.

Human reason is a rather ignored phenomenon, even if it is the most exquisite and precious entity known to humankind. Our reasoning capacity seems completely inconspicuous and transparent to us, it functions seamlessly in the background, most of the time we are not even paying attention to its activity, and most healthy human beings simply assume its presence. We just label it "common sense" and leave the unfathomable depths of its complexity and profundity unexamined. Reason is "common" only among human beings, we observe it in no other thing or creature known to us, natural or artificial. Human reason is qualitatively so unique that nothing else even comes close to it. We also have an immense trust in it. Even if we are aware that this capacity of ours can surprise us with irrational notions and beliefs (which we mitigate with disciplines like science and independent journalism), we entrust our lives fully to it. For example, we are so sure in our own thinking — if we recognize that our starting premises can be trusted (i.e. we are not lied to, misinformed, or sick) — that we fully entrust our lives and things we value to our thinking processes daily. We trust in the reasoning capacity of other humans too (even if they are driving the car or the airplane we are in.) Our reason is indeed the trusted command-and-control center for anything we plan and do.

The origin of trust in human reason

If we reflect on it, it is self-evident that the most important and indispensable scientific instrument used in every branch of science — without exceptions — is the human mind with its capacity for reason (including reason's capacity for objective thinking.) Science is not possible without reasoning human minds. Far from being an illusion, reason is our superpower. It is the most exquisite and powerful thing on this planet. If we accept this premise, and if we then focus our attention on the human reason itself, and on the levels of trustworthiness of the reason, we can, in broad strokes, follow the genealogy of science in a somewhat unusual, but rather essential, way. This is an important exercise for our deliberations here.

Considered in such a way, science as we know it indeed surfaced shortly before the Age of Reason when the individual human reason was recognized as a trustworthy and sovereign agent and placed above traditions and irrational beliefs. Looking at one step before that, we see that both the Scientific Revolution and the Age of Reason were sparked by the liberating impulse of the Renaissance around the 15th century. "Rebirth" is another name for the Renaissance because in many ways it represents the rebirth of the philosophy of classical antiquity (marked, among other events, by the re-establishment of the Platonic Academy in Florence by a cohort of Neoplatonists around Marsilio Ficino and Pico della Mirandola, who published the *Oration on the Dignity of Man*, often dubbed the "Manifesto of the Renaissance.") Why is the reappearance of Platonic wisdom — after about two millennia — significant here? Platonic doctrine is widely recognized as foundational for Western culture because of its recognition that human reason can be trustworthy and capable of comprehending *truth* and *wisdom* (and increasingly so if it undergoes cultivation and development.) Philosopher Alfred North Whitehead famously remarked that the entirety of Western philosophical tradition is but "a series of footnotes to Plato." Furthermore, if we look one more step back, it is also recognized that Platonic (and Neoplatonic) wisdom has its roots in the circles around Pythagoras and the mystical community he founded about 2,600 years ago. It is commonly assumed that it was Pythagoras who first used the term "philosopher", or "lover of wisdom," or even more literally "one who cultivates intimate and affectionate receptivity for wisdom." (Bertrand Russell remarked in his *A History of Western Philosophy* that Pythagoras "was intellectually one of the most important men that ever lived" and that he does not know of anybody "who has been as influential as [Pythagoras] was in the sphere of thought.") Neither Pythagoras nor the early members of his school and mystical community left behind written documents (their teachings were closely guarded secrets, and members took vows of silence.) However, we know enough from indirect sources to ascertain that the true birth of philosophy — and thus of the fundamental trust in human reason and its capacity to be further cultivated in "receptivity for wisdom" — were very likely conceived there and then. And already at that foundational stage, the paramount importance of cultivating the human mind's capacity for objective thinking was considered essential: for example, both Pythagoras and Plato requested their students to engage in mathematics as their first step in ennobling their capacity to reason (the famous phrase "Let no one ignorant of geometry enter here" was purportedly inscribed at the entrance to Platonic Academy).

Therefore, in the first approximation, if we follow the developmental path of human reason as we know it today, we can draw a straight line from the time when Pythagoras was able to develop intimate and affectionate receptivity for wisdom to Platonic Academy and Plato's written (and unwritten) doctrines one century later, to Neoplatonists (most prominently exemplified in Plotinus and the philosophical circle around him in the 3rd century), to the Renaissance, to the Age of Reason, and finally to the pursuit of science in modern times. In many ways, when we do science, we are continuing a long line of endeavors of the human reasoning minds that started in the school of Pythagoras more than two millennia ago. Even if simplified (and guilty of omission of many significant milestones that happened during the history of science), this first approximation of the genealogy of science may help us in our attempts to reflect on the importance of a deeper understanding of our minds. It may also help us pursue methods that will increase our abilities to willingly cultivate them and harness their irrational aspects.

It can therefore be argued that the ability of individual human reason to terminate its complete reliance on irrational beliefs and traditions, and to reliably perform inquiries about the world by means of thinking, was forged when the discipline of philosophy was born. This achievement of reason and its thinking capacity is not a small accomplishment, and pure empiricists among us are missing the broader context: observation via senses is only half the story – how our reasoning minds weave such observations into a meaningful representation of reality is still a big mystery. AI with such reasoning capacity (as computer scientist Yann LeCun says, "AI with common sense") is not within reach of any of our current efforts and disciplines. Cognitive scientists appreciate the depth of this mystery, Alison Gopnik recognizes that "one of the deepest and most ancient problems in philosophy is what we might call the problem of knowledge" and "there seems to be an unbridgeable gap between our abstract, complex, highly structured knowledge of the world, and the concrete, limited, and confused information provided by our senses." Noam Chomsky remarked that when such questions of "reason, or choice of action, when those questions arise, human science is at a loss, it has nothing to say about them, ... these questions remain in the obscurity in which they were in classical antiquity."

How did pioneering philosophers advance human reason? How can we?

Considering all this, the question naturally arises: what did the founding philosophers like Pythagoras, Plato, and Plotinus actually do? What is the process that enabled them to advance the individual human reason so that it can diminish the dominant irrational aspects and successfully cultivate "intimate and affectionate receptivity for wisdom." And also, why were they so secretive and selective about their teachings? Pythagoras's school and mystical community guarded their teachings so effectively that history has no direct knowledge about their methods. About a century later, in his *Seventh Epistle*, Plato said that his published (written) works were only meant to help his readers approach the more profound "knowledge of the subjects to which I devote myself" and about which "I have composed no work ... for there is no way of putting it in words like other studies" because "acquaintance with it must come rather after a long period of attendance on instruction in the subject itself, and communion therewith, when suddenly, like a blaze kindled by a leaping spark, it is generated in the soul and at once becomes self-sustaining." It appears that by the time Plotinus started to teach, about six centuries after Plato, veils began to lift somewhat. His Neoplatonic teaching is accessible to us in his *Enneads*, where he provides substantially more details regarding the methods he used to attain his philosophical and mystical insights. Especially noteworthy are insights (both his and Plato's) about the inherent connection between ethics and knowledge. This is also highlighted by Plotinus's critique of Gnostics — contemporaneous religious adherents who sought mystical insights and utilized methods somewhat related to his — for not grounding enough their quest for knowledge in rigorous reasoning and ethical living. It is in this Neoplatonic form that philosophy most directly influenced and sparked the Renaissance in the 15ᵗʰ century, leading to the Age of Reason and the development of science as we know it today.

The critical question for our time is whether we could gain something today by re-examining and studying the methods used by the founding figures of philosophy. The sole concern of this ancient wisdom and its disciplines revolves around the intimate processes in human minds. Philosophy was practiced in a way that is radically different from how we utilize it today. During Plato's time, philosophers *practiced* philosophy, they didn't just *talk* or *write* about it. Founding philosophers didn't consider their discipline to be about purely academic and theoretical musings, philosophy was understood as an intimate inner process of virtue development, as something one *does*. Freely chosen ethical living is something one does, not something one only analyzes and talks about. Such ethical life was deemed a necessary precondition to rise to higher levels of knowledge. For these purposes, pioneering philosophers developed, among other methods, *spiritual exercises* (a term used by the renowned philosopher of classical antiquity Pierre Hadot, e.g., in his work *Philosophy as a Way of Life*.) At its inception, philosophy was not thought of as a spectator sport.

Humanity is in great need, we are slowly realizing it, and the ancient wisdom indeed has words of counsel for us. Because its disciplines are centered around the intimate processes in human minds, such disciplines always start with the intense cultivation of the inner life of thoughts and feelings, and with acknowledgment of their vital importance. The origins and movements of our thoughts and feelings are elusive to us, but they are not some shadow-like contraptions that are passing accidentally through our minds, they are in fact fundamental to our lives and our reality. Thoughts and feelings are real forces behind every action human beings will and perform. Because their origins are hidden from an untrained mind, they are not always under the control of our reason. In other words, they can be irrational and thus can make us unfree, or expressed in Buddha's famous words, such thoughts and feelings cause "greed, hatred and delusion." It is for this reason that Schopenhauer stated that "a man can do what he wants, but not want what he wants." In line with Platonic wisdom, it is argued in this book that raw self-interest, which is universally recognized as selfish, egotistic, and destructive, is always an effect of irrational aspects of our mind. As such, raw self-interest reflects the absence of rational organizing forces within the individual human mind. A marker for the presence of rational organizing forces in mind is what Plato referred to as the virtue of *justice*. In this view justice is not something imposed from outside, it is an inner quality within the human mind. In the Platonic view, the absence of justice is a form of sickness. Plato recognized that the attainment of the virtue of justice is an essential prerequisite for an individual human being to attain and retain a healthy life (mental and physical), and it is also essential for the long-term existence of a healthy society. From this point of view, unless we acknowledge the power of our own thoughts and feelings, and unless we learn how to cultivate them (this is where the true battlefield is!), dark clouds above humanity are all but sure to continue to gather.

How would we go about it if we decided to open the door to ancient wisdom in our hearts again? Most importantly: this cannot happen as a direct result of any proclamations, activism, collectivist actions, policies, laws, peer pressures or the like. This is an intimate process that can only happen as a completely free deed at the level of the individual human mind. Pressures from the outside can only be misguided. Furthermore, it will be argued here that for people steeped in the modern Western mindset permeated by the scientific way of thinking, the natural port of entry would most likely be methods of inner contemplative training and meditation based on the Platonic, Neoplatonic, and related doctrines (including their unwritten aspects.)

Long history of *Philosophia Perennis*

It should be recognized that these methods didn't develop in a vacuum, and — even though we don't know details about historical connections and influences — they obviously share many tenets and practical wisdom with other ancient disciplines devoted to mind cultivation. They can be all gathered under the title of *Philosophia Perennis*, a term coined by Leibnitz to refer to a timeless wisdom that transcends all doctrines and cultural contexts, focusing on fundamental principles that are universally true. Therefore it should be noted that the above-mentioned Western-based methods can be seen as consistent with and, in many aspects, closely related to many Eastern traditions like Buddhism, the ancient Hindu wisdom (as expressed in the Vedas, Upanishads, in Patanjali's Yoga Sutras, and in related narratives like the Bhagavad Gita), Tao Te Ching (of the Chinese Taoist philosophy), Sufi tradition (prominently exemplified by the poet Rumi at the end of the Islamic Golden Age), and also with other Western traditions like Christian Mysticism, Kabbalah, and others. An insightful and informative guide through many of these disciplines, relevant figures, and methods associated with the cultivation of intimate processes of the human mind can be found in Aldous Huxley's *The Perennial Philosophy*. In it, he also articulates why we (now urgently) need this wisdom: "Our present economic, social and international arrangements are based, in large measure, upon organized *lovelessness*" and "in all the historic formulations of the Perennial Philosophy it is axiomatic that ... at least a minority of contemplatives is necessary for the well-being of any society."

In the hope that this foreword at least partially succeeded in setting the stage for our exploration of artificial intelligence and of the reasoning human mind, we now turn our full attention to it. The following chapter outline provides a brief overview of the material. The chapters are purposefully ordered to facilitate the narrative; they build upon each other and together tell the story. I expect that readers who read all chapters, in the order they are presented, will get the most out of the material.

Book overview

Part I

Chapter one, ***Building the Foundation: Why is the Human Mind Special?*** is the introductory chapter that lays out several important assumptions and fundamental positions for the conversation about the human mind. The emergence of artificial intelligence is considered an urgent call to deepen our understanding of human intelligence and the human mind. The influence of dominant worldviews on human reason is deliberated. Forces at work in the individual human reason and the driving forces behind ethical behavior are contemplated. The connecting links between individual freedom, the intentional cultivation of human reason, and ethics are explored in relation to ancient Platonic wisdom and its methods for disciplining the human mind. This chapter serves as a preparation for the material that follows, and it also makes several important forays into the key subjects.

Chapter two, ***Science of Mind, Its Successes and Struggles***, addresses several important ideas underpinning our current scientific paradigm, exploring its successes, potential prejudices, and blind spots in the quest to understand the human mind. It examines the impact and cost to human society of the prevalent physicalist belief system. Despite being unproven, this belief system, often masquerading as scientifically validated, promotes a crude reductionist view of human existence, and contributes to rising levels of suffering and existential despair in humanity. The physicalist belief system compels human beings to settle for the false notion — based on outdated science — that we are all mere collections of physical particles, adrift in cosmic dust, each of us merely a thing among things, believing that our development is solely due to the evolutionary process best understood as "survival of the fittest." Contemporary scientific results debunking these pernicious physicalist beliefs are presented. The chapter concludes with a discussion about the essential role of the human reasoning mind as a scientific instrument in every scientific endeavor.

Chapter three, **Technology and Artificial Intelligence in the 21ˢᵗ Century**, begins with an exploration of the role that 21st-century technology plays in human lives. It then considers several aspects of AI, including its recent accomplishments. Following this, the chapter transitions into a detailed discussion about the promises, limitations, and dangers associated with AI technology. It aims to point out that most dangers related to AI (eight are considered) do not stem from AI itself, but rather from humans and how we are likely to use AI. The real danger lies in the dominance of untamed raw self-interest in human minds, leading to the potential misuse of AI to everyone's detriment.

Chapter four, **Human Self as Gleaned Through the Lens of Science**, presents a brief overview of our current understanding of the human self and agency, as it can be gleaned from the contemporary scientific perspective. It examines the uniqueness of the scientific context surrounding theories of the human mind and related disciplines. The chapter then explores models of the mind and several important insights gained from infant research, attachment theory, and contemporary psychoanalytic and psychodynamic theories. The concept of *potential space*, as introduced by Donald Winnicott, is contemplated as a "playground" of the human self. A practical example of these theories in action is provided through an examination of child psychotherapy, as presented in Selma Fraiberg's seminal paper, *Ghosts in the Nursery*.

Part II

(in progress, not published in the first edition)

Chapter five, **Depths of the Human Mind**, introduces ideas about the human mind rooted in ancient wisdom and theories of the mind. This chapter discusses how sages of old preserved their wisdom through stories, myths, and legends, using mental images encapsulated within these narratives to ensure the transmission of their insights, sometimes for thousands of years. We will use the example of the *Breaking of the Vessels* story from Jewish mysticism to elucidate some important aspects. We then turn to sages of classical antiquity to ponder their insights about the human mind and the methods they used (Plato, the Academy he founded, his so-called *unwritten doctrines*, and Neoplatonists take center stage here). We consider Plato's notion of *dialectic* in its fullest meaning, as a method for spiritual ascent. The chapter then proceeds to present a conceptualization — appropriate for our purposes — of self, agency, emotions, intelligence, and will. Equipped with these concepts, we seek to apply them to a discussion about artificial vs. human intelligence. The notion of sentience in AI is also addressed. We then turn eastward, and the Buddhist notion of non-self (Anattā/Anātman) and the concept of Atman=Brahman from the ancient Hindu scriptures are considered. Finally, some important hints from the research on psychedelics are also presented.

Chapter six, **Human Mind and Relationships**, further develops the themes from chapter four and addresses a topic essential to our humanity: human relationships. Why, exactly, should we care for each other? What constitutes relationships among human beings? What is the spiritual meaning and consequences of human relationality? What happens when we can't relate, especially when very young children are deprived of nurturing relationships? This chapter also examines how the infiltration of technology into our relationships — in the form of social networks, AI companions, and AI romantic partners — brings some benefits but also enormous risks for humanity. Developing emotions for AI machinery has its own set of unique perils, which I try to address here. With these thoughts about human relationality as a backdrop, and to the extent that I am in a position to discuss it, the chapter attempts to identify the necessary prerequisites for modern human beings to live together in a civilized world. Finally, a necessity for the *economy of care* is presented.

Chapter seven, **A Radical ~~New~~ Old Approach to the Human Mind, From the Inside**, addresses the practical methods and the intimate process of cultivating the individual human mind from several angles. It provides a cursory overview of the long history of disciplining and training the human mind in meditative practices from time immemorial. First the Buddhist and then the Western meditative practice, informed by personal experience, are described in detail. Finally, the idea of a worldview rooted in liberated ethical intuitions is presented.

Chapter eight, **Beings of Freedom and Love, Stuck in a Limbo** provides some final thoughts.

B.K.

January, 2024

PART I

1 Building the Foundation: Why is the Human Mind Special?

Ready or not, AI is Coming

Artificial Intelligence technology is experiencing a precipitous advance. Despite initial shortcomings and problems,[1] this development has the potential to become a watershed moment, a paradigm shift for human society, possibly of the kind the Industrial Revolution brought us, likely even much more potent.[2] Until recently, it was widely believed that general intelligence[3] is a uniquely human capacity, but it is obvious now, with the advent of more advanced AI, that machines can demonstrate intelligent behavior in several domains. It should be recognized that AI machinery presently does this by parasitically leaning on the siphoned aggregate of human intelligence,[4] but nonetheless, this development raises a slew of burning questions. Will AI benefit or harm humanity? Could it take away livelihoods for many, polarize us further, replace us in the long run? Could it create new and worthy opportunities for humans, usher in an era of prosperity? Will AI become sentient, conscious? Are AI partner and companion relationships good for us? What is intelligence anyway, and what role does it play? What is the human mind?

Epochal Opportunity?

At the same time, this pivotal moment also represents an epochal opportunity. This opportunity may not be obvious, and in some ways, it has little to do with AI directly. It is about human minds and what we know about them. Because we don't have a good understanding of what human minds are, we are easily confused about what AI is, and the line between the human mind and AI can appear blurred to us. This moment is beckoning us to find ways to profoundly deepen our understanding of the human mind and human nature, of what it means to be a human being, and through that process to align AI and the human species in a beneficial way. This book puts forward an argument that in order to make AI successfully aligned with us, it is necessary to understand better and recognize who we are. It is also necessary to dare and thread some new and potentially unexpected paths while pursuing that goal.

Why do we need new paths? AI technology is in some ways still nascent, but it is rapidly gaining strength. It is already proving to be very disruptive, and we are not currently proving ourselves capable of managing this. Not even close. AI technology leaders are literally begging to be regulated,[5] which is unheard of, and many among them are even contemplating the chances of human extinction due to AI.[6] However, any regulation, containment,[7] or responsible use of a powerful tool like AI would *require effective global cooperation*. This is proving to be a bar set too high for present-day humanity. Any objective observer of the situation on our planet would have to conclude that members of the human species — in their present state — are way too selfish, glaringly unwilling to cooperate on a global scale, and utterly unprepared for impending global challenges.

There are many levels on which one could analyze why we have this defect, some of them being political, sociological, and psychological. Based on age-old insights — articulated already during the time of classical antiquity — we will seek here to acknowledge, revive, and promote the argument that at the root of this vice lies our human characterological predisposition to be overly self-interested. In some ways, this is obvious to us, but we don't seem to be able to find good ways to grow out of it. It has been recognized that, to a great degree, we all identify, think, and feel about ourselves in a self-interested way. And it is often claimed that this is just how human nature is and that we likely can't grow out of it.[8] This claim can and must be challenged. Our overly narrow self-interested nature is the true battlefield of our time. It is precisely this aspect of our nature that enables us to dehumanize our fellow humans, to see them as objects, numbers, unimportant, uninteresting, not worthy of equality of opportunity, and not deserving of our time, effort, shared experience, or care. Our self-interested nature urges us to insulate ourselves, to experience ourselves confined inside the boundary of our body, our home, our tribe, our nation, and to experience everything and everybody outside this boundary as not belonging, as others, as something else. If we don't overcome it to a sufficient degree, and balance it with our altruistic tendencies, we will not be able to deal with a host of cataclysmic challenges already coming our way, AI technology being just one of them.[9]

What does it mean to "overcome self-interest to a sufficient degree"? Based on the magnitude of the tempest staring at us, and the level of collaboration we would need to achieve, we are not talking here only about the usual humanist discourse on selfishness vs. empathy. Yes, this discourse is essential too, it promotes the argument that human beings also have an innate compassionate side and that the popular belief about our inherent selfishness is woefully inadequate. Because there is already a considerable amount of literature on the subject, there is no need for repetition here.[10] It should suffice, as a tiny summary, to mention here a few thoughts from Frans de Waal's book *The Age of Empathy*: "A society based purely on selfish motives and market forces may produce wealth, yet it can't produce the unity and mutual trust" and we are at a point where "we need a complete overhaul of assumptions about human nature" and must make full use of our innate "capacity to connect to and understand others and make their situation our own."[11] So, assuming that a good number of people among us have internalized this view, and we understand that the maxim "greed is good" must be buried and forgotten if civilized humanity is to survive, the question still looms large, what exactly are we to do presently?

We can identify several levels on which this battle must be fought. One is certainly at the level of collective worldviews or cultural narratives we hold. The other is more individual, in the darker primitive regions of our minds and hearts.

Worldviews and Us

As historian Yuval Noah Harari points out,[12] human beings mainly think in stories, rather than only in facts, and it is primarily the stories we end up trusting that become historical markers for the creation of worldviews. All major religions and cultural epochs have their carrying narrative. In most cases, we can't easily identify the cause or the point in time when a major worldview is created. Being born as the "idea whose time has come," a new worldview seems to spread its wings, assume dominance, and powerfully hold sway over large groups of people and over long periods of time.[13] All major religious or cultural worldviews can be observed as phenomena of such nature. We internalize worldviews via their cultural narrative (beliefs, values, mythology), and they affect the inner core of each of us, what we think, feel, and what motivates us. The worldview we accept informs us about who we individually are and what our relationship with society and the universe at large is. A person holding a ruthless Machiavellian worldview will almost certainly relate to their environment and other people differently than a person holding an all-embracing Buddhist worldview. The worldview we hold is deeply seated in our psychological nature (consciously or unconsciously) and influences all our actions. One of its features is that it is often hiding in plain sight and is simply taken for granted, we are often not even aware that we harbor a certain worldview as our essential life philosophy.

To explore this thought a bit further, let us attempt to characterize — in a few broad strokes — two currently prevailing worldviews with respect to self-interest and an individual's place in society. On one hand, we have a worldview that is prevalent in the modern Westernized developed world. While its foundations are rooted in the ancient cultural heritage that spans many global civilizations, it can be considered young in historical terms, having been significantly shaped by the powerful influences of the Renaissance and the Age of Enlightenment.[14] This worldview has endowed us with modern science, advanced technology, new art impulses, and a heightened emphasis on reason. Along with these advancements, it has brought about significant liberation and enhanced the dignity of individual human beings. Yet it is increasingly becoming obvious that this worldview's promise of humanism and infinite progress is starting to fray on the edges. In addition to its bright and inspiring side, it is also showing its bleak, isolating, and depressing side. Despite some talk (in limited pockets of society) about matters essential for humans — such as connectedness, empathy, attachment, community, and care — individual self-interest is regarded to be at the core of human nature in the modern Western perspective. This worldview is gradually revealing its shortcomings and its incompleteness. It precipitated an abundance of impressive achievements in the material world and enabled significant forces of progress, but this contribution only marginally relieved the existential pain we experience, and in some cases made it more intense. We are still dealing with the same kind of pain that led Hobbes to characterize human life as "solitary, poor, nasty, brutish, and short."[15] Through the stories of the Western worldview of our day, we — modern human beings — are urged to see ourselves as disjointed separate individual units (mechanisms actually), situated on a tiny planet, circling randomly in the vast cosmic space, like specks of dust, each fending for ourselves during our short life span, essentially alone, mainly ruled by our instinctual nature (so have fun while you can!), without intrinsic free will, purpose, and meaning.[16] For anyone who fully buys into stories of such a worldview, it is next to impossible to act truly cooperatively, with lifelong compassion for fellow humans, and in unison with them.[17] No good answer has yet been provided to the burning question: if this worldview were true and complete, why would we even bother?[18]

On the other side, we have the much older, traditional, group-centered worldviews, where self-interested behavior is subordinated to the interests serving the "greater good" (as it is often called) of a specific group. In this case, group members identify with the group to a significant degree. This can take many forms, most commonly we see it as loyalty, commitment, support, and sacrifice for one's nation, political party, tribe, cult, sports club, religious or spiritual group, and the like. People who strongly espouse such a worldview often experience a strong sense of belonging to a given group, and willingly conform to traditions, societal norms, and even authoritarian structures of the group.[19] This comes at the expense of the individual freedom of group members, as traditional views are not freely chosen, they are enforced from outside, and maintained by society. When quick group actions are necessary, these worldviews do have an advantage (especially in the presence of a strong authoritarian structure), as they can channel individual impulses in a way that becomes beneficial for the group. Some traditional worldviews promote wisdom that can effectively curb selfish individual impulses, ensuring harmonious group life.[20] However, this beneficial influence and such harmony-creating wisdom often stop at the group boundary, which can be discriminatory. Interests of people from different backgrounds, who belong to different groups, parties, nations, tribes, sports clubs, religions, etc are usually either not considered or are treated with hostility. Group-centered worldviews of our day tend to be tribal in nature, beneficial for one's own tribe (and for conforming tribe members), but often detrimental to other tribes, who are seen as competition. On the whole, group-centered worldviews do not hold the promise of unifying us all under a single banner.

Looking from a global perspective, these are the two dominant worldviews we hold. They might overlap, each of them has many tributaries, and there are people who hold dear some aspects of both dominant worldviews. Nevertheless, neither of them — in their current form — seems to be a strong enough platform for the global cause. If we are to accomplish effective global cooperation and action, we will have to find a new path, a path that can deliver some form of a universal, cosmopolitan worldview,[21] accepted by the majority of people, one where each of us freely chooses to identify with the whole of humanity, where our innermost self-identification and our self-interest widens to the point to include everyone's well-being, and where that majority of people acts as one. It is slowly becoming obvious that this is the only way forward open to us. Such a worldview has often been ridiculed, called utopian, unrealistic, or worse (and treated with disdain, not unlike how the youngest child is treated at the beginning of many fairy tales.)[22] Yes, of course, it is true, formidable forces in our human nature need to be overcome for this to become a reality. But the impending cataclysmic challenges coming our way — overwhelming AI being one of them — have been delivering a clear message for a while: embrace the challenge as an opportunity and unite, or perish!

Can Lead be Transformed into Gold?

A cosmopolitan worldview will not manifest out of thin air. Also, such a worldview does not stand a chance unless enough individual human beings adopt a position that this indeed represents a possibility,[23] and resolutely embark on the journey of *free individual self-transformation*. Now, for some casual readers, this is the point in the book where things might slowly start to feel weird, or over the top. What is "free individual self-transformation," and is that really what is necessary to enable us to rise to the challenges of modern times? Please bear with me, we have a long agenda here, but yes, this narrative is indeed slowly moving toward "the road less traveled"; however, it will be demonstrated that this road has always been available, and it is not uncharted territory.

Before we go further, this seems like a good place to state one of the main messages this book will be trying to convey: *self-interested human nature can be transformed; the capacity to accomplish this individual transformation is innate, it is available and lies dormant within every human mind.* This book represents an endeavor to provide some background and support for this process of individual growth and transformation, and to outline methods for accomplishing it. Such methods have deep roots in the past, marked by a rather quiet and somewhat veiled history, which I will seek to portray (even if my account must be cursory and incomplete.) It should be noted that this is not a self-help book, and the methods outlined here require a commitment and investment of effort. Among other things, this transformative process has the potential to deliver *connecting and unifying inner experience*, but its early stages are in many respects solitary and individual, as it is a prerequisite that it must be freely chosen and striven for. Nobody can be compelled to it, as the decision to thread this path, and all activities related to it, can only happen in our innermost space, where only one being has access – the one using the word "I" to reference it. At the same time, this self-transformative process is communal, as it leads to an inner experience that unveils unifying bonds and delivers the realization that human beings are in many important ways connected to a much higher degree than we commonly realize and experience.

Fervent Beliefs and Other Roadblocks: The Promise of Science and Are We Living Up to It?

Self-interested human nature can only be transformed one at a time, at the source, by the individual human selves who harbor it. The profound deepening of our understanding of the human mind, and the active forces within it, is a necessary step in this endeavor. Alas, from where we stand today, a radical deepening of our understanding of the human mind indeed seems like a tall order. This is mainly due to the biases of the currently established paradigm related to how we learn, discover, and acquire new knowledge about the phenomena in and around ourselves. It is evident that the dominant cultural and scholarly paradigm today is steeped in our modern scientific thinking. Natural science as we know it is a relatively young enterprise, it is just a few hundred years old, but in that short time span, it managed to radically transform the way we live by achieving deep insights into the inner workings of the material world and by spinning off the field of technology. In many ways, wherever our modern culture attained greatness, we owe some aspect of it to the scientific way of thinking. For modern humanity, science must point the way toward any new understanding, including that of the mind. On the other hand, science as a discipline — as we have it today — seems ill-equipped to deal with the phenomena of the mind.[24] It is not lost on me that such a statement may come as a surprise to many and result in the dismissal of everything else this work is attempting to say.

One possible way to approach this is to consider the argument made by Irvin Yalom, a renowned psychiatrist and existential psychologist, where he explained why, in his written works, he needed to use a novel (fiction) format to teach about the human side of what is happening in psychotherapy. He stated that scientific prose "did not permit [him] to convey what was truly the critical part ... — the deep, intimate, human, risky, caring (even loving) texture of the therapist-client relationship."[25] The sole focus of psychotherapy as a discipline is the human mind and relationships between human minds, and while it does involve a sophisticated process, we know that psychotherapy can work and can be very effective, even life-saving. Thus, the notion that the language of science — as we have it today — can be an impediment to conveying what is happening with human minds during psychotherapy should give us pause. We might want to consider the possibility that, even though our modern natural science has the unprecedented ability to uncover the secrets of the material world (or what we understand under that term today), it is — in its present form — lacking the ability to penetrate the "critical part" of what we know and experience as the human mind.

If we (even tentatively) assume that this is indeed the case, that our modern science lacks tools for such an inquiry, one can ask why that might be? It sure doesn't seem that the scientific method itself is in the way – observation and critical inquiry into phenomena, gathering data, pondering and testing hypotheses seem fair game in any kind of investigation. The issue would seem to lie elsewhere. In the following chapters, I will attempt to argue that we have been, in some ways, confounded by the enormous successes of modern science in (what we are used to call) the material realm, to the point that we are limiting its domain and thus stifling its further growth.

Science has long outgrown its pioneering roots when the likes of Copernicus and Galileo were bringing new science-based ideas forward, despite the violent resistance of the established dogmatic worldview of the day. They were branded heretics and were engaged in a struggle against a towering mountain of a powerful belief system. We live in a different time now, the tables have turned, science has become an established discipline, and one can argue that, as a side effect, science is now less pioneering and more rigid, also more corporate.

We should pay heed to this because the process of empowerment and establishment also brings with it a vulnerability in the form of conformity, daze, ignorance, or worse. Experience teaches us that we should be guarded against forming firm beliefs and speculations without solid evidence, and against unfounded projections regarding future scientific discoveries. Most importantly, we shouldn't seek to restrict the domain of science only to fields in which our past successes occurred. This urge to draw a certain boundary around science is mainly driven by the power of habits and by the authority of the scientific establishment and influential scientists. Max Planck, a renowned Nobel laureate in physics, famously stated that "science progresses one funeral at a time." While this is a paraphrase of a longer statement he made,[26] it is helpful to remind us that there is nothing intrinsic to science or to its subject that seeks to limit our pursuit of knowledge – obstacles often have their origins in our rigid psychological habits. By limiting what science is allowed to research and by referring to everything outside that arbitrary fence as non-science, we are indeed limiting what knowledge we can attain. Richard Feynman, another renowned Nobel laureate in physics, said during one of his famous lectures (while presenting the seemingly unexplainable quantum behavior of matter in the double-slit experiment): "You will find [nature] delightful and entrancing ... [and] it is necessary for the very existence of science that minds exist which do not allow that nature must satisfy some preconceived conditions." Feynman understood that this is indeed difficult for us, but insisted that we can overcome it because "difficulty really is psychological" and is a "reflection of uncontrolled but utterly vain desire to see [nature] in terms of something familiar."[27]

With respect to the research of the mind, in many ways, science has been idling at a crossroads for quite a while. Most attention was directed toward neuroscience and its quest for answers. However, despite many decades of researching and pondering about the human mind, even though some fascinating progress has been made in the field of neuroscience, with our current scientific toolbox we can't even clearly identify and define phenomena or aspects of the mind — like consciousness, thinking, feeling, qualia, and will — let alone properly research them. These and related phenomena of the mind represent everyone's daily experiences, they affect us all deeply; however, we can only tinker on their edges with the currently accepted scientific approach.[28] The needle is moving though; for example, just a few decades ago it was next to impossible to publish any scientific work about the concept of consciousness, and just talking openly about it might have been a career suicide for a scientist.[29] We are past that darkest period now, and the hope is that we will have the courage to widen the research domain even further. As a matter of fact, an opening for a radically new science of the mind has started to emerge and has already been advocated for,[30] several prominent thinkers have started to ponder and point to some possible alternatives,[31] and we no longer have a good excuse to postpone this quest. The argument for the need for a radical new consideration of the human mind in the scientific endeavor will be further considered later in the text.

This being the case, we may ask: what might inform this new scientific endeavor? Are there already any stakes in the ground, do we have some established starting points — possibly forgotten or ignored — to depart from in a scientific way? The human mind, human self, relationships among human selves, and their relationship to the surrounding world, have been considered a mystery to us for thousands of years. Since the dawn of classical antiquity, philosophy has been one of the main vehicles for pondering these phenomena – in addition to myths, legends, and related powerful narratives. So, we should ask whether philosophy, science's older relative, provides any solid anchors in the form of insights into what the mind is. How about spiritual traditions, psychology, mysticism, or religious thought? Can spiritual disciplines, available to us since time immemorial, help us find and develop wisdom about the training and disciplining of modern minds? Do we have any hints from the research on psychedelic drugs? Are all insights and teachings from these fields irrelevant, or outdated, now that we have neuroscience? Or did we dismiss some of their essential achievements all too quickly because they were too unfamiliar, too different from the new dazzling paradigm of modern natural science? This work will argue that we indeed have solid starting points to build upon in an objective scientific way. It is essential, however, that future research in this direction must find new ways that lead into the mind itself, directly, using the trained and disciplined human mind objectively – as a scientific instrument. It is a misguided prejudice to consider the mind to be only an "emergent phenomenon" caused or constructed by some other process in a "physical substrate" (i.e. brain), as is often speculated by many scientists of our day.[32] Accepting new ways might prove hard to do, an old habit or "psychological difficulty" (to borrow Feynman's words once more) can be hard to break or overcome, but it is an important crossroad for those who want to give the new path a chance.

In order to build upon these starting points, we need to shift our perspective somewhat. Even though we witnessed the emergence of several new theories with respect to the relationship between physical and mind phenomena in the last few decades,[33] it can be argued that the materialist or physicalist theories still hold the strongest grip on our collective worldview, especially the Western worldview. This is because our first instinct (at least for people attuned to modern science in its present form) seems to be that we simply wish away and eliminate all phenomena directly attributed to the mind by dismissing them as byproducts, as "illusions" or "hallucinations"[34] and postulate that they are somehow secondary, i.e. that they must be an effect of some underlying "physical process" and need a "physical substrate" in the brain where we should be able to find their "causes."[35] This instinct is very deeply ingrained, and it appears as obvious and natural to many people today. A renowned neuroscientist Antonio Damasio's position sums this well up – he states that even though the notion "that we have a firm grasp of what the brain is and what it does is pure folly," he *believes* that "problems that seem intolerably mysterious and unbearably hard are likely to be amenable to biological account."[36] Reasons behind this fervent belief seem understandable: for a number of phenomena, especially ones related to our sensory perception and motor control (as an aside for now, we should note that these particular features and phenomena are not unique to the human mind, animals have them too), we see a very strong correlation between the activity in the brain and what happens in mind. It is an obvious fact that the brain plays an important role here. However, it is also a fact that, after decades of active research, as far as the science of the brain is concerned, we have only correlations and speculations to show for it, nothing more.[37] The fact that an observed (e.g., via fMRI scan), or artificially induced (e.g. neurostimulation) activity in the brain correlates with an activity of somebody's mind (as they testify to it) does not automatically mean that the observed brain activity unidirectionally causes that activity of the mind. If we don't understand the underlying process, we shouldn't claim "causal evidence." Scientists know very well that correlation is not causation. Still, nonetheless, in this case, due to our deeply ingrained beliefs, causation is almost unanimously assumed, as can be seen in the way scientific postulates and speculations are proposed. It may sound weird, even spooky, possibly frightening, that the human mind may not be directly caused by brain activity, but be it as it might, that shouldn't be what influences scientific inquiry. Francis Crick, who received the Nobel Prize for DNA discovery, was open to this when he stated that there is a possibility "that the facts support a new, alternative way of looking at the mind-brain problem that is significantly different from the rather crude materialistic way many neuroscientists hold today."[38] Even if it sounds weird or spooky, it shouldn't be dismissed solely for that reason (it can be argued that Einstein's theory of relativity is also weird, but that doesn't mean that it is incorrect; thus, weirdness should be dismissed as a subjective opinion and should be of no consequence here).

An example may illustrate, by using an analogy, the need for a possible alternative approach.[39] Instead of *mind* and *brain*, let us consider a possible analogous relationship between two other phenomena, *music* and *a musical instrument*. Let's assume that an old piece of instrumental music (for example, a violin sonata composed in 1720) is played on the newly constructed 21st-century violin. Obviously, the only way we can hear the music is if it manifests itself through a violin. But it is not likely that anyone would conflate the piece of music itself with the violin on which it is played, or seek to find the creative source ("cause") of that music in the violin ("physical substrate"); similarly, we wouldn't say that violin creatively "constructs" music, or that music itself somehow "emerges" from the violin. We do understand that a musical instrument is necessary if we are to hear the music via our senses and thus make it manifest, but we wouldn't look for the origin of music in the wood or in the strings of the violin. Even if we can affect the sound of music by touching wood or tinkering with the strings of the violin while it is being used to play music, we wouldn't assume that we can in this way pinpoint the true creative source of the music to be in the violin. We understand that violins do not create or cause music, as the violin sonata was composed long before the violin was made. There is indeed a *correlation* between what we hear and the violin sonata composed long ago, but the violin *is not causally involved* in the creation of the violin sonata, the instrument only manifests music, it does not cause or create music. In this book, we will be pondering the relationship between the mind and brain in an analogous fashion, and we are particularly interested in the mind itself on this path.

The only reason why we are venturing into this discussion about the mind-brain relationship here is due to the need to challenge the dehumanizing physicalist ("crude materialistic" in Crick's words) interpretation that seeks to reduce our minds to physical mechanisms of sorts. The notion that we should view ourselves only as sophisticated machines is based on unproven and incorrect opinions.[40] Such notions are often dressed in clothes of science and appear to have persuasive armor, but, at best, they represent rushed assumptions of a yet immature scientific endeavor. They represent a belief system, plain and simple. If they were just that, no special attention would be needed, people believe all kinds of things, but the effects of such a belief system are not benign – a rather harmful worldview is being conjured up by it. Paired with the scientifically outdated, woefully incomplete, and one-sided interpretation of evolution (Herbert Spencer's "survival of the fittest," still assumed as a fact by many),[41] this belief ended up engendering raw individual self-interest and human isolation, and it has been gnawing at the roots of our humanism since its inception in the 19th century. The science of our time finds itself in a strange position, where it is unable or unwilling to see any other choice but to promote a worldview proposing that we are fundamentally just complex machines, evolving to support our "selfish genes,"[42] dead stuff in complex motion, and nothing else. This position results in a betrayal of the humanist ideals of its roots in the Age of Enlightenment. The causal connecting line from the physical brain to the mind is unproven, it is, in fact, "highly disputable" and "merely an assumption,"[43] but the fervent belief of many scientists in the field still seeks to support this dogma of the scientific establishment, as if we are under a spell of sorts. The scientific establishment does accept that we don't fully know what the term *physical* means or what *life* is (or what the concept of *being* in "human being" is, for that matter),[44] but nevertheless, it is claimed that we know, we just know, that everything is only "physical," and that "life" has nothing to do with the concept of "being." The silly phrase "we have no evidence to the contrary" is often used as the main line of attack by defenders of crude materialist interpretations. Their message is aggressive and persuasive, but if this physicalist view were true, we would be forced to conclude that human beings have no real agency, no free will[45] ("atoms or selfish genes made me do it"), no real purpose, what we call meaning is just an illusion of sorts, we are just "robots"[46] who find it useful to persuade ourselves that we are autonomous beings, and everything is pre-determined by movements of physical stuff (as described in the laws of physics of our day.)[47] So in this case, there wouldn't really be much that any of us could actually do, we couldn't be active participants and creators of our future. For example, we couldn't really counteract climate destruction, guard against the impending fall of democratic systems, harness AI technology, etc, if they were already predetermined to happen – billions of years ago. Sounds crazy, but I am not making this up. As a matter of fact, we indeed have scientists and philosophers today who claim just that (folks supporting *free will determinism*).[48] We also have some prominent thinkers who are hoping to have it both ways, believing that everything is predetermined, but also that we can somehow still have free will (supporters of *free will compatibilism*);[49] or that it simply might be fine to use a convenient vocabulary and say that we are "choosing," even though we know that we are just a bunch of atoms and "atoms are going to do whatever they were going to do."[50] So yes, we find ourselves in a weird place, and we are rather complacent about it.

This "physical-brain-causes-mind" dilemma indeed represents a true conundrum if we don't shift the perspective and look at the big picture. It is just an intellectual trap made of smoke and mirrors, so let's try to examine it carefully. The thought process that freezes us in this spellbound state happens due to the powerful reign of prejudices within the modern materialist interpretations of science – it can be expressed in very simple terms: "everything that exists (including our brains) is made of physical stuff" AND "physical stuff follows deterministic laws of physics" THEREFORE "mind must also be made of physical stuff (in the brain most likely), and thus it must be fully pre-determined." In this way, we are urged to conclude that our mind and agency are not what we might believe – they are just doing what they are pre-determined to do by physical laws, set in motion billions of years ago, everything else must be some kind of illusion somehow. The problem with this line of thinking is that it has several unproven prejudices packed inside. Concepts used in this line of thinking are in fact not well understood by science, and their interpretation is all too easily biased and distorted: not only do we not know what the term "mind" means (scientifically speaking), but science also accepts that we don't know exactly what the term "physical" means. As Noam Chomsky says, since Newton unintentionally challenged a purely mechanistic mindset by discovering gravity to be "action at a distance," the word "physical" lost its original meaning and became more of an honorific designation, like the words "real" or "serious."[51] The birth of quantum physics has made this even more apparent by undermining the long-established beliefs in the certainty of the strict mechanistic causality of all phenomena. What follows is a one-paragraph tiny summary in plain language (with additional explanations in notes) of some essential points of quantum physics that bear on our topic. This is necessary since physics is often incorrectly invoked as a justification for theories stating that everything has already been pre-determined, but the fact is that unbiased physics does no such thing.

Physics of our day considers everything that we call physical matter to be waves of sorts, everything that exists can be seen as just waves of probability, which can be calculated with Schrödinger's equation. Any particle, that nobody has yet observed, is considered to be everywhere (in "superposition"), we can't even call it a particle at that point, it is just a wave of probability, it is here and there and everywhere, and we can only assign a number value to it — interpreted as probability — for every location. Experiments show that, when an observing consciousness appears, the observed phenomenon (described by Schrödinger's equation until that point) "collapses" its wave into a particular localized physical phenomenon, which we can then observe as physical particles with our senses. Nobody knows exactly how that is supposed to work, this is like a black box to us,[52] there are several contending speculative theories (all of them much weirder than anything you will read in this book, all of them unproven too),[53] it is a mystery in physics, referred to as the *observer problem* (a.k.a. *measurement problem*.) In the words of renowned physicist Sean Carroll: "there are real mysteries associated with quantum mechanics, especially what precisely happens when an observer measures a quantum system."[54] Even the concept of *probability* itself, underlying all calculations in quantum physics, is something we are not sure how to interpret. Is the final outcome a blind chance of sorts? Yes? No? Maybe? We have no idea. As Bertrand Russell famously expressed: "Probability is the most important concept in modern science, especially as nobody has the slightest notion what it means."[55] Therefore, although the science of physics enables us to effectively manipulate matter in experiments and technology, any claim that we fully understand what is under the hood, what "physical" or "material" reality means, is a stretch of the imagination to a great degree.[56] And if we don't fully understand what physical reality is, how can we claim that it is fully deterministic? In

Richard Feynman's words, the future of phenomena observed in quantum physics "is unpredictable: it is impossible to predict in any way, from any information ahead of time."[57] Or is maybe only some of it deterministic? Honestly, we really have no idea. We do know that the behavior of macro phenomena of the so-called dead matter (for example, in mechanics – two billiard balls in motion) can be considered predetermined, but we are going far out on a limb in assuming that the mind can be reduced to such phenomena. When we do that, it is only our habits and our prejudices talking, putting on display the "utterly vain desire to see [nature] in terms of something familiar" (Feynman again.)

Despite the fact that the idea of determinism is highly disputable, and only a figment of our imagination, we do have some eminent scientists peddling it as a truism. This is exemplified by the recent (2023) book *Determined* by renowned biologist Robert Sapolsky. In an interview about the book, he stated that "all we are is the outcome of what came before, and what came before that, and what came before that... we are nothing more or less than the sum of biology over which we have no control... personal responsibility doesn't make any sense."[58] One can understand that, if somebody has a powerful instrument of scientific biology in their hands, everything out there might look only like a "sum of biology," but we should note that such statements are only assumptions, not backed by any kind of scientific facts. It is fine to have thoughts like this as philosophical musings of sorts, but nobody should assume that science undergirds such statements. They represent mere assertions, as Sapolsky also (partially) accepts in *Determined*: "no single result or scientific discipline can [disprove free will]. But—and this is the incredibly important point—put all the scientific results together, from all the relevant scientific disciplines, and there's no room for free will."[59] But what, exactly, does "no room" mean? There is a myriad of phenomena our science can't yet explain. We can't fully explain a simple thing like a human hand movement, let alone the phenomena of growth of organisms, or of thinking, feeling, will, and consciousness – and at the same time we seek to proclaim that we understand whether the human mind has free will? Seriously? For all we know, our scientific theories might have only scratched the surface, a myriad of universes might be needed to account for the unknowns. And Sapolsky might actually agree with this, as his rhetorical question "Why would we bother getting up in the morning if we're just machines?" is answered by "Hey, don't ask me that; that's too difficult to answer."[60]

In addition to all this, we seem to have a need to believe that our knowledge of laws of physics is solid and almost unchangeable (even many eminent physicists do), as if we have already discovered everything important there is to discover – as if the so-called *core theory* of physics will always be able to explain everything relevant we will ever discover.[61] In other words, we seem to be asking that nature must follow our physics textbooks. Also, in the scientific community, there is a strong belief, a conviction, a prejudice actually, that we have discovered all *fundamental forces* that can affect matter, "we are done"[62] has been proclaimed; physics of today tells us that there are only four (gravity, electromagnetism, and two nuclear forces acting on very short distances)[63] and that's it. This conviction is unwise and may prove premature given the fact that there is an abundance of phenomena in nature that we still haven't explained. Great enigmas abound in manifestations of all stages of developing life and what we call living beings (e.g. causes underlying the *developmental bioelectric networks* and *epigenetics* of living organisms are a complete mystery to us presently.)[64] This is an important point because the crude materialist's defense often rejects any notion of the concept of mind that doesn't align with established physicalist preconception of matter, claiming that such concepts would invalidate the laws of physics. Such a claim assumes that adding something fundamental to the canon of known laws of physics is impossible without invalidating them (by this logic, consider if we first learned about gravity, and later about magnetism; would it be correct to state that magnetism is impossible because it "invalidates" the law of gravity? This would be like saying magnetism, which can pull objects up against the force of gravity, is miraculous and contradicts our existing physics textbooks.) At any rate, we will revisit these topics in greater detail in the coming chapters, but this short consideration should already suffice to put forward the following statement: if our science were completely honest, it would have to admit that it doesn't fully understand what either matter or mind is, and we don't really know whether the mind is a manifestation of physical matter, or is it maybe the other way around?[65] Or are mind and matter one and the same thing, representing two faces, two aspects, of one and the same nature? From a scientific point of view, all these options are possible.

We should also note what the founders of modern physics have said about this topic – as Galen Strawson reminds us in an article about the statements the three winners of the Nobel prize for physics have given when interviewed in 1931 in The Observer of London: "Erwin Schrödinger ("the material universe and consciousness are made out of the same stuff"), Louis de Broglie ("I regard consciousness and matter as different aspects of one and the same thing") and Max Planck ("I regard consciousness as fundamental")."[66] Planck even elaborated further: "I regard matter as derivative from consciousness. We cannot get behind consciousness. Everything that we talk about, everything that we regard as existing, postulates consciousness."[67]

Therefore, we need to accept that our presently entrenched scientific way of thinking doesn't reach far enough with respect to either of these two central phenomena (mind & matter) to be able to characterize their relationship. Claims of some influential scientists of our day must be challenged: it is contrary to the spirit of scientific endeavor to state that science will in the future be able to prove that the mind is just secondary and emergent and that we will find a causal link pointing from the physical brain to the human mind. Nothing points us in that direction except the fervent beliefs of the scientific establishment.

Every human mind to some degree naturally rebels against the notion that it is just a mechanism of sorts, fully determined by some non-living/non-being stuff. (Luckily, all justice systems worldwide are still following common sense, ignoring the physicalist/determinist view completely, and generally assuming that human beings are active agents with free will.) It will be argued here that this inner rebellion is a welcome healthy force, that it can be helpful in releasing us from the reductionist trap, adjust our scientific theories, purge them of prejudices, and through that enable a cultural narrative that can help reinstate human beings to their rightful position. Contrary to what some in the scientific establishment are telling us, we are not just a bunch of atoms, separate from each other, and moving purposelessly. Human beings should be empowered to wake up to the reality of who we are and take the helm in guiding human history. And quickly.

Therefore, let us now continue our discourse regarding the shift of perspective about the mind. In fact, we already have scientists and philosophers who have, in the last few decades, slowly started to ponder the need for a new kind of inquiry into the nature of the human mind. The first step was acknowledging the problem we are trying to solve. *Consciousness*, as one of the phenomena of mind, seems to attract the most attention. A stake in the ground was placed by Thomas Nagel in 1974 in his widely cited paper on consciousness *What Is It Like to Be a Bat?* [68] in which he introduced an operational definition of the conscious experience of an organism as "something that it is like to be that organism — something it is like *for* the organism" often referred to simply as "what it is like." It can be argued that this paper laid the groundwork for the debate which intensified in the 1990s. Francis Crick acknowledged the problem in 1994 and stated that "at the present time [solution to the problem of consciousness] seems far too difficult";[69] he also introduced the "astonishing hypothesis," where he stated his *belief* that we are basically "nothing but a pack of neurons",[70] but he also acknowledged that consciousness is a territory unconquered by the science. David Chalmers introduced the term "hard problem of consciousness" in 1995,[71] thus pointing to the elephant in the room, and recognizing that we do have a problem, a hard problem – we don't know why it is that we have an inner experience, a subjective experience that accompanies physical processes of perception and information processing (colloquially referred to as "why couldn't we simply be zombies"). He reminds us that "there is nothing that we know more intimately than conscious experience," but at the same time he realizes that this "poses the most baffling problems in the science of the mind" and that to "make progress on the problem of consciousness, we have to confront it directly." This scientific and philosophical debate about consciousness is only tangential to our topic, but it is worth noting here, as it is indicative of a need for a new kind of "direct" inquiry, which is required if we are to understand the intrinsic phenomena of the mind. The consciousness debate has been active ever since, it branched somewhat into related concepts of *self, agency,* and *will* (there is a note with more details about this at the end of the book),[72] it has spawned several contending interpretations,[73] even if no clear consensus has yet emerged among scientists and philosophers about why (or how) it is that we have a first-person inner subjective experience.[74]

The Direct Inquiry into the Human Mind and Transformative Experiences

This "direct" inquiry into the human mind requires that we start by acknowledging that *human beings are active agents who can have inner experiences of thinking, feeling, and acting intentionally.* It is rather curious that this statement is even necessary; at some level, this is an obvious everyday experience of every generally healthy human being. However, given how hard our intellectual culture has worked to deny it for more than a century — attempting to persuade us that the obvious features of our agency and our minds are questionable (even illusory or non-existent) — this fact must be pointed out, elaborated, and defended. These phenomena of our inner experience are real and available to us. In order to approach them objectively, with a researcher's mindset, we need to develop a curiosity for observation and a will for critical inquiry in this domain.[75] We also need the devotion, patience, endurance, and courage of a resolute researcher, even more so compared to what is needed for the research into "physical" phenomena (why this is the case will be reflected upon later.)

What about scientific instruments in this domain? There is no science without instruments for observation, so first and foremost, it is necessary to become familiar with and learn how to control scientific instrumentation in this domain. In the same way that an astronomer needs to understand how to use and control a telescope, a chemist a spectroscope, or a biologist a microscope, a researcher in the domain we are discussing needs to become proficient in the development and use of the most exquisite instrument known to us – the human mind. Undeniably, even if we consider it to be all too obvious and don't pay much attention to it, *the human mind is already the central instrument in all branches of science* (and not only its analytical thinking features), as there would be no objective science without the objective human mind. One can easily argue that we don't appreciate this fact deeply enough, and we certainly don't invest much effort into understanding, developing, improving, and calibrating this most important of all scientific instruments.

Direct inquiry into the mind may not be a common endeavor nowadays, but it is not a new idea (even if it needs to be adjusted for modern times). As a matter of fact, any notion of it naturally gravitates towards an age-old idea, found in many traditions (sometimes in their discreet corners), rooted in a special kind of mind training and the resulting inner experience. Such an experience reveals — with the power of a force of nature — that *human beings are primarily minds, who have a common source and connectedness.* From the vantage point rooted in this experience, our "physical" nature is seen as secondary, as a derivative, as a filter of sorts, as an "individual user illusion" (referred to as *Maya* in Eastern traditions, Schrödinger simply termed it *deception*.)[76] Such an idea is foreign to many people entrenched in the modern Western worldview, to say the least. It is counterintuitive to many (including myself until a certain point in my biography), but its gentle knocking is back at our doors. This idea is essential for the message I am trying to deliver in this book.

Most importantly, it will be argued here that a wide enough embrace of this idea — and an endeavor aimed at understanding and gaining abilities to increasingly control and transform our individual inner natures — provides the only way to forge a possibility for cooperative human action on a global scale. Therefore we will come back to it from several angles, but it is worth mentioning here, in the introductory notes, that one of the goals of this individual transformational endeavor is the inner experience of what — already in classical antiquity — Plato (and Neoplatonists) referred to as the idea of *The Good* or *The One*.[77] Plato hints at it,[78] and Plotinus unambiguously (even if somewhat cursory) describes a process that leads to the inner experience of *unity with The One*.[79] In contemporary philosophy, these concepts are recognized, but they are often treated as purely academic and theoretical philosophical musings. However, they carry a profound meaning and were originally arrived at via *spiritual exercises* ("*exercices spirituels*," a term coined by a renowned philosopher Pierre Hadot, e.g. in his work *Philosophy as a Way of Life: Spiritual Exercises from Socrates to Foucault*.)[80] During Plato's time, philosophers *practiced* philosophy, they didn't just *talk* or *write* about it, philosophy was understood as an inner process of virtue development, as something one *does*. Philosophy, like life, was not thought of as a spectator sport.

This observation merits a brief glance at history. The emergence of philosophy in classical antiquity brought a growing independence of the individual human spirit and autonomy of human thought by emphasizing *reason* and *inquiry*. This undoubtedly laid the foundational groundwork for the Age of Reason, for modern science, and, more broadly, for much of modern Western thought. (This statement doesn't seek to diminish the significance of other cultures and epochs with their profound insights—such as Confucianism in China, Vedanta in India, or the intellectual contributions of the Islamic Golden Age.) Within the philosophical tradition of classical antiquity, Platonic philosophy occupies a central role. It can be argued that the depth of its insights stands unparalleled in the history of human thought, having served as a benchmark against which other ideas are measured for over two millennia (the Platonic Academy was founded in 387 BC in Athens). This long-standing influence is underscored by the philosopher Alfred North Whitehead, who famously remarked that the entirety of Western philosophical tradition is but "a series of footnotes to Plato."[81] However, it seems that we are unable to absorb the entirety of this profound wisdom in one go, so we approach it piecemeal. Over the course of history, the Platonic impulse has been rediscovered time and again. Its transformative powers of humanism are embraced and utilized, only to be set aside, sometimes for centuries, before re-emerging. Each resurgence has heralded a tectonic change. The most evident of these were through Neoplatonism and the Renaissance. Neoplatonism emerged in the 3rd century AD and played an essential role in interweaving wisdom and humanism into religious and mystical life over successive centuries. The last major revival of Platonic thought came in the 15th century, fanning the flames of humanism that drove the Renaissance, a term which literally means the "rebirth" of classical antiquity. This is when a cohort of Neoplatonists, centered around

Marsilio Ficino, established the Platonic Academy in Florence and Pico della Mirandola published the *Oration on the Dignity of Man*, often dubbed the "Manifesto of the Renaissance." Platonic thought set many intellectual and cultural currents in motion that would later become central to what we recognize today as the Age of Reason or the Age of Enlightenment. Its influence has never fully disappeared after that. Yet, curiously, many contemporary thinkers brush aside the foundational ideas of the Platonic worldview, forgetting historical lessons about their humanism and their transformative power, viewing them as unfamiliar to their own experience, deeming them thus more myth than reality, treating them as a fairy tale, unlikely to be true, as an "ugly duckling"[82] of sorts. Of course, there are many noteworthy exceptions; eminent philosophers, such as Iris Murdoch, Julia Annas, and those in the scholarly orbit of Gregory Vlastos (among many others I fail to mention!),[83] do recognize the profound depth and significance of Platonic thought and appreciate it as a robust underpinning for Western civilization as we know it. In her book *The Sovereignty of Good*, Iris Murdoch points to the existence of *The Good* and breaks it to us that we are, in fact, not robots, "we are moral agents."[84] We will return to this topic later.

Looking eastward from ancient Greece: some might find it surprising to learn that the inner transformational experience we are discussing is regarded here to have the same essence as the one referred to by Buddha as *nibbāna* or *nirvana,* which is said to be attainable by following the *Noble Eightfold Path* (addressed later in a dedicated section.)[85] Fundamentally the same transformative process is also described in ancient Hindu, Mystic, Gnostic,[86] and multiple other sources.

It is also worth noting that related inner experiences have been reported during recent trials involving psychedelic drugs.[87] However, transformative experiences achieved using psychedelics are neither guaranteed nor controllable, and they do come with some (under-researched) risks. While these experiences have been truly life-changing for many individuals, it can't be assumed that they are always and inherently accompanied by inner growth, as they are the result of physical body suppression via a substance.[88]

Schrödinger and "this grandest of all thoughts"

Several prominent thinkers of recent times have written devotedly about insights and direct mind experiences of this nature. They see our understanding of striving towards such experiences as a necessary step to awaken the humanism we desperately need today. Their works are studied, debated, challenged, and embraced, but it seems that the aura of inability to independently confirm them without extensive training of the mind stands in the way of their wider acceptance (or rejection, for that matter). We will devote our attention to many aspects discussed in these works later, so it should suffice to just mention a few notable examples here in the introduction.

Erwin Schrödinger, a Nobel laureate who endowed quantum physics with its most utilized mathematical tool, fully embraced the idea — most explicitly in his work *What is Life?* — that the conscious mind is in some way fundamental to the universe. He views the individual self to be only a partial manifestation of the eternal all-encompassing self which pervades the universe. Schrödinger recognizes that this idea has remained a stranger to the "Western ideology" of our time, but reminds us that this "insight is not new. The earliest records ... date back some 2,500 years or more. From the early great Upanishads the recognition Athman = Brahman (the personal self equals the omnipresent, all-comprehending eternal self) was in Indian thought considered ... to represent the quintessence of deepest insight." In his view, modern Western ideology clings to the "naïve idea of plurality" but "consciousness is a singular [and] there is only one thing, and that what seems to be a plurality is merely a series of different aspects of this one thing." Schrödinger points out that this same insight was independently attained by "mystics of many centuries" and calls it the "grandest of all thoughts."[89]

Aldous Huxley's deep concern about the state of the world precedes our current challenges by several decades. His book *The Perennial Philosophy*[90] represents an attempt to identify and explore the universal principles recognized and embraced by enlightened individuals across many religions and spiritual traditions throughout history. He saw the perennial philosophy as a promising antidote to the divisions, conflicts, and crises facing humanity. Huxley critiques contemporary Western society for its materialism and lack of spiritual insight. At the heart of the perennial philosophy is the idea that reality is unified and that there exists a single, transcendent principle from which all existence springs. One can't fully grasp the principles of perennial philosophy simply through intellectual understanding alone. True comprehension comes from the direct mystical or spiritual experience of the deeper self — attained through growth via meditation and related spiritual disciplines — which connects us to the universal reality. Huxley draws upon a wide array of religious and philosophical sources – mainly from Christian mystics, Hindu scriptures, Buddhist teachings, and Taoist texts.

In his works *The Doors of Perception*[91] and *Heaven and Hell*,[92] Huxley also explores the nature of inner experiences under psychedelic substance. He found that his own psychedelic experience strongly resembled the mystical experiences reported by religious and spiritual figures throughout history. He suggests that both psychedelics and certain spiritual practices can grant access to similar, if not the same, realms of heightened awareness and perception. It is worth noting that, while Huxley speaks of the potential benefits of psychedelics in granting access to profound states of consciousness, he also acknowledges their risks and warns against their casual or recreational use.

Erich Fromm is a widely read humanistic philosopher, psychoanalyst, and social psychologist. His insights regarding the interconnectedness of individual well-being with societal structures left a lasting mark on humanist philosophy. His posthumously published work, *The Art of Being*,[93] was originally titled *Steps Toward Being* and intended to be the second part of his last book titled *To Have Or to Be*.[94] In it, Fromm concludes his societal analysis with a realization that "the full humaniza-tion of [individuals] requires the *breakthrough* from the possession-centered to the activity-centered orientation, *from selfishness and egotism to solidarity and altruism.*" He termed this breakthrough the *Great Liberation*: "Perhaps the most fundamental form of expressing the goal and the meaning of living is common to the tradition of both the Far East and Near East (and Europe): the "Great Liberation"—liberation from the dominance of greed (in all its forms) and from the shackles of illusions. This double aspect of liberation is to be found in systems such as Indian Vedic religion, Buddhism, and Chinese and Japanese Zen Buddhism, as well as in a more mythical form of God ... in Judaism and Christianity ... In all these teachings, inner liberation — freedom from the shackles of greed and illusions — is inseparably tied to the optimal development of reason … This relation of freedom from greed and the primacy of reason is intrinsically necessary. Our reason functions only to the degree to which it is not flooded by greed. The person who is the prisoner of his irrational passions loses the capacity for objectivity and is necessarily at the mercy of his passions." In terms of methods used for the Great Liberation, Fromm points his readers towards the practices of concentration and meditation as "basic preparations for learning the art of being." He was familiar with Buddhist meditation (main sources: Nyanaponika Mahathera and D.T. Suzuki), and most material in this book is devoted to it, but he also shows great respect for Western mysticism, for example for the teachings of Meister Eckhart.

Sigmund Freud's *Civilization and Its Discontents* (1930) is one of his most widely read works.[95] The work begins with Freud reflecting on his correspondence with a friend, Nobel laureate Romain Rolland, "renowned for his humanitarianism and pleas for tolerance between peoples and nations."[96] In it, Rolland had referred to his own mystic experiences of the "feeling of eternity" or "oceanic feeling" – a feeling of oneness with the world, of "indissoluble connection and belonging with the entirety of the exterior world." Freud uses it as a backdrop for this work, lamenting that this "statement by [his] honored friend … caused [him] considerable difficulties" because he "cannot discover this oceanic feeling" himself. He thus limited his research into human nature, following his "impression that people generally measure with incorrect standards, strive for power, success, and wealth for themselves and admire them in others, but underestimate the true values of life," even if by doing that "one is in danger of forgetting the colorful diversity of the human world and its spiritual life" such as Rolland's inner experiences of "oceanic feeling." Rolland remained a major influence on Freud's work, their extensive correspondence started in 1923 and lasted until Freud's death in 1939. Another Nobel laureate, Herman Hesse, also greatly respected Rolland, and dedicated *Siddhartha*, one of his most recognized and widely read works, to him.

Free Will? Individual Freedom and Moral Intuitions

The topics of human free will and its relation to ethics are of fundamental importance for our discourse about the human mind. This will be further considered in greater detail in subsequent chapters, but it is necessary to stake out some key positions here in the introduction. (Philosophy is not the main focus of this book; however, a few essential perspectives on various philosophical theories are briefly outlined for the sake of clarification.)

As already mentioned, the crude materialist notion that human beings are only complex machines, automatons without free will (of the "atoms or selfish genes made me do it" kind) is considered here as unfounded and misguided speculation[97] (this applies to both hard determinist and compatibilist positions).[98]

Modern philosophical views in the vein of structuralism, post-structuralism, and postmodernism — which assume inherently weak agency of human beings, who thus often end up being playthings of dominant forces in nature, language, and society[99] — are considered here as largely incomplete, defeatist, and misguided.

Building on this sentiment and based on the insights expounded later, the position that *human beings have agency and the potential for free will* is fundamental in our considerations. Furthermore, *we human beings can attain freedom of will to the degree that our reason prevails, and we are unfree to the degree that forces of irrational passions and drives control us.* The "reason vs. irrational forces" battlefield will be revisited from several angles, but we can already state now that this position is in line with Platonic (also Neoplatonic and related) methods and insights of classical antiquity, with key ideas about the sovereignty of human individuality articulated during the Age of Reason and Enlightenment, also to a great degree with psychoanalytic and psychodynamic notions about the *existence of unconscious forces in the human mind*, with modern humanistic psychology, and with those aspects of existentialist philosophy that are rooted in humanism and authentic exploration of freedom of individual human beings. This position can also be summarized in modern language with Erich Fromm's statement that "freedom from greed and the primacy of reason is intrinsically necessary. Our reason functions only to the degree to which it is not flooded by greed."[100]

(As an aside only at this point, it should be noted that this position can also be seen as consistent with and in several aspects related to many Eastern traditions as well. It is compatible with the Buddhist interpretation of why the human mind can end up unfree (in short: the mind is suffering due to contamination with greed, hatred, and delusion)[101] and it is in line with the Buddhist image of the unfree human mind that is like "a deer entangled in snares."[102] It is also consistent with the ancient Hindu wisdom passed down to us in the earliest Hindu scriptures, the Vedas, and their philosophical interpretations the Upanishads, in Patanjali's Yoga Sutras, and in related narratives like the Bhagavad Gita.[103] Tao Te Ching, of the Chinese Taoist philosophy, also speaks of freedom from desire and artificial constructs (like imposed beliefs or societal norms) that leads to a true understanding of reality and inner peace.[104] Similarly, in the Sufi tradition, as exemplified by the poet Rumi at the end of the Islamic Golden Age, we are urged to recognize the "prison" of self-imposed boundaries and worldly worries that cause greed and resentment, and we are encouraged to seek freedom via spiritual awakening.[105])

Therefore, out of all aspects of the human mind, the capacity for *reason* and specifically for *objective thinking*[106] can be considered *the first stepping stone* of the royal road to liberation and freedom[107] for modern human beings. There are important implications of this statement for human ethical behavior (also for the theory of knowledge), which we will address later, but for now, we need to intimate the fact that it is the capacity for objective unbiased thinking (without distortion by personal feelings, prejudices, cognitive illusions,[108] or other unconscious irrational forces) that is the necessary condition for human beings to freely make decisions and to freely act. This statement does not seek to diminish the value of other capacities of the human mind, like feeling and volition, as they will be characterized later. The process of thinking is accessible as a direct inner experience to every (healthy and developed) human being, even if it is shrouded in mystery for modern science.[109] The "blooming, buzzing confusion"[110] of bodily sensory impulses provided to our minds is organized and interpreted to us by means of thinking.[111] Even pure ideas (e.g. in mathematics or philosophy) are identified, organized, and pondered by us by means of thinking. The thinking process is how we get to know things and ideas and how we include them in our inner mental space. Without exception, all our science and philosophy are fully dependent on our capacity for thinking and our trust in it. In many ways, thinking is our most important scientific instrument, as there would be no science without objective thinking. Cognitive scientists and philosophers of various stripes often refer to the process of thinking as "subjective," but this label is rather misleading. Of course, thinking is witnessed individually, as a subjective experience, but even the basic thinking process has the truly baffling (mysterious?) capacity to *connect* a thinking person with something objective and real, with the reality as it is, independent of individual subjectivity. Yes, it has become common not to challenge, but to simply accept the empiricist notion suggesting that human thinking is just one separate mind's interpretation of the world – only an inner experience, fundamentally distinct from the external world in some sense. However, this is merely an assumption, rooted in worldviews or belief systems we hold. Scientifically speaking, we, in fact, don't know what thinking is, thinking capacity is rather elusive and intangible to the modern reductionist mindset. Therefore, this *connecting and unitive aspect* of the human mind's thinking capacity is easily overlooked and commonly left out of cognitive science considerations. In spite of this, emotion-laden descriptions akin to "a satisfying rush of insight" and "a distinctive joy"[112] are used by cognitive scientists to character-ize the moments when thinking reveals to us meaningful connections in what was otherwise utter confusion. I will venture out at this point and simply state that the feelings of "satisfaction" and "joy" can manifest themselves because the thinking process *unites* us in a meaningful way with the world of objects, ideas, and beings we perceive. *Thinking removes the separateness, lifts the veil off the confusing reality, and reveals the otherwise hidden connections and meanings to us.*[113] Hence the experiences of satisfaction and inner calm, we get to know that we are part of the world we understand. In fact, if we couldn't think — even if all other capacities in our nature remained — our human existence would be tormenting and hardly bearable.

(Even if just in passing, we should note here that modern cognitive science does recognize the depth of the problem regarding how we acquire knowledge by means of thinking. Alison Gopnik points out that "one of the deepest and most ancient problems in philosophy is what we might call the problem of knowledge. There seems to be an unbridgeable gap between our abstract, complex, highly structured knowledge of the world, and the concrete, limited, and confused information provided by our senses."[114] In its search for answers, cognitive science proposes, among other theories, the *computational theory of mind* and the theory of *connectionism* as possible speculative frameworks to elucidate the thinking process, suggesting that the mind might operate like a computer, either processing information via algorithms and mental representations or through the interactions of a network of interconnected units.[115] These frameworks are hypothetical and don't offer a true account of the process of thinking (even if we can recognize that, for example, some aspects of connectionism — the concept of "neural networks," which are then given human-created content and trained by human beings — are at work in modern AI technology, we shouldn't refer to any of it as thinking.))[116]

Our trust in thinking is not misplaced – if we don't manipulate the input into the thinking process (wrong facts, lying, sensory illusions, unconscious biases, traumatic experiences that compromise our epistemic trust,[117] etc.), we can be sure that it will provide a meaningful output true to reality. Some people may argue that this is a big "if" to ask for, as many factors often influence our thinking, and thus its ability to convey to us the objective reality is questionable. It is not uncommon in scientific circles of today to hear an opinion that our minds are actually tricking us all the time, that they are —

to cite one instance — so "effective at hallucinating that we [only] believe [that] we see the world objectively."[118] However, the truth is that if we dig a bit under the surface, we will find the raw thinking capacity that can convey the objective reality to us and connect us with it. Our *percepts* (sensory perceptions or even pure ideas) are joined by *concepts* (supplied to us via thinking) that provide the meaning and context for our perceptions. That is the reason why we rely on it the way we do; even scientists rely on it when they run experiments and write about them in scientific journals. This fact doesn't seem to be appreciated enough in modern cognitive science. We inherently fully rely on and trust thinking to ponder all our experiences, science, and philosophy (we trust thinking even to understand and pass judgment on this sentence.) If a mathematician figures out and publishes a successful proof of a theorem, which has application in rocket propulsion, all mathematicians — if they are informed about the problem at hand — would be able to read, agree, and understand it based solely on the thought process everybody uses, and rocket scientists will be able to successfully apply it in their design and verify it in that way too. No trickery here, this is awe-inspiring, we have built civilizations with this. We will have to come back and ponder this feature of thinking deeper, but at this point, we may state that *thinking can transcend our individual human nature and connect us with the realities of objects and ideas we observe.* In general, this is an easily overlooked fact, as thinking seems transparent and effortless to us. We all too easily take for granted its capacity to transcend individual boundaries and reveal the meaning, connections, and context of our observations. This statement may not be easy to accept for many people who harbor the modern materialistic worldview. It may even sound unsettling or spooky to many of us. We are used to considering human beings as "physical" units completely separate from the "rest of the world" (everybody is just another thing among things). In order to accommodate this prejudice, we are willing to ignore, or wish away, a multitude of phenomena we encounter daily. Contrary to ancient Platonic wisdom, today we are willing to assume that the true reality is unknowable to us, and this has been an entrenched belief of the theory of knowledge for several centuries now (basically after Hume and Kant ventured to speak about it in the 18th century).

It is also worth noting that we do know that the basic framework of our ability to think is neither learned nor acquired, it is innate. Most cognitive scientists agree about this fact. Thinking capacity (sometimes referred to as *reflective function*) is simply innate to human beings, available and roughly uniform across the human species,[119] in a similar way the ability for language is innate (every healthy and developed human being can use language with a roughly uniform proficiency.)[120]

OK, fine, but why should the province of reason be called a battlefield? For one possible answer to this, we once again reach for Platonic wisdom. In his dialogue *Phaedrus*,[121] Plato presents his well-known *Chariot Allegory*, with the charioteer at the center, who needs to acquire the skill to guide "horses" – the forces within the human mind. Charioteer uses the power of reason that needs to develop and grow so that it can gain the upper hand in controlling the (mostly) unconscious forces. We will revisit this charioteer allegory again, but need to contrast it here with three often-mentioned statements: one by David Hume that "reason is no match for passion, "[122] another by Sigmund Freud that the individual reasoning self, the "I", is "not even master in its own home"[123] and that "our intellect is a feeble and dependent thing, a plaything and tool of our instincts and affects,"[124] and lastly the statement by Immanuel Kant that "out of the crooked timber of humanity no straight thing was ever made."[125] Sentiment inspiring all these statements (and their many offshoots) is often used to support the belief that human nature is rather weak, selfish, generally not capable of noble endeavors, that we are for the most part wildly self-interested, "evolved" mainly for survival and to "propagate our genes", and that our altruistic behavior is at best just a glossy veneer[126] we put over our selfish animalistic passions and drives. It can be argued that this belief, with its persuasive stories, is a powerful driving force overshadowing many human motivations and actions today. But this belief is deceiving, and it is in many ways fundamentally wrong. This belief represents something truthful only if we observe human nature and the human mind statically, and not as a developing entity. Yes, reason may not be a "match for passion" if it doesn't grow, develop, and increase in strength. We see this, for example, if we consider our deeply ingrained habits: they might be hard — but not impossible — to control and overcome. Overcoming them requires some sort of intentional training and discipline. In a related way, human reason can be cultivated to the point that it is strong enough to command the irrational passions and drives. This is how the human mind can, by degrees, be developed into a reliable and objective inner scientific instrument of sorts, and this is also how we can commune with the "better angels of our nature" within, heeding the intuitions of Charles Dickens: "the shadows of our own desires stand between us and our better angels, and thus their brightness is eclipsed."[127]

Individual human beings can attain freedom, but the path to it is through inner growth. It will be argued here that this process belongs to a particular human developmental phase, similar to how the development of permanent teeth and maturation during adolescence belong to a phase. It should be viewed and approached like other developmental phases, with an appropriate growth mindset. The important difference is that this developmental phase requires our fully conscious and willed participation. Furthermore, this inner developmental growth process should no longer be considered optional, it is indispensable for many human beings living in the 21st century. If we consider the impending challenges of our times, it becomes palpable that mastering this developmental process represents the only way forward open to us if we are to continue developing as a civilized society; otherwise, the irrational forces of our untamed natures (in a short Buddhist nomenclature: greed, hatred, and delusion) will — when pressures start mounting or resources start running low and passions start running high — pit us one against the other and tear us to pieces, together with our culture and our civilized way of life. We should have no illusions about this prospect. Thus, we are dealing with an existential question, and the real issue is not whether reason is a "match for passion," rather it is how the power of reason can grow and strengthen so that it *becomes the ruler of our irrational drives and passions.* In the same way that we don't ask whether a mathematics student who just mastered basic skills in arithmetic is a "match" for solving a complex calculus problem, we ask only about the appropriate path and schooling the student needs to take to grow. It is unwise to consider our minds static; it is innate to their nature that they are very dynamic and eager to learn.

Our minds need to become stronger and grow so that the inhibiting obstacles of unconscious forces are no longer a "match" for them. We need to do that so that many, if not all, individual human beings are liberated and can attain the highest ideals. In Plato's terminology, the highest ideal a reasoning mind (nous) can attain is what he termed *The Good* (agathon), manifested through the internal virtue or ideal of *justice* (dikaiosune). The idea of justice represents much more than what we today commonly consider under the same name, it has a boundless spiritual dimension, but it is within reach of human beings in its form as a *virtue*. Plato recognized that the attainment of the virtue of *justice* is an essential prerequisite for an individual human being to attain and retain a healthy life (mental and physical) and it is also essential for the long-term existence of a healthy society (polis/politeia/republic).[128] Human beings with minds that are enlightened and liberated by such virtue can accomplish what to most of us today may seem impossible – they can freely, out of themselves, without any compulsion, choose actions that are fully in harmony with other individual human beings, for the benefit and wellbeing of all. To many readers, this might sound like a wild claim. How do we know this? Is it just Plato talking? For starters, at this point in our considerations, an analogy with a much simpler phenomenon may help to elucidate this assertion: if two individuals look at the same physical object (a red rosebud for example), even if they look from two different sides and have completely different sensory input (different percepts), they can simultaneously *think the same concept* (mental representation, the concept of rosebud), *thinking* can be seen as that *dynamic unifying force*, and both of their thoughts — and actions related to their physical observations — can easily be in harmony and understood by everyone. So, in the same way that — at our present developmental stage — our thinking reason can easily deal with objects given to us by sensory observations, we need to become competent in dealing with concepts and objects of a more subtle inner nature. Without further disciplining, training, and growth (toward what we vaguely refer to as "wisdom" today), we ordinarily cannot see and understand, or can only barely discern, more subtle "objects" of our inner nature. Such wisdom can be instrumental in informing us about the deeper nature we and our fellow human beings harbor. (We can sometimes experience fragments of this wisdom in dreams when the filters of our daily consciousness retreat into the state of sleep, but this most commonly happens in a disorganized and uncontrolled fashion.) Indeed, what is *just* and "what's the right thing to do"[129] is much harder to understand and to agree upon if two fully separate and narrowly self-interested minds, with little shared experience, ponder the same phenomenon (for example, when a wealthy capital owner and a laborer ponder the fair price of labor.)

Indeed, as the wisdom since before classical antiquity teaches us, the human mind is special, it is not just a thing among things, and it is in our developmental path that our minds can grow, that they can become liberated from the inner oppression of irrational habits and drives, and that they therefore can, in time, gain the ability to willingly choose actions in unity and harmony with other individual human beings. This is true because *all human beings ruled by free reason are acting from a common source, their actions are the result of their moral intuitions, and it is impossible for their interests to collide.* From a certain viewpoint, which every human being can attain in principle, this fact represents common sense, and it is directly observable via insights attained by methods expounded later. (These methods also seek to answer the call, articulated by voices like Adrienne LaFrance's while writing about the incoming challenge of intelligent machines, urging that we must put "more emphasis on contemplation as a way of being" and we should ultimately not settle for anything less than being "floored by the universe as it reveals its hidden code" to us.)[130]

When Plato spoke about the *world of ideas*, — tangible to our minds — and about the idea of *The Good*, this was not a metaphor or philosophical contraption he invented, it was the fact he observed in moments when he was able to follow the method of dialectic to the very end, and to "generate in the soul" a state akin to "a blaze kindled by a leaping spark."[131] Plotinus outlined the spiritual exercises he followed to apprehend such reality. It is widely accepted today that Plato's philosophy is what gave birth to the whole of Western civilization (as already mentioned, Alfred N. Whitehead famously said that the entirety of Western philosophical tradition is but "a series of footnotes to Plato.") But we still don't dare to fully go there, into the inner sanctum of Platonic thought of ancient mysteries; hedging our spiritual bets and choosing cowardice, *we don't do* philosophy like Plato and his students did, at best *we just talk* about it.[132] But it is this insight, which was observed by initiates like Plato, Plotinus, Buddha, Meister Eckhart, and many more, that speaks — with a power of a force of nature — of the common source, of the single mind, of the common cradle for the whole human race. If attained, a single glimpse of it has the power to provide inner peace, courage, and conviction, to provide liberation to human reason; and *individuals with free human reason always act in harmony, they can never collide by following their self-interest, because their self-interest at that point includes everyone and everything.* Only truly free people can love, with pure unconditional love – or *agape* as ancient Greek philosophers referred to it. When our minds are selfish and oppressed, we have a veil of illusion drawn over our sight, and thus cannot reach up to the experience of true connectedness and love.

Before we conclude this section, let us once more dive into Plato's *Republic*, where he examines the polarity of the ideas of *justice* and *raw self-interest*, which he illustrates with the *Ring of Gyges* story,[133] posed to Socrates as a challenge. The story is about a shepherd named Gyges, who finds a magical ring that gives him the power to become invisible at will, thus allowing him to do anything he wants without fear of being punished. Gyges uses this newfound power to satisfy his personal desires as best as he can: he enters the court, seduces the queen, assassinates the king, and ultimately takes over the kingdom. The question Socrates needs to answer is this: don't people behave justly only because they fear the consequences of being unjust, don't "all men believe in their hearts that injustice is far more profitable to the individual than justice?" In other words, why would any individual human being choose justice out of their own free will, if they were not compelled by external forces of law, public shame, perceptions of their reputation, or even by "good opinion of the gods ... [who promise benefits of the heavens that only] rain upon the pious"? The question is profound. In many important ways, the future of human civilization depends on the answer we arrive at. To answer the challenge, Socrates starts a philosophical quest to determine the nature of justice itself and realizes that this is an almost impossible task if only a single individual is considered in isolation. Thus, he and his two interlocutors decide to design a functioning society (Republic) to examine the concept of justice systematically. The narrative and arguments are thoroughly captivating, they are a testament to why Platonic wisdom has been studied for more than two millennia and is still as relevant and insightful today as when first written. In it, Socrates ultimately argues that only just individuals can create a just, uncorrupt, and healthy society in which everybody prospers. Furthermore, at the level of individual human beings, a just life is the true source of happiness and health. Conversely, an unjust life, despite offering the possibility of delivering the satisfaction of individual passions, cravings, and drives, pursues these short-lived pleasures at the cost of individual (physical and mental) health and long-term happiness. This is because such a life leaves the unjust person in a primitive state, enslaved by the irrational forces of their "appetites" and "passions." Consequently, such person can never become a "master in their own home." They remain "the crooked timber" from which "no straight thing can ever be made." While they "can do what they want," they are, in fact, enslaved, unable to "want what they want." This represents the response of ancient wisdom to the assertions of Hume, Freud, Kant, and Schopenhauer.

The new paradigm is slowly dawning upon us, one with a much more dynamic moral landscape, where commonplace ethical norms, commandments, categorical imperatives, thoughts about the veil of ignorance, and social contracts — even if they are presently still holding their ground — are becoming increasingly evaded, disregarded, and irrelevant. This change is at the same time frightening and carrying a promise. It is bringing forward a world in which *only a deed out of love can truly be a moral deed.*[134] 21st-century technology demands 21st-century ethics, primitive ethics won't be able to sustain civilization in the long run.

Only people who have elevated themselves to the experience of inner freedom and developed a capacity for love can view and fully partake in what Plato observed and called ideas of *Good* and *Justice.* "Love should be inseparable from justice," we are reminded by the insightful Platonic scholar Iris Murdoch.[135] Ultimately, the whole Western civilization —

despite our ignorance and our failings — still stands upon the ideas of Justice and Good, even if its foundations are starting to loosen and tremble. Thus, the liberation of individual human minds is the battlefield of our time. Are we up to the task? Time will tell, and soon — certainly during the earthly lifetimes of many of us.

Creating an Opening for Wisdom

Several important aspects need to be pointed out regarding the methods for striving for individual transformative experiences given later in the main material. Regarding individual motivation, it should be noted that it is not only the end goal that matters; just acknowledging and entering the path can bring immense benefits individually and communally. In many ways, aiming for the end goal attainment is less important than staying in the process (focusing on the result can even be a major impediment if it takes the form of a fervent personal ambition.) It is this *process* of striving for the transformative experience of unity that creates an opening for true wisdom in us. This is the wisdom that helps us recognize our common humanity and thus renders it unbearable for us to treat other beings only as instruments for our exploitative individual intentions. If attained, the full experience of unity ultimately liberates us to see ourselves and others in an intimate light, face to face, no longer through a glass darkly, so that fellow beings can be viewed as ends unto themselves. However, even early stages on the path provide many benefits for the practitioner, as they open the way for a yearning to fashion the world so that all beings can thrive in it, and to rebel against every instance of oppression of fellow humans.

At the same time, it is nevertheless important to consider the communal aspect of this process more as a side effect of the individual transformation, rather than its primary goal. Whoever is familiar with this process and the inner experience it cultivates, has a deep respect for the fact that *the individual freedom of all human beings must be considered inviolable* as it is the only true foundation for ethical behavior that is possible today and in the future. Freedom is a prerequisite even for the very first step in this individual transformative process. *Any group or cult-like organizing, that seeks to limit individual freedoms in any way, or introduce discriminative group boundaries to this process, is completely foreign to it.*

Moreover, many roads can lead to this path. It does not need to be followed because of a wish to get rid of one's self-interested nature, it can simply be followed for the sake of individual improvement and liberation, as it does result, among other things, in a stronger inner platform to stand on – in greater inner confidence, patience, endurance, resilience, stability, and capacity to control one's habits. It can also be followed simply as an honest pursuit of wisdom (not to demonstrate it and impress other people), just because we are inspired from inside or — in Plato's words — driven by eros and love for wisdom, by true enthusiasm and fire from inside.

One important characteristic of this transformative process is that every single human mind counts in an essential way. This is not said casually. Every single human being can choose to bring their *unique innate virtue* to the big fair of humanity. In ancient Greece, philosophers recognized this and called such a virtue *arete*.[136] The endeavor considered in this book is based on the individual and unique arete, it is not a zero-sum game as it doesn't involve competition; however, that doesn't mean it is easy or battle-free.

Finally, unlike most other disciplines of the modern world, where somebody's life conditions may prevent them from pursuing their goals, this is one domain where everyone truly has equal opportunity; the only asset required for the journey is the individual human mind (the most exquisite thing any of us can possess.)

2 Science of Mind, Its Successes and Struggles

2.1. Why is Modern Science Struggling to Explain the Phenomena of the Mind?

Science undoubtedly stands among humanity's most successful endeavors. Its accomplishments radically transformed how we live by influencing just about every activity humans perform. Not only has science increased our understanding of the world and enabled technologies that improved the lives of many, it has also enriched our cultural life and bolstered human freedom and dignity. This legacy of science is awe-inspiring.

We can observe that the development of science, in important ways, runs parallel to the development of human reason. It is only reasoning human minds that engage in science, thus making human reason the key protagonist in the narrative of scientific progress. Our capacity for reason began its rapid ascendancy in classical antiquity with the emergence of the discipline of philosophy. Philosophy initiated a gradual shift away from worldviews anchored in irrational beliefs and authoritative dogma, ushering in an era of increased trust in individual human reason. This Promethean awakening impulse didn't bear many visible fruits immediately. Instead, it spread more or less quietly — mainly among the educated minority who could read — and simmered slowly for about two thousand years. It then reemerged as a powerful force during the

Renaissance and the Age of Enlightenment. Starting roughly with the Copernican Revolution in the 16th century, the scientific worldview grew in strength and soon established itself as the primary driver of human cultural evolution.

However, the explosive growth of science came at a cost. Humanity had to relinquish something to advance in the sphere of natural science. A certain narrowing of focus had to happen, at least temporarily, so science could become successful to the extent it did. This aspect has been cogently captured in Philip Goff's book *Galileo's Error*.[137] In it, he describes how Galileo Galilei, often hailed as the father of modern science, asserted in his 1623 work *The Assayer*[138] that it was crucial to reduce the focus of the "natural philosophy" (now known as natural science) solely to phenomena that "could be captured in the purely quantitative language of mathematics."[139] Phenomena of the mind, encompassing subjective experiences like qualia, cognition, emotions, and will, were deemed unsuitable subjects for the emerging field of science. Instead, they were relegated to the mysterious realm of the "soul" and remained largely unexplored. Thus, Galileo created a new field of natural science by leaving the phenomena of the mind "outside of its domain of inquiry and placing them in the conscious mind. This was a great success, as it allowed *what remained* to be captured in the quantitative language of mathematics."[140] At its inception, natural science as a discipline chose methods best suited for exploring the material world as revealed to our senses. This proved to be a wise decision, but it resulted in a limitation on the domain natural science could research. This limitation still lives with us today. The only problem is that many people attuned to the modern scientific worldview seem to have forgotten this happened. They ignore the fact that the methods of natural science — in their present form — are neither intended nor suitable for exploring the mind.

As already discussed in the introductory chapter, the field of natural science appears to be at a standstill regarding mind research. Our current understanding has not progressed significantly beyond what was known in classical antiquity over 2000 years ago. Many scientists and proponents of science, optimistic that no radical change is needed, are focusing on neuroscience and brain research. They believe these areas offer the most promising paths for unraveling the mysteries of the mind. However, as we have shown in our introductory chapter, despite many decades of extensive exploration, our progress has been minimal. To move ahead, we must consider the possibility that a radical new approach is necessary to augment the established canon of scientific methodology. This idea, suggesting the need for a revolutionary approach, is not new. Several scientists and philosophers of science, driven by genuine curiosity and open-mindedness, have advocated for such a shift. Notably, Nobel laureate Sir Paul Nurse has stated regarding our prospects for finding satisfactory answers about the phenomena of the mind, "I do not think we can rely only on the tools of the traditional natural sciences to get there."[141] Thomas Nagel views the "dominant scientific naturalism" as "incapable of providing an adequate account" about it, and Philip Goff and Galen Strawson both call for a new "revolutionary" way of thinking, which they deem necessary to tackle the problems of mind research.[142]

Basic phenomena of the mind, such as thinking, feeling, and acts of will, are ever-present. Every human being constantly experiences them, both in wakefulness and, to some extent, during sleep. However, the laws underpinning these internal experiences cannot be captured in the same way as the laws governing external phenomena, which are supplied to us via our senses. Inner experiences are direct, authentic, and intimate. In contrast, we learn about external phenomena indirectly; they seem outside and separate from ourselves, following the objective laws of nature, which appear strict, rigid, and unchangeable to us. This separation between the inner (*subjective*) and external (*objective*) realms appears to us as logical, neat, and even comfortable and safe.

But — and this is an important "but" — there is a vital and fundamental *link* between our inner and external worlds, a somewhat uncomfortable and possibly unsettling (spooky?) link, which we have an instinct to wish away, eliminate, and ignore. Nevertheless, there it is. Always. Without this link between our inner experiences and what is happening outside of us, we would be utterly adrift; a cohesive understanding of our surroundings would be unattainable – not only that we couldn't do science, but we also wouldn't be viable as living creatures, there would be no possibility to comprehend any phenomena observable to us. As highlighted in the introducetory chapter, the key component of this vital link is revealed in our capacity for *reason* and specifically for *objective thinking*. Both Platonic doctrine and contemporary cognitive science agree that our ability to think is innate. Scientifically speaking, we don't know why and how that is possible, but it is an undeniable fact that we possess the faculty to think and understand the world. Thinking reveals to us the objective lawfulness behind the observed phenomena. And thinking appears to us as an inner experience, not as an external fact. When we set aside our customary perspectives, it becomes evident that our internal experiences are of various kinds. And, among them, our capacity for objective thinking is essential for our species, not just for understanding our inner world, but for comprehending external realities as well. It is precisely through the inner experience of thinking that we learn everything we know about the world around us and about ourselves. Even the most basic fact — that we exist — is conveyed to us solely via an inner experience in our minds. In the 17th century, René Descartes famously declared: "I think, therefore I am" (*"cogito, ergo sum."*) I can doubt almost everything, but since I can think, I am — at the very minimum — sure that I exist. The inner experience of thinking is intimately connected with human agency – with the very individual self that does the thinking activity.[143]

No external scientific instruments are essential for direct research of the phenomena of the mind. The foundational constituent of science — human reason and its capacity for objective thinking — is of course indispensable as a tool, as is the case in any other research, but the particular methods of natural science, appropriate for investigations of the material world around us, need to be augmented or replaced with methods suitable for direct explorations of the mind. For this purpose, training and disciplining of certain capacities of the individual human mind is necessary. *In order to properly exercise our capacity to reason, to attain an objective stance in regard to the inner phenomena of the mind, a strengthening of our inner capacities is necessary.* Methods for doing this are age-old and proven, even if they were kept out of the spotlight until recent times (we will devote our full attention to this aspect in the seventh chapter.)

2.2. Evolution, and its Pernicious Misunderstanding as "Survival of the Fittest"

Our first chapter devotes significant attention to dismantling a destructive belief entrenched in the modern scientific worldview. This belief erroneously portrays human beings as merely complex deterministic machines composed of physical matter, devoid of intrinsic agency or purpose. We now shift our focus to another prevalent belief, related to the popular interpretation of human evolution. This belief, too, contributes to a collective sense of helplessness and resignation. While it is not our intention to delve deeply into arguments surrounding the theory of evolution — as this is not directly connected to our main topic — it is necessary to address several aspects of this debate in the context of the ideas presented in this work.

The one-sided interpretation of evolution, characterized by the phrase *"survival of the fittest"*[144] is a harmful prejudice. This interpretation is scientifically outdated, incomplete, and deceptive. It tacitly serves as fodder for a socially destructive belief justifying the raw individual self-interest. The "survival of the fittest" mindset indirectly peddles the conviction that we are in constant competition against each other, that one's strength can and should be used to overpower and dominate others, and that each of us is in significant ways isolated and alone. Consequently, people who harbor this conviction accept that bare-knuckled self-interest is always lurking under the surface as an essential aspect of human nature. Justifications for "Social Darwinism," the understanding of justice as "might is always right," and notions like "greed is good" and "every man for himself" are being propelled as "wise" by this belief, even though they might better fit as examples in Harry Frankfurt's book *On Bullshit*.

There are several levels on which this destructive belief can be exposed for what it is. One is addressed in *The Age of Empathy*, a book by primatologist Frans de Waal,[145] where he dismisses it as an "ideological prejudice" and a "mere projecttion" (mainly created by certain "economists and politicians"). While we can espouse a selfish and ruthless nature, we can also choose not to. De Waal reminds us that "many animals survive not by eliminating each other or keeping everything for themselves, but by cooperating and sharing."[146]

If we want to examine the phrase "survival of the fittest" on a level close to its origin, we need to consider the two key concepts of the theory of evolution – that of *evolution* itself and of *natural selection*:

1) *Evolution* means development. We can observe that life is not static and that all living beings are connected as part of one continuous developmental movement. We also have compelling scientific evidence that organisms have evolved over time – living beings we observe later in the historical record use features developed earlier, modify them, and build on top of them. The available fossil record, studies of developing living systems, and DNA-based evidence suffice to establish the theory of evolution as a fact. In the words of biologist Sean B. Carroll: "We now know from sequencing the entire DNA of species (their genomes) that not only do flies and humans share a large cohort of developmental genes, but that mice and humans have virtually identical sets of about 29,000 genes, and that chimps and humans are nearly 99 percent identical at the DNA level."[147] Evolution has been happening all along.

2) On the other hand, the science of *natural selection* — considered the main contributor to the process of evolution — is much less settled. In fact, evolutionary biology has been undergoing a radical makeover, a revolution of sorts, in the last

few decades. The reason for this is that the 80-year-old, neo-Darwinian, gene-centric notion of natural selection can no longer support the experimental facts. In truth, much of it was always a mere assumption not rooted in empirical facts.[148] Therefore, a major remodeling of the theory is well underway. The new understanding of evolution — as a *process mainly driven by the active agency of organisms with intention and purpose*, as opposed to random-chance events — has been establishing itself as a scientific reality[149] (more details about the new theory, now known as *Extended Evolutionary Synthesis*, have been placed in the endnotes.) We now know that both genetic information encoded in DNA and epigenetic information (which is not encoded in DNA but is involved in determining when and which genes are utilized) are directly influenced by the purposeful, goal-oriented behavior of an organism, rather than solely by rare, random-chance events.[150] And variations created in this way can also be passed on to the offspring. Moreover, the genome is no longer seen as a program that predetermines an organism's development; rather, it is selectively, purposefully, and creatively utilized by the organism throughout its life cycle. In his book *The Music of Life*,[151] eminent physiologist Denis Noble uses a metaphor that poignantly captures the whole theory: "the genome is not at all like a program that 'deter-mines' life ... the genome is like an immense organ with 30 000 pipes" on which the agency of organism plays polyphonic "music." Associations between genes and specific traits of an organism are not fixed, and they can be overridden by the organism itself when necessary.[152] That is one of the reasons why scientists cannot, in principle, definitively answer questions about which genes cause specific traits or outcomes (except in very rare cases.) With the new insights, the ubiquitous concepts of "selfish genes"[153] and "blind watchmaker"[154] have lost their persuasive power, although they still, unjustifiably, continue to captivate the minds of many.

(As an aside here, it should be noted here that, while we human beings intuitively recognize the presence of active *agency* in living beings and can easily associate concepts of *intention* and *purpose* with it, all these concepts and phenomena remain rather elusive for modern science that is rooted in the materialist/physicalist belief system. It is arguably for this reason — as many "evolutionary biologists feel uncomfortable recognizing organismal agency"[155] — that simple operational definitions are still preferred in the field (read: they sound less spooky to some people.) So, for example, it is said that "agency" is simply represented by "goal-oriented behavior," but it is recognized that this behavior is "neither predetermined, nor random."[156] This suffices to consider the meaning of the term *agency*, as used by modern evolutionary biologists, compatible with the one used in this book.)

New ideas take time to get accepted, we humans tend to cling powerfully to old habits, hence this scientific breakthrough about evolution peculiarly feels like the best-kept secret in science.[157] Experiments, scientific papers, books, and conferences in this field have all been happening for quite a while. However, all of it is barely touching the mainstream news cycle, school and university textbooks are very slowly updated to reflect it, academic establishments are resisting it (often completely avoiding the debate), evolutionary biology and psychology are still rife with speculative *just-so stories*[158] that are not being corrected, and it just seems that the only people talking about this revolution in science are either scientists or philosophers of science. The vast majority of people seem to still believe either in the outdated neo-Darwinian gene-centric evolution or in some form of Creationism. The new idea —

that living beings are active agents with intentions and purposes, who can affect their own (and their offspring's) development — is rather slow to pierce the shield of existing beliefs and penetrate the popular mindset.

Why does this all matter for the notion of "survival of the fittest"? These new insights allow us to finally remove the spell of a preposterous belief that we, human beings, are just survival machines fighting each other for resources, or as Richard Dawkins blatantly put it, "survival machines—robot vehicles that are blindly programmed to preserve the selfish molecules known as genes."[159] We now know that these claims are out of touch with reality and can only be rooted in a belief system. It is about time that humanity dismantles and puts such beliefs in the dustbin of history. If we acknowledge that human beings have agency and purpose (what a discovery, right?), we also recognize that we are free to choose which parts of our nature we want to identify with, nourish, and promote.[160]

2.3. Evolutionary Molecular Biology on the Frontiers of Science

Despite its significant discoveries and achievements, evolutionary biology remains a young and developing science, with many of its fundamental assumptions yet to be proven. For this reason, it may not be prudent to assign it the most central place in the worldviews our culture espouses.[161] Instead of assertive proclamations that we are just one step away from unlocking the mysteries of life and the human mind, a higher degree of humility would likely serve us better. Several frontiers in the science of life clearly remind us of this, even if they point us in exciting directions. Here are three examples from the frontiers of evolutionary biology.

2.3.1. The Developmental Process That Made Us Homo Sapiens

The developmental process that made us into Homo sapiens (or rather into *earthlings with a reason*, in a more literal translation) is proving hard to understand and demystify, it is a sort of riddle for us. We know very little about the development of the human capacity to reason, arguably our greatest and most sophisticated feature. Paleoanthropologist Ian Tattersall appreciates this fact by saying that "we modern human beings have an astonishingly recent origin and a sudden one. In evolutionary terms, we acquired our extraordinary symbolic reasoning capacities virtually overnight."[162] At this point, our science is largely in the dark regarding this riddle, and individual scientists only speculate about it based on the belief systems they subscribe to. Many scientists harbor the physicalist worldview and thus try to seek the answers in the matter of our brains, even if Nobel laureate Paul Nurse reminds us that "how all this emerges from the wet chemistry of our brains provides us with an extraordinarily challenging set of questions."[163] Similarly, speaking about properties of the mind, like consciousness and intelligence, stem cell biologist Paola Arlotta stated that "we really don't understand, even how they can emerge from an actual real brain, and therefore we cannot measure or study."[164] Neuroscientist Erik Hoel also reminds us that, in fact, "no current theory of consciousness is scientific."[165] An important aspect of a reasoning mind is the ability to utilize language. Here as well, Robert Berwick and Noam Chomsky conclude that "language does indeed pose a severe challenge for evolutionary explanation."[166] Our science would serve us better if it were more humble in its attempts to proclaim that we have certainty in this domain.[167] Scientifically speaking, we actually don't know whether our minds are based on "material substrate," or is it the other way around, or are they one and the same phenomenon with two faces? Presently, we seem only to have belief systems of various stripes to inform us about this. And it is not at all clear how we would even start to apply our existing notions of evolution or natural selection to this domain. And should we? Or would our attempt to explain attributes of the mind in this way amount to an attempt of "the tail" to "wag the dog?"

2.3.2. The Growth and Maturation of an Entire Organism (morphogenesis)

Yet another great enigma in our scientific understanding of life arises when we consider the development of an organism in its entirety. It is recognized that every living cell within an organism operates according to processes that can be described as both orchestrated and purposeful. For example, we can observe how a specific embryonic stem cell ends up differentiating into a nerve cell rather than a muscle cell, and each other cell type also follows a precise developmental pathway. Every cell performs its designated function at exactly the right time, as if guided by a common architectural blueprint dictating its role. This unfathomably complex choreography reliably leads to the formation of a fully developed organism. Some cells remain quiescent for years before springing into action, as exemplified in humans by the changes that occur during the emergence of permanent teeth or during puberty, while others, like those driving the heartbeat, act swiftly.

Information about the complex aspects of bodily anatomy and properly timed physiological actions of an organism must be reliably stored somewhere and somehow. When we examine the human brain, we see it begins as a tiny 3-millimeter neural tube and evolves into an organ containing over 100 billion neurons at birth. To accomplish this feat, the brain must expand at the remarkable rate of roughly 250,000 new nerve cells per minute (and form more than one million new neural connections every second) – a true marvel of organismal biological engineering.[168] These phenomena raise a longstanding question: how does each cell "know" its precise function and timing during development? Which parts of the genome within the cell should be used and expressed, and at what times and locations? Our present scientific knowledge doesn't reach far enough to answer this question. And the notion that all cells in a developing organism receive purposeful, top-down signals based on some centralized developmental blueprint is hard to escape.[169] At the same time, this notion challenges some entrenched scientific perspectives. Historically, scientists have shied away from the term *purpose,* as it implies some form of *agency*, a concept that is met with discomfort by many in the field (even though we all constantly experience agency in our own mental space.)

This conundrum is biology's hard problem. Paul Nurse acknowledges the challenge: "How all of this spatial order develops is one of the more challenging questions in biology. … At present, we only really understand fully the structure of biological objects that are direct assemblies of molecules. … Understanding how structures form at larger scales, in objects such as organelles, cells, organs and whole organisms is more difficult."[170] Speaking specifically about brain development, Paola Arlotta echoes this sentiment: "Nobody knows what the entire code of development is, … we know bits and pieces of very specific aspects of the development of the brain, … how the two cells interact to make the next level structure, that we might know, but the entirety of it, how it's so well controlled, it's really mind-blowing."[171]

Two promising and paradigm-changing research fields have been exploring new frontiers and providing a glimpse into some aspects of the development of living organisms: *epigenetics* and *developmental bioelectricity*. And they both strongly hint at the purposeful organismal agency.

Epigenetics

Epigenetics studies changes in gene activity that don't involve alterations to the underlying DNA sequence.[172] Instead of changing the DNA code itself, epigenetic changes modify how the genes are expressed, by turning specific genes "on" or "off." One way to think about it is via the already mentioned analogy with music. We can think of the human genome as a grand piano. All the keys (genes) are there, but not all of them are played at the same time. Epigenetics is like the pianist's choice of which keys to press, how hard, and in what sequence, creating different melodies without changing the actual keys. There are several paradigm-changing discoveries within the field of epigenetics. First is that an organism, as an active agent (pianist), reacts to environmental influence epigenetically (plays the keys of genome piano as necessary) to adapt to this influence. This is not a random-chance process that evolves over millions of years, we can observe it in the adapting organism during in vivo experiments, and it is obviously goal-oriented. Second is that epigenetic changes can in some cases be passed down to offspring. This means environmental factors or experiences of the parents — and how they reacted to it — might influence gene expression in their children without changing their children's DNA sequence. We know that factors such as stress, exposure to toxins, and diet can lead to epigenetic changes, affecting how genes are expressed, and that dysregulation in epigenetic patterns can lead to diseases. Implications of this are wide-ranging, not only for our understanding of living beings, but also for medicine, and, most importantly, for understanding how the kind of social environment we create deeply affects all human beings and their health, all the way down to their bodily structures. Moreover, we may ponder how our own inner world, our own thoughts and feelings — which ultimately create either a stressful or nourishing social environment — influence our own bodies and also everyone else's around us. We can only imagine the kinds of music our epigenetic selves play on everybody's genome when we are full of love, as opposed to full of greed or hate. Thus, speaking from a purely biological point of view, it is not incorrect to state that if we hate somebody, this action is akin to physically hitting them, and when we love another being, this is helping both of us grow and thrive.

Developmental bioelectricity, a force field of life?

Developmental bioelectricity (often referred to as *bioelectricity networks* or simply as *bioelectricity*) is a remarkable discovery.[173] Even though it has been researched and publicized since the early 2000s in its current context, it also feels, alongside epigenetics, like one of the best-kept secrets in science. Bioelectricity patterns provide the means for an organism to unfold its anatomy during the development. The experiments in developmental bioelectricity, in fact, challenge the assumption that genes contain information that determines complex aspects of bodily anatomy. Before the discovery of developmental bioelectricity, even though we knew that DNA in genes contains information specifying the protein building blocks for an organism (low-level hardware of sorts) and that developmental genes (e.g. toolkit/Hox) are involved in some aspects of morphogenesis (the acquisition of shape and structure by an organism), we did not know how the complex features of bodily anatomy are determined or their unfolding accomplished. Genes do not seem to specify the complex features of bodily anatomy nor how it unfolds from a single cell into a whole organism.[174] However, all cells in an organism need to know somehow which proteins to manufacture (which keys to play on the "epigenetic grand DNA piano"), when to start, and when to stop a given action, all depending on their place and role. We now know that the purposeful intelligence that governs this process can be observed in the overarching intricate bioelectricity pattern present in all living organisms. Every cell of a living organism actively participates in the maintenance of this bioelectric pattern (observable via fluorescent voltage-sensitive dye during in vivo experiments), and every cell derives cues for its own activity from this pattern. Scientifically speaking, at this point we don't understand exactly how, but these patterns are also able to play the role of memory, they reliably store and retrieve information, as they are the keepers of the blueprint of the whole organism. This is demonstrable during initial organismal development and during the regenerative actions. Cells of an embryo follow the instructions stored in the bioelectric blueprint during development, and cells also do it if an injury occurs to regenerate and repair the injury. Experiments with flatworms, which fully regenerate after injuries, are fascinating. The majority of them were performed and published by Michael Levin and the team from his Tufts and Harvard labs.[175] For example, if the information stored in the bioelectric blueprint of a flatworm is intentionally "hacked" before an injury (e.g. by changing the bioelectric pattern with ion-channel drugs in targeted cells), this hacking action is stored in the bioelectric pattern. The bodily tissue repair is then predictably affected by that modification after the injury, without any changes in the DNA-based genome. Intelligence radiates through the bioelectric coordinating actions – in the face of perturbations and obstacles, multiple paths of cell actions are quickly discovered and utilized to accomplish the same organismal action. The first encounter with these experiments can indeed feel like science fiction.

At this point, it may be noteworthy to mention two 19th-century ideas about evolution and organismal development. One was introduced by Jean-Baptiste Lamarck (*Lamarckism*, the idea that organisms can pass on traits acquired during their lifetime to their offspring), and the other comes from Henri Bergson (*Élan Vital*, a hypothetic vital force that orchestrates and drives the development of living organisms.) They both had evolutionary implications but were generally viewed with skepticism and often outright dismissed and ridiculed by proponents of the neo-Darwinian theory and by scientists in general. They were considered incompatible with the widely believed ideas about the genetic basis of inheritance and development, which were considered "evidence-based" (arguably the phrase often (mis)used to justify settling for reductionist notions and unwillingness to research deeper). Now that the rigid gene-centric notions of inheritance and evolutionary development are considered outdated in scientific circles (establishment is also slowly catching up), these and related ideas have become ripe for reconsideration and update. As for Lamarckism, the field of epigenetics and its discoveries have opened new vistas for its reconsideration. Denis Noble expressed the sentiment of many scientists in the field by proclaiming "Lamarck is back."[176] A considerable number of scientific works that endorse this sentiment have been published,[177] and we already have textbooks that spell this out: "Lamarck and his ideas were ridiculed and discredited. In a strange twist of fate, Lamarck may have the last laugh. Epigenetics, an emerging field of genetics, has shown that Lamarck may have been at least partially correct all along."[178] On the other hand, it seems too early to claim that the idea of Élan Vital, or some form of it, is also back. However, observations made during experiments with the developmental bioelectricity patterns in living organisms are giving us reasons for some reflection in this regard. We now know that an organism follows the organizing pattern manifested in the bioelectricity network. This overarching pattern informs its activity, particularly its bodily development and regenerative capacity. There exists a blueprint for each organism, and we can observe that at least some aspects of it are revealed in this intricate bioelectric pattern. At this point, scientifically speaking, we do know that each cell participates in it, but we don't yet understand what the true source (or force?) behind the organization of these intricate bioelectric patterns is and how is it possible for them to reliably store and retrieve highly complex and structured information. We do recognize that bioelectric patterns unquestionably manifest intelligent agency and purpose, and they contain (or convey) important highly structured information, with timed developmental cues, for every cell of an organism. Experiments also show that cells within an organism constantly exchange information via the bioelectricity network (e.g. damage to a tissue on one leg is signaled to the cells in the corresponding location on the other, uninjured, leg). Furthermore, experiments are demonstrating that the inter-organism bioelectricity information exchange is also taking place, revealing a sort of collective intelligence at work (e.g. groups of embryos in the same medium exchange information about the injury to a single embryo.)[179] All this may sound radical today, even unbelievable, to many among us who harbor the conventional scientific worldview (quickly becoming outdated and obsolete in the light of new experiments.) Be it as it may, it is definitely food for some serious thought, and for further research. And, needless to say, in our time we need human reason to lead the way on this path, not blind irrational beliefs of any kind.

This chain of thought brings forward reflections about the topic pondered by one of the science icons. Back in the 1940s, Erwin Schrödinger wrestled with the problem of the resilient orderliness and regularity of living organisms and presented his thoughts in a series of lectures, which later were expanded and published in his work *What is Life*. In it, he considers the necessity for a new scientific paradigm. He wrote the following under the subtitle *New Laws to be Expected in the Organism*: "from all we have learnt about the structure of living matter, we must be prepared to find it working in a manner that cannot be reduced to the ordinary laws of physics. ... The unfolding of events in the life cycle of an organism exhibits an admirable regularity and orderliness, unrivalled by anything we meet with in inanimate matter. ... We must be prepared to find a new type of physical law prevailing in it. Or are we to term it a non-physical, not to say a super-physical, law?"[180]

It is not obvious whether scientists, and humanity in general, are ready for a "super-physical" (whatever it may be) in our worldviews. But then, we might be arriving at a point where we have to face this possibility. I will go on a limb here and notice that, with the experiments in developmental bioelectricity, we might be knocking on doors of something new and different. There are already first experimental indications, opening a possibility that even bioelectricity networks may not be the ultimate source of governing developmental blueprints. Rather, bioelectricity could represent the first manifestation of a deeper (unknown to science) source that is indirectly observable with our present scientific instruments. It seems plausible that bioelectricity is only a dynamic imprint, an interface of sorts, of another — underlying — phenomenon that conveys agency and is formatively involved in this imprint's existence. Experiments[181] with planarian flatworms are telling. (The body of a flatworm fully regenerates after an injury – even if cut into hundreds of pieces, each piece grows into a full planarian, from head to tail.) Experiments in which their bioelectricity pattern is hacked in such a way that it instructs their bodies to grow a "monster" head (head is severed after the hack, and in two weeks grows back) are successful – planarians do grow heads of different (remotely related) species, but there is a twist. The twist is that, after a while, the body of this "monster" planarian reverts by itself, without any intervention, in just a few weeks, so that it again becomes a good old planarian – "monster" head metamorphoses back into a nice planarian head, eyes and all. This experiment highlights a possibility that a deeper principle might exist (dare we say a force? and was Schrödinger onto something after all?), which in this case manages to override the hacked bioelectric pattern and restore the biological shape to match the original blueprint in these experiments. We can only wonder how all that works when nature itself scrambles the bioelectric pattern in order to create it anew, like in the case of butterfly development. During the two-week chrysalis stage, the caterpillar undergoes a remarkable transformation, completely reorganizing its body into the shape of a butterfly (while intriguingly retaining information/memories from its caterpillar stage).[182] There is more: if a flatworm learns how to find food in a simple maze, the memory of that learning is preserved. Even if its head (with the brain) is cut off, when the head regenerates in about two weeks, the flatworm regains the memory of the learned process. This demonstrates that "the *information is likely stored outside of the brain* and it [likely] has to be imprinted onto the new brain as it develops."[183] Bioelectrical networks seem to have something to do with memories of living beings in general, not only with the processes of organismal development. If we try to scale this insight up, all the way to human beings, important questions are opened regarding humans as well – specifically regarding our capacity for remembering and recalling memories and the possible involvement of bioelectrical medium, or the principle underlying it. Memory is indispensable to the human sense of self and its continuity, thus the principle behind it is of great consequence (this topic is addressed in a separate section in the second part of the book.)

2.3.3. The Mother of All Questions in Evolutionary Biology: Origin of Life

And finally, of course, there is the foundational question in evolutionary biology: that of the *origin of life*. We have made some attempts to find scientific answers to this question, both experimental and theoretical, but nothing more than mere assumptions and conjectures ever came out of them. Everything science claims about life's origin is "highly speculative."[184] Scientifically speaking, we are not even exactly sure which phenomena to call life. We intuitively feel that there is a big gap between the phenomena of life and non-life, but "perhaps surprisingly, there is no standard definition of life, although scientists have wrestled with this question across the ages."[185] Our operational definitions of life rely on the fact that "everything that is alive on the planet is either a cell or made from a collection of cells."[186] If we accept that, the origin of life question becomes: how is it possible that a chaotic assembly of chemicals can turn into something as complex and orderly as a cell that can maintain and replicate itself. This mystery undoubtedly stands as one of science's most profound challenges. We have plenty of speculations and guesses, but scientifically speaking, nobody really has a clue. If we add to this the newly acquired insights about the organizing principle of life being manifested in the intricate bioelectricity networks we observe in living beings, the enigma deepens and grows more perplexing. Rather than clinging to feeble speculative ideas, it may be more prudent to gather the courage, stop marketing hypotheses as facts, and accept the uncertainty until we can advance our understanding in this domain.

Evolutionary biology is still a young discipline, but it has already come a long way and has provided us with many insights into our nature and development. It has thus been a beacon of light, slowly establishing footholds for reason in our worldviews. Like most endeavors of human reason, its path has been meandering towards its quest for truth. But persistence and honesty in this quest don't fail to yield results in due time. As we have seen, new discoveries in this scientific field now have the potential to liberate us from the clutches of deceptive and pernicious traps we stumbled upon, and we also get to keep the prize – the rational stance in our worldviews.

But we should never forget that if we gather the courage and dare to remove the veil, we will see nature "delightful and entrancing,"[187] she is also wise, lifegiving, immeasurably beautiful, and deeply caring for its creation, even in times of hardship when it may not feel that way, especially in those times. We can only hope that, having trodden this path, we have embraced a new understanding, reverence, and humbleness towards the secrets of the phenomena of nature as they reveal themselves to us. May that be our future guide in all scientific endeavors.

2.4. Existential Despair and Physicalist Worldview of Modern Science

Mental health experts from all disciplines have consistently been telling us that human beings need: 1) *productive work*, 2) *loving relationships*, and 3) *a sense of meaning* for their mental health.[188] Societies that create opportunities and foster a supportive environment for accomplishing these needs are healthy societies. Sigmund Freud, the founder of psychoanalysis, was once asked what constituted psychological health, and his answer was the ability "to love and to work." Psychiatrist Viktor Frankl added "meaning" to these essentials.[189] Indeed, an inability to engage in long-term relationships or in meaningful work is indicative of a form of sickness. Without fulfilling these needs, human beings cannot fully develop or lead healthy lives. We shouldn't even need experts to point this out to us, this truth should be considered self-evident, an obvious fact of life: we need a sense of meaning, loving relationships, and productive work. We seek them like plants seek light, and we suffer and get sick if we are unable to find them. But then, we somehow seem to have created a cultural narrative and society in which neither of these fundamental human needs are a priority.

Of all our mental health needs, human relationships are the most existentially important. They form the cornerstone of our humanity, serving as the central hub from which all meaning, purpose, and motivation for any kind of engagement or work emanate. Both traditional wisdom and modern science converge on this essential truth about human beings: the formation of meaningful bonds with others and the nurturing exchange of care are universally recognized as foundational to mental well-being, more than any other factor (we explore this further in the fourth chapter). This is an established scientific fact with virtually no controversy. For infants to grow into healthy and strong adults, healthy attachment relationships with caregivers are indispensable. In the realm of psychotherapy, therapeutic relationships, perhaps more than any other factor, are key to healing psychological traumas. In the words of psychologist and psychiatrist, founder and pioneer of the *Attachment Theory*, John Bowlby:

> "Intimate attachments to other human beings are the hub around which a person's life revolves, not only when he is an infant or a toddler or a schoolchild but throughout his adolescence and his years of maturity as well, and on into old age. From these intimate attachments a person draws his strength and enjoyment of life and, through what he contributes, he gives strength and enjoyment to others. These are matters about which current science and traditional wisdom are at one."[190]

While there is an important place for solitude[191] and for the ability to be alone[192] in human life, even those who thrive in solitude during extended periods of time owe important aspects of their maturation and formative experiences to relationships, and their work is often in some way connected to what other people are doing, thinking, or feeling. Therefore, the significance of healthy relationships — with friends, family, classmates, co-workers, comrades, buddies, colleagues — is essential for a healthy life (just as unhealthy or abusive relationships can be detrimental.) This is a truth that resonates universally, everybody seems to know and understand, at least on some level, that care and human connections are fundamental to a healthy and fulfilling human life.

This being the case, if we would imagine an independent rational observer, say a visitor from another universe — equipped with this knowledge that relationships are crucial to human well-being — it is obvious that they would be perplexed by the way we live our lives. They would have to conclude that many Western societies in the so-called developed world are structured and organized in a way that is fundamentally anti-relational. The things we care about as a society, endeavors in which we invest our best and brightest efforts, how we appreciate, nourish, develop, honor, and commit ourselves to human care and human bonds, are not only inadequate, but they also often seem to be heading in the opposite direction. In many respects, we actively undermine these relational values by prioritizing raw individual self-interest over relationships and care, ignoring the psychological traumas this inflicts on people.[193] And all of us are impacted by the consequences.

(This book includes a chapter dedicated to the central role of relationships in defining our human identity. In it, we venture to explore why human minds are inherently relational and discuss the reasons AI cannot replicate this relationality. We also talk about the necessity for the inauguration of the *economy of care*, in which the main participants are relating humans (rather than AI.) All that will not be left unexamined, but for now, we need to set these topics aside and focus on understanding some of the reasons behind humanity's irrational anti-relational stance.)

A well-known book about psychological trauma, *The Body Keeps The Score*,[194] by psychiatrist Bessel van der Kolk, has been on the New York Times best-selling book list for more than three years now, and is still going strong at the time of this writing. It is, of course, great that this material is reaching many people, it is in books like this that we can read about the healing of trauma and, among other things, that *"restoring relationships and community is central to restoring well-being."* But the fact that it has been on the best-selling book list for such a long time is telling us that many people have been grappling with psychological trauma. In fact, there are many signs telling us that we presently have a horrific mental health epidemic staring at us, and it has been unfolding, with increasing intensity, for quite a while. The situation in the United States is particularly grim as described by economist Anne Case and Nobel laureate Angus Deaton in their recent book *Deaths of Despair*,[195] which focuses on uncovering social and economic forces behind this phenomenon: life expectancy in the United States has been falling for several years in a row, deaths from suicide, drug overdose, and alcoholism have been rising dramatically (every year they claim hundreds of thousands of lives), people in working-class communities have fewer and fewer prospects, which all too often results in broken families and many deaths of despair. Case and Deaton outline how capitalism is reshaping itself into an untamed self-interested destructive force that helps corporations grow their power at the expense of working-class communities, thus propelling inequality to new heights. Ironically this process is most visible in the health-care sector, which was supposed to be about health, and about care, but which metamorphosed itself into a ruthless redistribution machine, pumping working-class income and resources into the pockets of the wealthy. Similar news about the existential despair of people and of communities has been reaching us from many other directions as well, and just the titles of several recent books and news articles are telling volumes:

- *Why Americans Are Dying from Despair?*
- *The kids are not all right, and frustratingly, we don't really know how to help them,*
- *Surgeon General Advisory Raises Alarm about the Devastating Impact of the Epidemic of Loneliness and Isolation,*
- *America Fails the Civilization Test,*
- *America's Teenage Girls are Not Okay: Rising teen anxiety is a national crisis,*
- *The Men — and Boys — Are Not Alright,*
- *America's Life Expectancy Crisis: Stress is Weathering Our Bodies from the Inside Out,*
- *Why American Teens Are So Sad,*
- *Stress in America: Generation Z,*
- *We're Missing a Key Driver of Teen Anxiety,*
- *Millennials aren't having kids. Here's why.*
- *The Silicon Valley Suicides*
- *Too many Americans, in almost all groups, are dying,*
- *Teenagers Are Telling Us That Something Is Wrong With America,*
- *The paradox of wealthy nations' unhappy adolescents.*

There is more, many more. It is undeniable that we are in the midst of a growing mental health epidemic, and we don't really know how to help ourselves. There are many ways to think about this phenomenon, and there are opinions and theories about "what to do?" Most of the theories (among the sincere and defensible ones) are presented by experts in their fields and seem to be very practical in their thinking. Solutions have been thought out: what to do about the opioid epidemics, about wealth redistribution or taxes, about education, healthcare, monopolies, minimum wage, basic income... And most of them (justifiably) either demand changes in policy and laws or seek to raise awareness about the need for such changes. They are, of course, noble causes we must implement, but alas, obstacles and forces pushing in the opposite direction seem to be insurmountable for us. Take just healthcare industry in the United States as an example: as Case & Deaton tell us, already back in 1963, economist and Nobel laureate Kenneth Arrow implored that the ruthless *"laissez-faire* solution for medicine is intolerable,"[196] and yet, here we are, 60 years later, using healthcare — under political protection — to redistribute wealth upwards towards the rich, at the cost of destruction of whole communities. Forces pushing in the opposite direction — irrational from the perspective of humanity as a whole — are formidable and seem stronger than our good intentions. They are obviously able to overpower and ignore any ethical norms, imperatives, rules, or social contracts known to us. Many experts seem to know exactly what needs to be done, so we have at least that part figured out. What, then, if anything, can we do about the powerful forces — embedded in our society and its cultural narrative — that are standing in our way?

If we step back, and observe the situation through the eyes of our independent rational observer from another universe, it seems appropriate to characterize this adversarial force as anti-relational: this force resists any action that favors supporting human beings if it comes at the expense of raw selfish self-interest. Greed would be another term for it (and we need to include in it the willingness to inflict the pain our greedy actions cause to others.) Existential despair people are experiencing has its ultimate roots in individual greed and in its powerful anti-relational self-interested position. In some ways, this might seem obvious, but further examination is needed.

How is it that greed can wield such power and ensure its persistence and long-term prosperity within human society? Is there truly something in human nature that enables this, something we cannot change, or has its justification been fortified by persuasive stories? Does our dominant modern Western worldview, informed by scientific endeavors, have something to do with establishing the primacy of greed in our society? A short excursion into some aspects of the history concerning the birth of the modern Western scientific worldview — during the Age of Reason when this worldview was forged — seems necessary in our search for answers.

The anti-relational sentiment was not always with us, at least not in this widespread and powerful form. Humanity has a long history of traditional societal values that are deeply rooted in relational context. Africa's *Ubuntu* way of life is centered around relationality and stands out as one noteworthy example. Traditional societies and their community-oriented worldviews were prevalent before the onset of the Age of Reason (also known as the Age of Enlightenment, propelled by the Renaissance in the 15th and 16th, and by the Scientific Revolution in the 16th and 17th centuries.) And it is evident that traditional community-oriented worldviews have been steadily in decline ever since. In all thriving traditional societies, human bonds have always been considered important, sometimes even sacred, and this sentiment has been supported by stories, myths, beliefs, the authority of elders, and by the sheer force of tradition if necessary. The well-being of the community always comes first in a traditional society, and thus relational context rules supreme, without too much regard for individual differences – tradition is always willing to sacrifice individuality for the benefit of the group as a whole. Of course, traditions have boundaries, they are tribal in nature and there is a line after which they start to discriminate; we have never easily extended traditional values of respect and care to other tribes or outside communities. Nevertheless, relational wisdom has at least been recognized and deeply respected within group boundaries.

Enter the Age of Reason that enabled modern Western society. Individual human reason re-awakened — after it was born in Classical antiquity through philosophy, and simmered for two millennia, — it burst onto the world stage and sparked the "rebirth": Renaissance, Scientific Revolution, and the philosophy of Enlightenment. These developments burned many bridges towards the traditional group-centered worldviews, and the return to them became an impossibility. This brought a new focus on individual rights, free inquiry, and questioning of traditional authority. The empowered human reason gradually found ways to emancipate individual human beings, bringing liberation and flourishing of new human pursuits, first of all in sciences, engineering, and commerce. Humanity benefited enormously from this development. However, we came to experience that the sword of reason has two edges and must be wielded wisely. We didn't. We used carefully only one edge, the most visible and obvious one, without considering too much the wider context in which this was done. Material achievements enabled by this were bountiful, but in pursuit of material advancement, there was little consideration of how to use these advancements for the benefit of the broader ecosystem, including humanity as a whole. We ended up leaving the individual human nature unchanged – liberated, more powerful, but one-sidedly self-interested. We did have attempts (albeit rare) to build a healthy communal life based on the ideals coming out of the Age of Reason. But it can be argued that most such endeavors — i.e. attempts to build utopian communes — failed in big part due to assumptions that human nature is noble by birth, and does not need to be transformed.[197] Traditional societies have means to tame self-interested aspects of human nature, but modern Western societies ended up having a blind spot and not caring for it nearly enough.

However, if one thoroughly considers the humanistic roots of the modern Western worldview, this blind spot — and the fact that greed survived the transition into the Age of Reason — may seem like a rather unlikely development. Many other irrational beliefs and powers oppressing humanity were either purged there and then or started their descent into irrelevance. In fact, it does seem surprising that we lacked the wisdom to understand the dangers of the one-sided pursuit of reason, and that we have proceeded without much consideration of the wider contexts and implications. The Age of Reason was ushered in through the humanist impulse of the Renaissance, a major part of which was the "rebirth" of Platonic and Neoplatonic philosophy. It was at the onset of the Renaissance that the new Platonic Academy was re-founded in Florence (with the support of the Medici family) and led by Neoplatonist and humanist philosopher Marsilio Ficino. This was a major cultural and intellectual hub of the budding Renaissance. It inspired many artists and intellectuals of the time, and it was the cradle out of which many cultural impulses were born. It is within the Academy that a cultural synthesis of Platonism and Christianity (the dominant tradition of the time) was accomplished, as its scholars successfully argued that Platonic philosophy was not in opposition to Christian teachings but rather could complement and deepen their understanding. Pico della

Mirandola published the *Oration on the Dignity of Man,* considered one of the great manifestos of humanism.[198] The fact that the Age of Reason stands in no small part on the shoulders of the humanism of Platonic philosophy — which revolves around the process of evolving and perfecting human beings so that they can grasp the foundational ideas of *Justice* and *The Good* — seems to imply that most notions of raw individual self-interest were destined to be curtailed or purged. It was well understood within the main cultural current of that time, that humanism is only possible if individual human beings willingly transform their nature so that they are no longer playthings of the irrational drives within. The clutches of greed and raw self-interest, which narrow the vistas and keep human beings in ignorance, were supposed to be on their way out.

We have to wonder then, how it happened that the humanist ideals were slowly pushed aside and — if we fast forward to our time — are now increasingly overlooked? If we go back in time, we can indeed trace humanist ideals and see them well represented from the Renaissance onwards, they resonate strongly in many cultural currents, even if they dress in different philosophies, like Enlightenment Humanism, Transcendentalism, Existentialism, Secular Humanism, and Critical theory, to name a few.[199] Humanist ideals didn't go anywhere, they are still with us, even if somewhat muted. But then, obviously, another powerful force must be at work in the human cultural narrative.

Indeed, we can trace a parallel cultural undercurrent from early on, developing as an opposition to the humanist culture, becoming manifest in the early 16th-century Renaissance. It appears to surface in Niccolò Machiavelli's political treatise *The Prince*. In it, Machiavelli advises leaders on how to acquire and maintain power, advocating for pragmatic and ruthless tactics

— employing cruelty, violence, and trickery — over moral or ethical considerations. One position, or rather one belief, about human nature is very explicit in this treatise, it tells us that: *it is because human nature itself is selfish and corrupt that dishonesty and cruelty are justified towards humans.* In Machiavelli's own words: "For this may be said of men generally: they are ungrateful, fickle, feigners and dissemblers, avoiders of danger, eager for gain" and thus we "must be prepared to act immorally" because "circumstances do not permit living a completely virtuous life."[200]

This impulse, opposite to humanism, indeed hinges on a single belief as its only justification, on a single opinion about human nature: human beings are selfish and unworthy; humanism therefore has no place among humans, and smart successful leaders are allowed to be practical and act immorally – their own selfish ends justify their unethical means. This simple justification has been recycled repeatedly, virtually without any modification, until our day. It has been used as a justification for views and philosophies opposing humanism. *The Prince* can be considered the founding document of Realpolitik and a handbook of Social Darwinism. It is imperative of our time that we notice the shortsightedness of this opinion: in it, human beings are perceived statically, not as beings that can and will develop – as implied in the Platonist and Neoplatonist cultural impulse. If we view humans through such a bleak prism and don't give them a chance to unfold their true potential, then, in fact, we do have to agree that some form of Social Darwinism and "survival of the fittest" represent the best culture we can have. If we, as humanity, succumb to this impulse — if we forget that cultural evolution has already been happening for the last few thousand years and is eager to continue — the day when we will stand on the ruins of civilization may not be too far away.[201]

After *The Prince*, we can recognize a related anti-humanist sentiment in the early 18th century, in the story published by Bernard Mandeville titled *The Fable of the Bees*, centered around a beehive that metaphorically represents human society. In this beehive, the vices and selfish behaviors of the bees are said to drive the hive's prosperity and efficiency; however, when the bees decide to adopt honesty and virtue, the hive's productivity and eco-nomic stability collapse, leading to its downfall. This satirical poem was supposed to illustrate Mandeville's argu-ment that private vices, such as greed and vanity, contribute to the economic benefits of society, suggesting that the selfish actions of individuals are the only way to arrive at positive collective outcomes. This fable is a sort of the holy book of neoliberal economics. It enshrined the idea of greed as a public good. The story is simple, persuasive, and infectious – a great device for demagogues and sophists. And yes, even a humanist like Adam Smith can be coopted by demagogues and inter-preted one-sidedly as a supporter of this kind of philoso-phy.[202] Things haven't changed much ever since, the slogan "Greed is good!" still resonates with too many among us.

We can see this anti-humanist stance in later cultural currents in the 19th and 20th centuries as well: in Realpolitik, in Objectivism (i.e. in most interpretations of Ayn Rand's philos-ophy), in foundational ideas of Postmodernism, in older interpretations of Freudian psychoanalysis (prior to the incorporation of relational theories under the psychodynamic umbrella: object relations, intersubjectivity, psychosocial de-velopment, self-psychology, and attachment theory), and in its most powerful manifestation so far – that of Social Darwinism.

Officially, Social Darwinism is viewed as a discredited and outdated ideology today, criticized both for its scientific inaccuracies and its unethical applications. In the past, it was used to justify social and political inequalities, including imperialism, racism, and cruel laissez-faire economic policies, promoting the idea that competition and struggle in society lead to progress and the betterment of humanity. In its most vicious form, it was also used to justify the Holocaust during World War II and the eugenics movement, including forced sterilizations and the euthanasia of people with disabilities. Social Darwinism has been widely criticized for its oversimplified application of biological concepts to complex social phenomena and for incorrectly providing a scientific justification for unethical and inhumane practices. So yes, technically Social Darwinism might be considered outdated and discredited; however, its foundational sentiment — epitomized in Herbert Spencer's phrase "survival of the fittest" — is very much alive and kicking. The existential dread and despair of many people in today's societies is the strongest testament to it. And again, the same simple story, the same belief, is used for its justification – it's just how human nature is and there is very little we can do about it.

We shouldn't be blind to the fact that powerful cultural icons and persuasive imagery have been built on the sentiment of "survival of the fittest." As already mentioned, Richard Dawkins's book *The Selfish Gene* is one example of it. In it, he proclaims that human nature is such that we are, in fact, just "robots" and "survival machines," and that "pure, disinterested altruism ... has no place in nature" (truth be told, Dawkins states in the book that he would be open to "discuss ways of deliberately cultivating and nurturing pure, disinterested altruism.")

(It is interesting to recognize that Dawkins' book *The Selfish Gene* appeared in the late 1970s, in parallel with several related impulses that permeated Western culture. The 1987 movie *Wall Street* is another example that vigorously influenced societal imagination in a similar direction, a line in it even says how "greed captures the essence of the evolutionary spirit." The philosophy of postmodernism also became prevalent in the 1970s and 1980s. Its main current — which also considers human beings statically, rather than developmentally — sparked a cultural movement that has been questioning the existence of any objective truths, asserting that all meaning and understanding are relative, subjective, and culturally constructed; it also embarked on an endeavor to deconstruct the idea of a unified, autonomous individual self, suggesting instead that agency of human self is dispersed, weak, constructed by various cultural, linguistic, and historical power structures. By exploring and establishing such positions, postmodernism, among other things, uncovered certain power structures in society and opened the possibility of challenging them, but at the same time, it insisted on the impotence of the human self and its powers of reason, and offered a means for individuals to disengage and dissociate themselves from ongoing events in the world.[203] In the same time period, a significant shift towards neoliberal economics in the West happened, bringing with it the ethical narrative that has "exalted some of the most distasteful of human qualities into the position of the highest virtues," to borrow the words of John Maynard Keynes. [204] The movie *Wall Street* provided some powerful wind for its wings with the sentiment that "greed, for lack of a better word, is good." Neoliberal policies are seen by many today as a powerful force behind the increased inequality, erosion of democratic institutions, economic crises, and diminishing public unity and trust. Neoliberal economics ignores the importance of societal connectedness and — despite the fact that it is undergoing its own evolution[205] — its underlying sentiment[206] remains a globally influential dehumanizing force.)

It is obvious that inferences from science are being made by Dawkins and by other authors writing in the same vein. They claim — without evidence (as demonstrated in the preceding material of this and the previous chapter)[207] — that science teaches how human beings are only deterministic bundles of atoms and molecules, how biochemistry will (in undetermined due time) be able to explain everything about human beings (including our minds), how we are only mechanisms of sorts, and how our evolution and development are driven by random-chance mutations and selection of our genes. All such statements are based either on mere assumptions or, at best, on outdated scientific theories. These assumptions about human nature imply that lucky ones among us become fit, enjoy life, and survive a bit longer; while unlucky ones suffer, despair, and die early. No agency, no purpose, and no meaning play any role in this view, they could only be illusions[208] of sorts. But yes, the claim is that science "discovered" all that. By inference, existential despair is to be expected — for the weak (or less fit) among us — and should simply be accepted as a reality of life. If all this were true, science would, in fact, support the idea of some form of Social Darwinism, this conclusion is inescapable.

Moreover, in the physicalist perspective on science, there is no place for any of the key factors we have identified as necessary for mental health. If our nature is such that we are just "survival machines," if "pure, disinterested altruism ... has no place in nature," and if all events in nature, including evolutionary development, are without agency, meaning, or purpose (at best they are illusions) — then loving relationships and meaningful work are not really possible. Mental health would be a sort of an illusion as well, mental hardship would be only some kind of an imbalance of chemicals in the "survival machine."

This is the genuine position of the physicalist scientific worldview today, even if it may sound weird to many people when expressed in this chain of thoughts. I suspect that most people holding views of modern physicalist science might even shy away from such formulations. And it is also possible that most people are spared suffering through these thoughts by the fortunate fact that they don't pay too much attention in school when this stuff is taught. If one really ponders about such a bleak view of reality, existential worries appear naturally, do they not? When a university professor, after teaching theories along these lines gets a message from a student — who did pay attention to what was thought — saying "Dear Professor …, What advice do you have for someone who has taken ideas in your books and science to heart, and sees himself as a collection of atoms? A machine with a limited scope of intelligence, sprung out of selfish genes, inhabiting spacetime?"[209] — this should not be shrugged off, this can indeed be a cry of a person feeling the approaching existential dread (or the grip of loneliness or depression.)[210] It is also one more testament to how ridiculous our physicalist belief system, dressed in science's clothing, has become.

Could we perhaps dismiss our worries by saying that these ideas involve some complicated scientific theories, and most people really don't even pay attention to them, they have better things to do, so people must be fine, life is not really predatory out there, "survival of the fittest" is just a story. Not really. All institutions in our system do pay attention, our for-profit corporations do, our health care and insurance companies do, and our technocracy and bureaucracy do as well. Our culture, education, institutions of science, governance, and economy are all affected by it. If somebody desperately needs mental health treatment, it's all too common that their medical insurance refuses to allow it, simply because it is not "evidence-based" (an abused buzzword)[211] that they need yet another therapy session, they should be fine after what they already got (or not... if despair becomes unbearable some people choose to end their lives; every 11 minutes a human being commits suicide in the US, every 2.5 seconds someone seriously considers it; and the suicide rates reached an all-time high in 2022 when nearly 50,000 killed themselves, we have science about that too.)[212] Even the survivors suffer, for example, as of 2023, the percentage of US adults who report having been diagnosed with depression at some point in their lifetime has reached 29%, and among women alone, the percentage is 37%![213]

The vast majority of corporations in our economic system feel fully justified to set themselves up to extract maximum profit for the owners of capital as the first order of business,[214] many big corporations do not shy from exposing people to suffering or death if they can get away with it,[215] and it is not high on their priority list to provide an environment for meaningful and productive work for their employees, or to help them with the flexibility to attend to loving relationships in their lives (in contemporary discourse, this consideration may even sound like a joke), or to seriously consider ecological damage and other externalities of their actions. Institutions of education also pay attention, and very often, especially in the United States, education is treated as a business — rather than as a cultural investment and societal necessity — with targeted efforts to extract as much profit through every student (during their "struggle to survive" the educational process), either in the form of tuition or predatory loans to pay for "their" education. Not every society is affected in the same way, Nordic countries are shining examples of how to promote humanist values in society while maintaining a vibrant life and economy,[216] but very few people are lucky to live in such systems. Overall, institutions in many modern Western developed countries are not primarily geared towards supporting our humanism, they sanction and serve the forces of greed first and foremost, and through that, they are pulling us all down. It is our task to uncover the supporting narrative that justifies and allows this process.

Therefore, the question is warranted: exactly how complicit is our science in the misrepresentation of human nature and thus in the dehumanization of culture and the creation of existential despair in a vast number of human beings? Here we clearly have to differentiate scientific facts from beliefs dressed in science's clothing. Science as a discipline relies on the curiosity of human reason, observation of phenomena, making hypotheses about the observed phenomena, skillful collection of data, their unbiased interpretation, and then finally human reason can make conclusions about the causes and laws active in the observed phenomena. This is how we arrive at scientific facts, this is pretty straightforward. Beliefs dressed in science's clothing are altogether different, they are conjured up by irrational forces in our minds, based on the worldviews we subscribe to, and they don't bother with the scientific method too much. Let's examine this on two fallacies that are the most damaging — ruinous really — to our humanism:

Fallacy #1: *Human beings are just complex deterministic machines consisting of physical matter, with no intrinsic agency, and no purpose (we* *can't identify what concepts of 'being', 'agency' and 'purpose' could possibly mean, they must be just some kind of illusion, or simply a way of talking.)*

   Fallacy #2*: Human beings, like all other living systems, evolved solely via a process consisting of random-chance mutations of chemical molecules in their genes, which are then selected for fitness. This is how the 'evolution by natural selection' works, this process is not influenced by any agency, and it is not driven by any kind of purpose (as stated in #1, 'being,' 'agency,' and 'purpose' must be fictions or illusions.) We don't know how 'life' could have started, but it must be that the first living cell somehow just assembled itself by a long series of random-chance accidents and was then able to maintain and reproduce itself; we believe that this likely wasn't too improbable, and after it happened, purposeless evolution and natural selection did all the development.*

   Many people harboring modern Western worldview seem to believe both these fallacies. Even if notions contained in them are scientifically outdated (by experiments), most scientists seem to believe them too. If we ask any scientist to demonstrate scientific evidence for any of these fallacies, they couldn't do it, because both #1 and #2 are merely assumptions, they are not scientific facts, they are beliefs, plain and simple. Throughout the history of science, we have never really been able to research in-depth the phenomena mentioned in these statements. This was already demonstrated in the preceding material in this and in the previous chapter,[217] so it will only be briefly summarized here. Regarding fallacy #1: scientifically speaking, we are not in a position to state what "physical matter" is, or how and when it follows deterministic laws. Thus, materialism/physicalism has a dark secret – we don't really know what matter is. Our best knowledge about it comes from quantum physics, which tells us that what we call physical matter is represented only by waves (which we interpret as probabilities), and that particles of an observed phenomenon can manifest themselves only in the presence of an "observer," an agent observing the phenomenon (this is the big unexplained mystery in quantum physics.) Founders of quantum physics therefore considered what we call physical reality to be only an expression of what we commonly call mind or consciousness (Schrödinger: "the material universe and consciousness are made out of the same stuff", Louis de Broglie: "I regard consciousness and matter as different aspects of one and the same thing", and Max Planck: "I regard consciousness as fundamental ... I regard matter as derivative from consciousness. We cannot get behind consciousness. Everything that we talk about, everything that we regard as existing, postulates consciousness.")[218] Also, future states of phenomena observed in quantum physics are unpredictable. We can't possibly state that human beings are deterministic "machines" consisting of physical matter without agency or purpose – based on what we know from physics or other sciences known to us. Science doesn't really tell us any of that. As for fallacy #2: evolution by natural selection in its neo-Darwinian incantation (random-chance mutation in DNA molecules + selection) is an outdated theory that refuses to die simply because the scientific establishment is too attached to it. As shown in the material earlier in this chapter,[219] experiments performed in recent decades, in the fields of developmental bioelectricity and epigenetics convincingly demonstrate that living beings develop as purposeful active agents, and not primarily (possibly not at all) via random-chance mutations.

Be it all as it may, most of us still seem to be rather attached to the physicalist/materialistic notions about reality, even if we intellectually admit that we don't fully understand what physical matter is. It somehow seems that these physicalist notions are tangible, it feels familiar and easy to think of everything being a sort of mechanism one can touch. Thinking of mind and consciousness as independent from this mechanism (possibly even being the very foundation of what we perceive as a mechanism) seems somehow unreal and intangible, to many it feels too much like science fiction.

But then, looking at it from another perspective: all of us constantly experience phenomena of the mind, we all unquestionably know that we are active agents with a purpose, we are conscious beings, we have thoughts, and feelings, and our will can accomplish purposeful actions. Our thinking grasps reality around us and informs us about it. All healthy human beings also have easy access to the *theory of mind*,[220] i.e. we are aware of ourselves and of other people around us and know that they are also beings who have minds with mental content, with thoughts, and feelings, and that they can act with a purpose; we can understand and anticipate their actions. We are actually very comfortable dealing with "meanings" and "purposes," and, as a matter of fact, we need meaning and purpose, we get sick when we can't find meaning and purpose. This is all very natural and seamless for all of us. We experience it all the time. But still, we won't believe that it is real and substantial. We just won't do it easily. It somehow seems "too spooky" to us, whatever that means. For most people harboring the modern Western scientific worldview, this is just hard. That's how far we have come after Galileo decided (as we mentioned earlier) that we must limit the domain of natural science to "tangible" stuff, which can be "captured in the purely quantitative language of mathematics," and leave the rest unexamined. The science we currently have is not equipped to even identify the phenomena of mind, except through their secondary effects, let alone to define or properly research them. So, the solution many scientists and philosophers of science have resorted to is to simply wish them away, not believe in them, and proclaim that they must be some kind of illusion somehow. There is no scientific evidence telling us that these phenomena don't really exist. There can't be such evidence.

Therefore, after a somewhat lengthy consideration in this section, we can indeed conclude that science remains the greatest gift passed on to us from the Age of Reason. Human reason can utilize scientific methods to learn deep secrets of the world around us. However, crude materialistic interpretations and belief systems based on physicalist scientific worldview have been wreaking havoc on humanity. Its beliefs that human beings are just "survival machines," without any intrinsic agency and purpose, engaged in a struggle termed "survival of the fittest" where "selfish genes" propagate, have created untold damage to our humanism. There is nothing scientific about those beliefs. It is precisely when the idea of human nature is hijacked, and the concepts of human agency and purpose are taken away, it is when humans are not seen as beings belonging to the community of beings, when they are perceived as meaningless blobs of molecules developing randomly without purpose, or only as numbers in statistic calculations, that they become dehumanized, they become "others" and "them" and "those people." Once they are dehumanized in this way, perceived as separate, as others, as not really belonging anywhere, they can be ignored, not cared for, and greedily exploited for individual benefit. Or worse. So, yes, science matters, and we should be very clear (and loud!) about what science is and what it isn't. If we let irrational beliefs run around dressed in science's clothing, we provide fodder for irrational impulses inflicting pain, despair, and destroying our humanity.

2.5. Is the Human Mind the Most Important Scientific Instrument?

All science needs scientific instruments. Statements of this kind usually invoke images of scientific hardware in labs and classrooms: telescopes, microscopes, spectroscopes, and the like. But there is more to it, please indulge me on this point for a moment, and let's briefly revisit the basics.

What is science? There is no single answer to this question, and an entire discipline, the *philosophy of science*, has emerged in pursuit of answers.[221] Perhaps surprisingly, we don't have a singular, universally accepted definition of science. This does not seem to concern the majority of modern scientists deeply immersed in their work; Steven Weinberg famously wrote that "philosophy of science is just about as useful to scientists as ornithology is to birds."[222] Be that as it may, when the emergence of a "new paradigm"[223] in science — a term coined by philosopher of science Thomas Kuhn — appears on the horizon, it might be prudent to revisit and restate some of our fundamental principles.

The word *science* is only a few hundred years old, it comes from the Latin "scientia", meaning *knowledge*. But there is more to science than just knowledge. We need to have some means to reliably acquire knowledge, and we also need to know that we can trust those means, trust that our knowledge is a true representation of reality. We humans utilize our minds for this purpose, we employ *reason*[224] and specifically, its capacity for *objective thinking.* Science, as a method for acquiring knowledge, is not possible without the instrument of human reason. We are the only species on our planet that can reason, that is why we are the only ones doing science. Thus, if we wanted to identify the essence of science, one possible way to do it would be to define it as an activity of *reasoning that results in knowledge.* Everything else in the scientific method could be considered technical details (e.g. how to use the hardware of telescopes, microscopes, etc, and how to formulate scientific papers, and the like.)

Demonstrating the essential role of human reason in science, cognitive scientists Alison Gopnik, Andrew Meltzoff, and Patricia Kuhl have shown that even infants engage in a form of scientific inquiry while learning about the world around them. Technical details of the kind of science infants are doing may not be conventional, but babies' use of reason and knowledge is a serious business. In their book *The Scientist in the Crib*,[225] these scientists explain that infants are born with an innate capacity for reasoning, which they use to learn and hypothesize imaginatively about the world. It can be observed that, in their learning process, babies clearly "formulate theories, make and test predictions, seek explanations, do experiments, and revise what they know in the light of new evidence … these abilities are at the core of the success of science."[226]

It is obvious that the process above, even when done by infants, entails much more than raw intelligence. Raw intelligence, whether human or artificial, can on some level be likened to a computing device that processes input data and transforms it into output data (which can all be of great complexity.) However, raw intelligence does not inherently seek explanations; it lacks agency, purpose, own will, intentions, or imaginative capacity. These attributes represent a broader context and must originate from outside the scope of raw intelligence itself.

At this juncture in our discussion, it seems appropriate to clarify some positions regarding the features of human reason. The term reason, as used here, has a broader connotation than intelligence. Reason serves as the organizing principle of the human mind, encompassing human purposeful agency and its capacities, which include cognitive, affective, and conative aspects (our thinking, feeling, and will). Among its other functions, reason, while interacting with the environment, also *regulates affect* based on deliberative cognitive processes, and *exerts control over conation* (which includes instincts, drives, wishes, cravings, and also inclinations and purposeful actions of the will.) In this context, the concept of reason aligns well with the metaphorical depiction of a *charioteer guiding the horses* (forces within the human mind) in Plato's dialogue *Phaedrus*.[227] It also resonates with Plato's view that human health (mental and physical) is dependent on the ability of reason to exercise all its capacities. This point is vital for our discussions and will be revisited in the subsequent chapters.

Returning to the topic of science: if we accept the premise that *reason and the knowledge acquired through reason are the essence of science*, then it can be argued that what we commonly refer to as science began much earlier than the Scientific Revolution (which happened in the 16th and 17th centuries.) From this perspective, the early roots of science can be traced back to Classical antiquity, when the discipline of philosophy — which awakened the full power of human reason — was born in ancient Greece, two millennia before the Scientific Revolution. Philosophy literally means *love of wisdom* or rather *intimate and affectionate receptivity for wisdom,*[228] and can arguably be considered the true birthing impulse of free human thought and of trust in human thought. This was the point at which we started to diverge from age-old worldviews that relied on authority and belief systems.[229] Indeed, the Scientific Revolution significantly enhanced the scientific method, but that can be considered as only an upgrade of the fundamental scientific instrument — human reason — which we had already embraced with the birth of philosophy.

We can conclude this segment with a summary stating that *the true foundation of science lies in the human capacity for reason, specifically for objective thinking, and our trust in it.*

3 Technology and Artificial Intelligence in the 21st Century

The content of this section might disappoint all readers hoping to find elaborate details about the technical aspects of AI. As you have probably noticed by now, there is not much talk about the specifics of the *Artificial* aspect of AI in this book, there is much more talk about the *Intelligence* features and the role intelligence plays within the human mind as one of its attributes. The good news is that there is plenty of material out there about the technical aspects of AI, explaining how equipment, software, data, and training pieces can be put together so that the whole AI machinery behaves in a way we consider intelligent. Several pointers to technical AI resources are provided in the endnotes.[230] AI is a tantalizing discipline with a very turbulent history, during which it has defied and proved many of its critics wrong. Its history is comparatively short, spanning about seven decades, from its humble beginnings in the 1950s to its significant successes when it bested humans first in chess, then in the game of Go, and subsequently AI demonstrated that it can be helpful to humans, for example, in the field of *natural language processing* (NLP) and by solving complex protein folding problems. Finally, it burst into the lives of hundreds of millions of people in the form of a chatbot that demonstrates highly intelligent behavior and appears very competent in handling the modalities of text, images, and sound. Several pointers to the material about the history of AI are also provided in the endnotes.[231]

3.1. Technology in the 21ˢᵗ Century

Few forces have been as influential in the lives of human beings as technology. Until recently, this force was mainly a vehicle for our liberation and empowerment. Granted, we didn't always use it wisely, destructive wars and ecological damage are obvious examples of humanity's immaturity and inability to always wield it sensibly. However, on the whole, the progress of technology has enabled the progress of the human race. We had to adjust whenever a technological revolution happened — trades, professions, and jobs were disrupted — but when the dust had settled, the outcome was almost always a more empowered and liberated human race. Technology happily took on the role of serving humanity. This has been true since our humble beginnings when we were learning how to carve stone tools and master fire, to the era of steam engines and weaving looms, refrigerators and washing machines, electric motors, cars, trains, airplanes, phones, computers, and the internet.

But then, sometime in the early 2000s, a different force started to surface and permeate the realm of technology. A rift of sorts began to appear. There remained the "good old" technology, a tool utilized by humanity, useful and empowering. But a new face of technology also started to emerge, presenting an altogether different creature, one that gradually began to impose demands on us. We came to depend on and like this new creature; it has been beneficial and made us more efficient in almost everything we do. But at the same time, there is a dear price to pay for it, there is a dark side to consider. This new wave of technologies feels far from indifferent to us; it seeks to penetrate our intimate spaces, infiltrating our inner processes of thought and feelings, and aims to control where we deploy our attention.

The perfect storm of powerful networked computers (most of them residing in our hands and pockets, many of us still call them phones for some reason), social networking platforms, and 21st century AI has wholly redefined our relationship with technology. Tools and technologies of old, like those created before the early 2000s, function as extensions of human agency. They follow our directions and our purposes, imposing no demands on us, except the need to know how to use them skillfully — perhaps to read their user's manuals. A hammer, a washing machine, a table saw, or a bicycle do not intrude into our inner processes. They do not try to capture and hijack our attention or persuade us what to do. In this way, human agency remains free and unoppressed, with human intentions reigning supreme in how the tools are used. However, this is no longer the case with modern technology.

Let's examine some aspects of how we arrived at this point, and also explore the role of AI technology in this process.

The real superpower of human beings has to do with what is happening in human minds. Whatever we are doing — building or destroying, caring or injuring — is first conceived in our minds. Despite what demagogues are proclaiming, human minds are not passive deterministic mechanisms or illusory contraptions,[232] our individual minds are agents with a purpose, who have specific forces at their disposal, like those of thinking, feeling, and will. Everything we ever do consciously starts in our minds, and where we put our will to work is decided by what we think and how we feel about the issue at hand. From time immemorial, it has been well understood that the most powerful force in human society is the one capable of affecting the narratives weaving through human minds. Great myth and storytellers know this, as do parents who understand the value of nourishing bedtime stories for their small children, effective teachers know it, but so are marketing strategists, demagogues, sophists, and ideologues who use propaganda. The battleground where human culture and the course of history are shaped is actually within individual human minds.

Until recently, technology was a minor participant in this process. Of course, the invention of the printing press in the 15th century was an important milestone, as it enabled the distribution of information on a scale not available until then. Newspapers and books affected human culture and actions in ways not known before. With the introduction of radio and television technology into our homes in the 20th century, things started to change even faster. US President Franklin D. Roosevelt understood the importance of the new media well: from 1933 until 1944, he delivered more than 30 "fireside chats," a series of evening radio addresses, consistently listened to by tens of millions of people, which were influential in transforming the American worldview from one of despair to one of hope during the Great Depression and World War II.[233] At roughly the same moment in history, it took just five weeks — following Adolf Hitler's appointment as German chancellor and the transfer of control of the radio broadcast to his Nazi party — for the Nazi propaganda machine to tilt the political votes in favor of the Nazis in the 1933 election, which enabled them to fully consolidate power.[234] From then on, radio and television were used either to inform or to manipulate human minds. But these developments seem to have been only an early warm-up act. There is no precedent in human history for the scale of technological changes directly affecting individual human psychology, which started to unfold in the early 2000s.

Social networking platforms[235] (and related human-attention-focused platforms) have been at the forefront of this process for the last two decades. They offer numerous benefits, and that's why it was so easy for them to get under pretty much everybody's skin, young and old alike. Social networks make it effortless to connect and maintain (some form of) relationships regardless of distance, to discover people and groups with similar interests, they provide access to information and facilitate learning, help build and support communities, help raise awareness and mobilize people around social and environmental issues, enable cultural exchange, and much more. At the same time, there is a shadow side to how social networks impact individual psychology and the social dynamics of societies. These platforms are specifically designed, by experts, to be habit-forming, even addictive. Social networks use AI extensively. Their AI systems may not be on par with the most recent Large Language Models like ChatGPT, but they don't need to, all they need is fast intelligent systems to learn and analyze users' behavior and psychological habits.

The business model of social networking companies (and of other companies in the same human-attention-focused business space) depends on acquiring and analyzing our attention. We all get to use social networks, home assistants, email, messaging, calendars, contact lists, storage drives, document editing, and more on many platforms – without any direct cost to us, completely free! How is that possible? What do these companies get in return from us, and how are the companies behind these platforms worth trillions of dollars (with most of them not making any tangible products)? In return, these companies get the most precious thing – the undivided attention of individual human minds for long stretches of time. They get to observe and analyze us in intricate detail, peek into our intimate inner spaces, and build our *psychographic profiles*. These database records include what we like, dislike, and do, as well as which mental content drives our decisions, preferences, and loyalties. That information is used to feed us targeted content and build our attention habits. All this may sound weird, but still, it may not feel like a big deal to many people. Yes, companies may obtain/sell/buy our personal attention records and try to sell us stuff, or get us to vote for somebody, or whatever, but this is not dangerous or even over the top, right? The fact is, however, that once the usage habits are established in social media users, these habits influence what is fed to them through the platforms. The media content they consume may influence what they think about, how they feel about specific topics, and, through that, what they ultimately do in real life. (This and many other related aspects are captured in the economist Yanis Varoufakis's 2023 book *Technofeudalism*.)[236] Social networks are hotbeds for misinformation, and they have also been used for targeted disinformation spreads, leading to informational echo chambers and societal polarization. And it may not matter that this wasn't and isn't the intention of platform designers, the fact is that their products enable this effect. The 2019 documentary movie *The Great Hack* is a powerful portrayal of how societal changes can be affected via social media manipulations. Unfortunately, we cannot always consider social networking platforms as harmless and benign agents in human societies,[237] even in open societies[238] that seek to foster and protect individual human rights and provide safety. This is even less true in societies with totalitarian regimes, whose very survival depends on powerful surveillance and control of their citizens' minds. We should also remember that open societies, with relatively strong democratic traditions, are only young fledglings in historical terms. Things may change, and we can already observe signs of severe strain in the fiber of many of our democratic institutions worldwide. Open societies may indeed turn into totalitarian ones under powerful pressures.

Even on the individual level, social networking platforms affect us profoundly because they are designed to be habit-forming and are supported by AI systems watching our every move and glance. They collect every bit of data they have access to from our screens, cameras, and microphones and analyze our activities down to minute detail: what we buy, which books we read, how much time we spend on any given photo on our screens, how fast do we scroll, when do we swipe left and when right, which parts of a video do we watch or replay, which newspaper articles do we read, how much time do we spend reading them, who do we message and what is the tone of our messages, who messages us, who do we support or give contributions to, how much time do we spend on devices, the list goes on and on. AI analyzes every detail of our behavior and our life of thoughts and feelings. Based on gathered data, our psychographic profiles are built and encoded into many numbers in our records that are supposed to capture our characters and inclinations. They compare our numbers with the numbers of vast populations they have access to, which AI uses in attempts to predict our decisions, thoughts, emotions, and behavior. In addition, it has also been established that social networks and extended screen time associated with them directly affect us in unhealthy ways. Their use, especially extensive use, has been linked to mental health problems, including anxiety, depression, low self-esteem, short attention span, and declining cognitive skills. They lead to reduced physical activity and sleep disruption, affecting our overall well-being. Cyberbullying and harassment can have devastating effects. Sustained concentration and contemplative thinking can become hard to attain. It is also known that social networking platforms collect vast amounts of personal information with little concern for privacy or security. The list is long, and we can't go into all the details here. Fortunately, many resources on this topic are available[239] and the 2020 documentary *Social Dilemma*[240] poignantly portrays this landscape.

In the historical context, the developments described above culminate in the arrival of modern 21st-century AI technology. Even before the powerful deep neural network based AI systems arrived right before the 2020s, AI technology had already been integrated into our everyday lives, helping us with mundane tasks, like helping us with text autocomplete, figuring out who is who in our photos, and detecting credit card fraud, among other things. What roles is the new powerful AI poised to assume in the future? Let's first try to take a broader look at several aspects of AI, and from that vantage point, we shall attempt to ponder the good, the bad, and the ugly of what might be coming towards us.

3.2. The Grand Entrance of AI

Modern AI systems were inconceivable just two decades ago. The sheer scale of hardware and software platforms they comprise today is staggering by the early 2000s benchmarks. The exact numbers have not been publicly disclosed, but we do know, for example, that Large Language Models (LLMs such as *ChatGPT* from OpenAI) are *trained* on hardware platforms with tens of thousands of processors (often substantially more), over many weeks, and their software is designed to represent several hundred billion *parameters* or more.[241] In order to be able to make meaningful *inferences*, such models must initially siphon their training data from the vast amounts of content created by humans, consisting of hundreds of billions of words collected from websites, books, articles, and other sources (there are indications that GPT-4 was trained on more than two trillion words). Most modern AI systems (at the time of this writing) are based on *deep neural network architectures*[242] and utilize various *machine learning* (ML) strategies. These systems are very versatile and can gain competence in many domains. During the extensive training phase, they "learn" about structures, patterns, and styles in the target domains (language, images, game strategies, etc). After the *training* is complete, AI can competently engage in domain problems.

One of the first widely recognized milestones[243] in AI based on deep neural networks was in 2016 when *AlphaGo* (a program developed by Google DeepMind) achieved a victory in the complex strategy board game Go by defeating world champion Lee Sedol.[244] The way AlphaGo was "trained" is a good illustration of some aspects of AI "learning" in general. Initially, this was done using supervised learning utilizing a large database of Go played by human experts (thousands of games.) AlphaGo software then played games against different versions of itself, learning from its own victories and defeats. This involved millions of self-play games and resulted in discoveries of new strategies and tactics, beyond what could be learned from human games. The whole process lasted several months, culminating in the March 2016 victory. The model's next iteration (2017) was *AlphaGo Zero*, which utilized only self-play, "based solely on reinforcement learning, without human data, guidance or domain knowledge beyond game rules."[245] This model quickly advanced, and it was able to outperform the previous version after only 36 hours of training, winning 100-0 against the previous version after 72 hours of training. Building on this success and relying on self-play for training, the latest iteration (2018) released by DeepMind was *AlphaZero*,[246] which can play not only Go, but also chess and shogi. It achieved superhuman results after just 24 hours of training. This demonstrates how AI, after the initial impetus and training by humans, can quickly surpass human intelligence by improving autonomously. Of course, even complex games like Go have clear rules that govern the game, which makes them most suitable for quickly testing and improving intelligent behavior. Nonetheless, the performance of AI in this domain is clearly impressive.

The next breakthrough accomplished by these AI architectures, also achieved by DeepMind scientists and engineers, was *AlphaFold*, a system that was able to predict *protein folding*. Proteins fold into complex three-dimensional shapes based on the one-dimensional string of amino acids that comprise them, but determining how proteins fold was extremely difficult before AlphaFold. Predicting the folding process is essential for understanding biological processes. This was considered one of the most important, yet unsolved, issues in biomedical research. During the 2020 CASP competition, a sort of Olympics for protein folding research, the AlphaFold program solved the intractable protein folding problem by accurately predicting three-dimensional protein structures for 98.5% of the human proteome. In a noble gesture, DeepMind made AlphaFold public and freely available to all, and Demis Hassabis described it as a "gift to humanity." The accomplishment of this milestone meant that AI technology moved beyond games in 2020, as AlphaFold solved a serious scientific problem with important implications for biomedical research, including drug discovery.[247]

The first forays of AI into realms closer to general intelligence — where AI cannot easily be trained based on known rules — have been accomplished in the domain of language by *Large Language Models*. Starting around 2020, these models were trained on unprecedented amounts of data for the first time, comprising hundreds of billions of written words. LLMs became widely known when OpenAI released *ChatGPT-3* in November 2022. ChatGPT can generate intelligent responses in many languages (and translate between them), based on the provided input at its prompt. It can also engage in other modalities like sound and images and generate software code in multiple programming languages, based on high-level instructions in human language. Within two months, ChatGPT had become the fastest-growing software application in history gaining over 100 million users. (More than one year after its release, ChatGPT remains the most advanced language model, measured by both classic benchmarks and professional exams designed for humans. However, at the time of this writing, the LLM field is very competitive and crowded, with several models still vying for dominance.)[248] This development, the descent of LLMs, received worldwide attention and quickly brought awareness of the possible impact of AI on human society. The fact that AI is demonstrating superior intelligence in the domain of language, where until recently we humans felt that we reign supreme, is bringing forward feelings of unease in many. It is deeply embedded in our experiences that we associate any manifestations of intelligent behavior — and competent use of language is intelligent behavior — with a purposeful agency, sentience, and beingness, even if we generally don't have a clear understanding of what any of these concepts represent. The fact that we are witnessing AI exhibiting intelligent behavior brings into sharp focus our limited understanding of who we ourselves fundamentally are, as beings with minds. This all feels unsettling, and many consider this development to be an urgent wake-up call. However, at this point, we are still trying to figure out exactly what we want to wake up to.

One more AI competence should be mentioned to complete the picture. AI is quickly gaining unprecedented capabilities in speech, image, and video generation and pro-cessing. Many new companies have sprung up in this field (too many to list here, and the competitive terrain is very dynamic at the time of this writing.) Several developments are notable, and some are even frightening. AI can now *synthesize naturally sounding speech*. When listened to through a loudspeaker, it is almost indistinguishable from human-recorded speech; it is context-aware, with realistic intonation, and can sound as if conveying the genuine emotion of a speaking human being. Moreover, AI can synthesize speech that sounds like a specific individual, living or deceased,[249] based on a short voice sample (*"voice cloning"*). The creation of *realistic sound effects* and *audio editing* have been highly automated. AI is presently making its first forays into *music composition* in various styles as well. On another frontier, image generation experienced a revolution with the introduction of *Generative Adversarial Network* (GAN)[250] models, which can create highly realistic images, including human faces, new characters and environments, and special effects in movies and video games.

Pondering new and emerging AI capabilities in speech, image, and video, and how they are used, it often feels like it's a jungle out there. The potential for technology abuse, which affects us all, is great. *Deepfakes* are becoming increasingly realistic and more disturbing: realistic but fake audio, video, and images raise concerns about disinformation, fraud, privacy, and security. There are dozens of online tutorials on creating realistic-looking and sounding *avatars* that look and talk like real people and can be utilized for online presence, meetings, and phone calls. The existence and proliferation of fake videos, images, and human voices justify an urgent call for regulation. Geoffrey Hinton has a point when stating that it might become "impossible to know what's true by having so many fakes out there. ... that's something you might be able to address by treating it like counterfeiting. Governments [make it] a serious offense to print money, it's also a serious offense if you're given some fake money to pass it to somebody else if you knew it was fake. I think [we need] similar regulations for fake videos and fake voices and fake images ... [we must] make it a serious crime, you go to jail for 10 years if you produce a video with AI and it doesn't say it's made with AI, that's what they do for counterfeit money ... These fake videos are so good at manipulating the electorate that we need them all marked as fake, otherwise we're going to lose democracy... it's fairly clear that organizations like *Cambridge Analytica,* by pumping out fake news, had an effect on Brexit, and it's fairly clear that Facebook was manipulated to have an effect on the 2016 US election."[251] Adrienne LaFrance adds that "transparency should be a core tenet in the new human exchange of ideas—people ought to disclose whenever an artificial intelligence is present or has been used in communication."[252]

Incorrect or misleading information and threats to democracy are not the only shadow side of the AI deepfake technology. This technology enables new forms of harassment and abuse, yet we seem neither sufficiently determined nor capable of arresting this development effectively. At a time when even basic legislation against deepfakes and nonconsensual pornography faces hurdles in many countries (including the US), the tools to create them are becoming increasingly accessible. As a result, child sexual abuse material and nonconsensual pornography, like revenge-porn or image-based sexual abuse, are being created and proliferated, exposing the underbelly of modern technology and its misuse. Some pointers relevant to this topic can be found in the endnotes, and the 2023 award-winning documentary *Another Body* clearly demonstrates the gravity of deepfake technology misuse.[253] The need for more vigilant and effective responses is urgent.

Creating art is also becoming a contested territory. Copyright infringements are becoming easy to accomplish and more common. The question of what represents the work of art seems to require a new chapter in the philosophy of *aesthetics*. In any event, the technology is becoming a formidable factor in this domain. AI can perform *style transfer* by recognizing and applying the style of one art creation (e.g., a painting) to new artworks. Then, there are *super-resolution* (enhancing the resolution of existing images) and *face-aging-and-rejuvenation* applications. With just a few words, images or videos are created by *text-to-image* and *text-to-video* applications. There is also *image-to-image*, *image-to-video*, *text-plus-image-to-video*, you-name-it-to-you-name-it. And all these applications are becoming increasingly sophisticated and ubiquitous. The impending impact on human experience and the art, entertainment, and communication industries seems inevitable. This tidal wave cannot be stopped, we must prepare to ride it out and learn to stay on top.

It is evident that the first wave of AI technology has arrived, it has already entrenched itself within humanity, and AI is not going away anytime soon. Its impact on us will depend on how fast we develop it and how successfully we regulate and integrate it in our societies. AI brings with itself a set of enticing promises, but also considerable limitations, and some grave dangers. We will attempt to consider them in reverse order, starting from the dangers, moving to the limitations, and finishing with the promising benefits of AI. Humanity will likely experience it in that order too, we will only see the good side of AI if we overcome its dangers and limitations.

3.3. The Ugly AI: Dangers

There are outright dangers the proliferation of AI brings with it. It is welcome news that the discourse about them is entering the mainstream.[254] With some insight, they are predictable, and we ignore their consideration and required actions at our peril. We should have no illusions about these dangers and shouldn't underestimate their potency, our ignorance in this domain is how some version of a dystopian society[255] becomes humanity's reality.

Some obvious dangers have already been mentioned earlier in this chapter. They are related to the utilization of AI technologies for deception, especially by means of fakes, deepfakes, and AI-generated false narratives.

[D1] Disinformation and misinformation
by means of AI

The most obvious societal danger stems from *disinformation* and *misinformation,* where semi-truths, elaborate fabrications,[256] and outright lies with hidden agendas are disseminated and amplified through online platforms like social networks, rating-driven news channels, various conspiracy theory forums, and the like. Open societies[257] and their democratic institutions are vulnerable to the malicious spread of disinformation and — if not adequately guarded and defended against this threat — may succumb to attacks via these channels. This danger must be resisted vigorously, and strict and effective government regulation[258] must be the first line of defense. As mentioned, Geoffrey Hinton's suggestion to treat fake media as fake money provides a good analogy and starting point. However, government regulation may not be enough as detecting and prosecuting offenders may be slow. Platforms used to disseminate disinformation must invest more resources and step up their efforts to detect the sources of disinformation and shut them down. To help with the scale, they could also collaborate and provide a single, easily accessible, monitored, moderated, fact-checking forum website — Wikipedia style (maybe with an associated comments page) — where citizens could post evidence about disinformation sources for everybody to consider and discuss. *AI detection* applications[259] also have their place in the toolkit for this effort. Of course, the "most effective tool is to increase media literacy among average readers,"[260] which, at its core, would be a long-term investment in the protection of open societies and, among other efforts, would include *reviving the humanities and civics subjects in education.* The fact that these fundamental disciplines are in decline is unconscionable and could prove fatal for open societies if not remedied. More truthful information is also an important component. Trusted free media and news platforms championing honesty and integrity are indispensable and deserve our support. Investigative journalists and authors deserve exceptional admiration for their courage and humanity. They reinforce many pillars on which open societies stand, and we are therefore all indebted to them. They need the whole society to support them in battles against massive manipulations. Investigative journalists and whistleblowers should never have to stand alone. Disinformation threatens civilization and proclaiming individual neutrality and remaining quiet is no longer an option, active engagement is necessary, in the words of Howard Zinn — who embedded this advice in the title of his book — *You Can't Be Neutral on a Moving Train.*[261]

[D2] Cyberbullying and image-based sexual abuse (IBSA)

As already mentioned, AI also brings new dangers at an individual level. Here, the reckless and malicious use of deepfakes for *cyberbullying* and *image-based sexual abuse (IBSA)* has already demonstrated its vicious effects. This danger has also exposed a lack of societal determination — sometimes even reluctance — to regulate and curb them.[262] Neither designating cyberbullying and image-based sexual abuse as a form of free speech nor protecting such abuse under the guise of tradition should be tolerated as a defensible position. Here, too, strict and effective government regulation is necessary. The cyberbullying, proliferation of child sexual abuse material, and nonconsensual pornography must be considered even more damaging than inflicting physical harm on a person, and they must be fought with tenacity. And here, too, proclaiming individual neutrality is not a viable option for living in a healthy society. Support and active action by friends, family, teachers, managers, wider social circles, and society are all essential. Our humanity must shine through such support.

[D3] AI autonomous weapons & the creation of human targets

Another often-discussed danger is that of *AI autonomous weapons* and the *creation of human targets.*[263] They are already being deployed and further developed, and many world armies will soon have them. Like most other dangerous AI technologies — assuming these tools of destruction are *aligned* with human intent — they don't directly represent a danger posed by AI. Humans deciding to use them are the real danger. Regulating them is a tall order for present-day humanity. But, even if AI of this kind is inherently complex to regulate internationally, it would make sense to create an intergovernmental organization, similar to the IAEA for nuclear proliferation, at the very least to engage in an ongoing conversation and make the proliferation and use of such weapons more transparent. Individual non-military use of such weapons should be strictly banned and vigorously enforced. For example, non-military use of armed flying drones with object/people recognition and targeting capabilities should be restricted to movie scenes only. The other aspect of AI autonomous weapons often talked about, that of AI-controlled robots *not aligned* with the intents of human beings who created them (à la *The Terminator* movie), must remain in the realm of science fiction. All AI weaponry that humans cannot fully control should be banned or discontinued. This shouldn't even be a debate. We will return to this topic in our discussion of the *alignment* problem.

[D4] Dangers of pervasive AI surveillance, in private and public sectors

AI technology can make tools for surveillance frighteningly powerful and effective. It can monitor, analyze, and interpret vast amounts of data (often in real-time.) Some of these tools are: social media monitoring, employee monitoring, facial recognition, voice recognition, gait analysis, predictive policing algorithms, location tracking and analysis, and various anomaly detection algorithms. Sophisticated AI tools are increasingly being integrated into the security/surveillance systems of many countries, companies, and organizations.[264] They can be utilized in many applications, ranging from public safety and security to marketing and consumer behavior analysis. Authoritarian and totalitarian governments are particularly eager to utilize such tools for invasive monitoring of citizens (the very existence of such regimes depends on their ability to monitor and control the lives of their citizens.) Surveillance technologies portrayed in George Orwell's dystopian novel *Nineteen Eighty-Four* (a.k.a. *1984*) appear like silly toys compared to what modern AI-empowered systems can do.

While AI surveillance tools can be very useful for identifying potential criminal activities or security threats and for applications like traffic management and urban planning, they can also be used in such a way that they endanger both the well-being of individuals and the existence of open societies. Protection of freedom, privacy, and individual rights, tolerance of diverse viewpoints, and the existence of transparent and accountable government are all fundamental for the existence of open societies. These principles must be defended at all costs, and open societies will therefore have to contend with a slew of perilous dangers in the presence of powerful AI surveillance. Some of them are: a) *privacy invasion* (e.g., tracking of individual's movements and behavior, predicting future actions, collection and storage of large amounts of personal data), b) *abuse of mass surveillance* (used for suppression of dissent, manipulation of information, and erosion of democratic freedoms), c) *lack of transparency and accountability* (both are necessary for how surveillance data is used and interpreted), and d) *chilling effect on freedom of expression* (fear of constant surveillance can deter people from exercising their freedom of expression and assembly).

Open societies need to balance the risks and benefits of AI surveillance technology. Legal and ethical frameworks, with sufficiently specified details, must be developed. Powerful independent oversight mechanisms must be established, with full access to used technology. Transparency must be paramount. Strict and enforced data privacy laws, clear guidelines, and limitations on AI technology use are all necessary. The use of AI surveillance technology must not endanger core values of privacy, fairness, and freedom in open societies. The dangers here are very great and must be taken seriously.

Careful deployment and legal and ethical frameworks are necessary not only at the societal level but also at the level of individual organizations and private companies. The danger of *privacy invasion at the workplace* (in companies and some government agencies) is particularly worrisome.[265] It has been widely recognized that *privacy is not just a personal preference but a fundamental aspect of human rights, dignity, and autonomy*. Privacy is essential for the development and well-being of individuals, including their mental health and self-identity. Privacy allows us to think, communicate, and express ourselves freely, without external pressures or fear of judgment and surveillance. Having a physical and psychological private space, where we can retreat, reflect, and relax, away from public eyes, is vital for our emotional health. Privacy enables us to live authentically, to choose what personal information we want to share and with whom and is necessary for building trust and meaningful relationships. Creativity and innovation also require private boundaries where individuals can experiment, take risks, and think creatively without external influence or observation. Our civilization stands on the Enlightenment values we must preserve, "reason, human autonomy, and the respectful exchange of ideas" and for this reason "privacy is key to preserving our humanity."[266]

If we acknowledge these facts about individual privacy, how should we approach the increasingly pervasive monitoring of employees in the workplace? Company managers, instead of using time-tested methods of directly talking to their employees and discussing productivity results rather than micromanaging their activities, have started to utilize tools that only measure the activities of their employees, down to minute detail. The increasingly advanced and AI-empowered surveillance technology ("bossware", a.k.a. "tattleware" or "workspace analytics") crept up on us without a proper warning and it is extremely concerning. It was supposedly intended to boost productivity and ensure security, but not only is bossware ineffective ("activity is not productivity")[267] and causes employee burnout, this powerful surveillance technology is also crossing the line into invasive oversight. This not only raises ethical questions about privacy, but it also erodes trust and creates an oppressive environment, often undermining morale and individual autonomy.

The Fourth Amendment to the United States Constitution protects citizens from unreasonable searches and seizures in the US, so for example, if the police or FBI or any other authorized government agency wants to track somebody's movements, they have to request a warrant from a judge. That is the only way to do it legally. However, for some reason, this doesn't apply to private employers! If your boss wants to monitor all your movements, peek through your camera at will, see what's on your computer screen, check your email or messages, or listen to your conversations, they can do it. Legally. And they basically use the same kind of software that is illegally used for stalking people.[268] This major breach of trust and privacy reflects a major power imbalance between the company managers and employees in our society. The existence of such an imbalance is also eroding the pillars of open society. And AI technology is increasingly mixing itself into this imbalance and tilting the scales the wrong way. By allowing this to happen, we are setting a very dangerous precedent.

Much has been written about this lately, for example in a recent Wired article titled *The Creepy Rise of Bossware,* we read that "bossware is everywhere, and it's getting more nightmarish. … more and more companies have turned to increasingly intrusive technology to monitor employees, track their locations, read their documents, and even use cameras and microphones to listen in or watch staff at work."[269] Widespread harms of bossware were discussed during the 2023 Stanford Social Innovation Review panel, *Bossware Is Coming for You: Worker Surveillance Technology Is Everywhere,*[270] and the following can be read in their summary: "Technology is giving employers ever-greater abilities to monitor, evaluate, and control workers, all in the name of efficiency. But "bossware"—as the growing constellation of surveillance and automated management tools is often called—has insidious effects on the health, well-being, and livelihoods of people." There is no doubt about it, the dangers of pervasive AI surveillance extend to private companies too and our legal and ethical frameworks must therefore extend to them as well.

Apart from the four dangers mentioned above — in some ways obvious and already widely talked about — there are other perils AI proliferation is bringing with it. Some of them are still unknown, and we will discover them as AI deployments become widespread. However, some threats can be predicted based on what we already know about AI and human nature.

[D5] The danger of AI uniting with self-interested neoliberal economics (or its remnants)[271]

Geoffrey Hinton used the following words to describe this danger of AI entering human society: "In a decent society AI would be great, it would mean everything got more productive, and everyone was better off, but the danger is that it'll make the rich richer and the poor poorer [and] that's not AI's fault."[272]

The history of technological progress over the past 150 years teaches us that the benefits of progress are not distributed equally, or fairly by any measure. Forces of raw self-interest in human society — which often manifest in the pumping of benefits from the poorer to the richer — are strong and do not hesitate to assert themselves whenever an opportunity arises. This is a known fact to all students of economics and history, and much has been written about it.[273]

The neoliberal paradigm, as it appeared in the 1970s and 1980s, often associated with the economics of Milton Friedman,[274] the so-called free market, and the policies of Ronald Reagan and Margaret Thatcher, can be seen as just another surfacing of a deep-seated force in humanity (we dwell on this notion in the second chapter, in connection with the phenomenon of existential despair.) Unlike many other irrational beliefs and powers oppressing humanity, this force was not purged by the arrival of liberating humanistic impulses of the Renaissance and the Age of Reason (it immediately continued to make itself manifest, for example in works like Machiavelli's *The Prince* and Mandeville's *Fable of the Bees*.)[275] This is the same force that later, in the 19th and 20th centuries, made us allow, among other things, the ruthless exploitation of human beings during the Industrial Revolutions (it is enough to recall the cruelty of child labor or the torturous plight of railway workers building the First Transcontinental Railroad in the US) and harsh, unhealthy, and unsafe working conditions (like those that caused the tragic Triangle Factory fire.) Today, at the time of this writing, this same force allows us to tolerate that more than 13 million children face hunger in the US — in one of the wealthiest countries in the world — and that more than 40 million people live in poverty.[276] At the same time, we have created a society where the wealth owned by the top 1% in the wealth bracket equals $46 trillion, which is more than tenfold the amount owned by the bottom 50% of people. Notably, just 735 billionaires possess more wealth than the bottom half of the US population.[277] Such reports don't often appear in the main news cycle, and they seem to rarely reach the ivory castles, country clubs, and yachts of the rich and powerful among us. Sometimes they do, like when Warren Buffet said in jest, "there's class warfare, all right, but it's my class, the rich class, that's making war, and we're winning."[278] Considering all this, we have to conclude that there is no urgent need for new technologies and more resources if we are looking to provide for the basic wellbeing of humanity, we just need a somewhat more level playing field where everyone can access the basics. Humanity doesn't lack resources and technologies to feed and provide basics for everybody on the planet. Based on what we already have today, there is no rational reason or need for any human being on the planet to be hungry, unhoused, uneducated, and without basic medical care. The fact that we live in a society that allows this is not a reflection of any rationally explainable necessity or adversity we face. We ourselves willingly allow that the world we live in is fashioned in this way. People among us who have their fingers on any levers of power willingly created a world that looks like this.[279] That doesn't mean that their will was rational and free, it was almost certainly irrational and invisibly enslaved in all cases, but this is a topic for another chapter (hint: contrary to the often stated belief, this fact of human nature has nothing to do with how humans developed during evolution or with the "evolutionary spirit" as proclaimed in the 1987 movie *Wall Street*).

In any event, a force in human beings is an active ingredient in this process. Every confrontation of humanity with this force brings pain and requires sacrifice before at least the basic regulations and protections for human beings can be put in place (if in doubt, it is enough to recall the events related to the Civil Rights Movement, or 1930s Labor Movement in the US). And this force works relentlessly to undo such regulations and protections as soon as the opportunity arises. This same force of raw self-interest enabled slave labor, robber barons, Great and other economic depressions, and today it is the driving impulse behind the dominant forces of corruption, plutocracy, and kleptocracy that increasingly rule our lives and seriously threaten the survival of our democratic institutions and civilized society.

This force has found its home in our minds and will not yield without a battle. It has been acknowledged and recognized in the history of thought (even if it was often viewed through a pessimistic lens). Various names have been used in ethical and psychological considerations for this force and its ports of entry into human minds. Hume simply called it "passion" ("reason is no match for passion"), Freud said that human selves are, in fact, "playthings and tools" for it, Kant said that humans could only be "crooked timber" because of it, Plato and Aristotle[280] used the term "appetite" and pre-scribed inner effort, within a virtue-based ethical framework, for how to battle and overcome it. We all harbor it to a certain degree, even if this is not always obvious, as this force strives to remain hidden in the primitive areas of our minds, and we don't generally like to think about ourselves as self-interested. In any case, we should live under no illusion that this force will stop controlling our lives out of its own accord. This fact is mentioned here only in passing, dealing with this force is an intimate process and it is a topic of the second part of this book. Additionally, it should be emphasized that, because overcoming this force can be accomplished only by means of individual transformation, we can't expect that societal-level prescriptions like "dictatorship of the proletariat"[281] and similar proposals can bring any lasting change.

Considering all this, if we honestly reflect on the market mechanisms that accomplished the unprecedented levels of inequality we have reached at this point,[282] hopes and illusions about the AI benefits being distributed equally, without imposing further exploitation and suffering on many human beings, will quickly evaporate. It is folly to expect that AI can enter humanity via the ruthless and inhumane forces of the market and still benefit all of humanity. Market forces will gladly take the reins, but they don't care for humanity. If the power of AI unites with and empowers the mindset of neoliberal economics, it is all but guaranteed that many ways will be found to use it to extract even more resources from the working majority (or to simply discard many people as unneeded)[283] and to transfer these resources toward the tiny minority that owns the capital and now increasingly controls the governance of our (increasingly plutocratic) societies. It is to be expected that the plight imposed on people will simply be ignored (possibly even blamed on them too, as is common in modern neoliberal discourse.) The fact that the neoliberal order itself is undergoing its own evolution and possibly approaching its own demise (this process started after the neoliberal mindset caused the devastating 2008 economic crisis worldwide)[284] does not work in anybody's favor. This process is only signaling that "the tectonic plates of American politics [are] shifting" — which should worry everybody else too — and the new paradigm pushing towards us can be described as consisting of "surviving neoliberal remnants, mixed with ethno-nationalist populism, authoritarian state surveillance capitalism, or out-and-out neo-fascism."[285] This sounds like a scary landscape to land AI onto.

Therefore, the expectation that AI technology will benefit human society — without a decisive change in individual human nature — is almost certainly naïve and likely bound to disappointment and rude awakening. The vast majority (within a tiny group) of people in a position to control the levers of societal power don't even seem to believe that there is such a thing as a human society to care for (society as the supposed beneficiary of the AI benefits). Margaret Thatcher famously said "Who is society? There is no such thing! There are individual men and women"[286] (this is the equivalent of saying that there is no such thing as a human organism, there are only individual atoms swirling around.) And most people in this small powerful group seem to (still) believe that the only force that can organize these separate individual swirling "men and women" is the force of the "free" market, a force that compels them to do what they must. "There is no alternative, not to the market," proclaimed Margaret Thatcher, or in the words of economist Brad DeLong, paraphrasing neoliberal icon Friedrich Hayek: "The market giveth, the market taketh away: blessed be the name of the market."[287] This mindset seems very entrenched in the ivory castle of power, even after the multiple devastating economic crises in the last 150 years (caused by the forces of the market going haywire) should have humbled them, when government bailouts (money from folks who work for a living) and deficit spending had to save us all.

It has been said that power corrupts minds, and not without reason. It is quite hard for the very wealthy among us, for the small group of people in the ivory castle — being walled off and with virtually no shared experiences[288] with the hoi polloi from the outside world — to understand the impact and the gravity of the decisions they are making. "I didn't believe that anyone lived like that," said Eleanor Roosevelt when she visited children in a poor neighborhood for the first time.[289] Without having shared experiences, it is hard for the very wealthy even to believe that an upward transfer of wealth has been engineered and happening, and that they are the beneficiaries of that transfer of wealth, while it also creates crippling inequality and leaves millions of people in poverty.

And today, it is also easy for them to engage in wishful thinking that the increased productivity brought by AI will increase wages and open enough new job opportunities. It is thus no wonder that we hear proclamations from above, like the ones telling us that "AI will save the world" or that AI "is owned by people and controlled by people, like any other technology."[290] Right... These and similar statements could and should become true, but that will only be possible if we quickly sober up and start enabling and acquiring a radically new mindset.

Economists Anton Korinek and Joseph Stiglitz remind us that AI will inevitably have implications for income distribution and unemployment. It is obvious that the rapid proliferation of AI "necessitates large adjustments" and must be "coupled with the right form of redistribution. In the absence of such intervention, worker-replacing technological change may not only lead to workers getting a diminishing fraction of national income, but may actually make them worse off in absolute terms." Also, society must be willing to "support the necessary transition and to provide support to those who are 'left behind'," otherwise we should "expect resistance to innovation, with uncertain political and economic consequences."[291] Such a societal position indeed requires a mindset change, it is indeed impossible "to have a strong democracy on top of a rotting social fabric."[292]

For such a mindset to take root among us, rules and regulations are not enough, a change must happen in a sufficient number of individual human minds. Think Ebenezer Scrooge. We need to finally heed the message Charles Dickens imparted to us 180 years ago.[293] *The Ghost of Christmas Yet To Come* has been knocking at our doors, yet Scrooge in us still clutches the "nobody gets something for nothing" note with his cold miserly hands. The hour is late for our planet and for our species, the time to wake up is now. We must thrust all our strength and abilities towards developing an individual interest in uncovering the hidden bonds among human beings. We must discover a willingness to include others in our inner space, and through that significantly widen our self-interest. Only such transformation can call forth a mindset that will seek to protect the planet we live on and to care and provide for all humans. Human beings should be provided with basics not because they "earned" them, but because we want to live in a society where humans work to express their humanness, rather than fighting for survival against other humans in the economic domain. The only domain in which human competition is healthy is the domain of culture (of any kind!) and creativity, and not the domain that provides basic economic necessities. It's about time to move away from the caveman mentality. Our species needs to move away from the idea that human work is solely, or even primarily, a means for survival. We cannot afford to pair 21st-century technology with a primitive caveman mindset, this will tear us to pieces. Human work naturally seeks expression in the domain of culture, where it can ennoble our will. This expression can and must take many forms. For some, it is found in science; for others, in art, gardening, trades, and, last but possibly greatest, in caring for others. Such care is an almost completely ignored area in today's economy. The *economy of care*,[294] where our most noble labor should be invested, is scarcely acknowledged, respected, or adequately rewarded. We need all these aspects of human work. The new mindset will help us internalize new ethics. We actually already have a model for such ethics (even if limited.) We can recognize it today mainly in the way most parents care and feel for their children.[295] Loving parents don't expect their small children to "earn their keep," they also don't think that their children are getting "something for nothing."[296] All this seems natural and ethical to us, we are just not yet advanced enough to be more visionary and to extrapolate this notion. Even if formidable forces in our nature are resisting and fighting this moral vision, we actually might not be that far, and a related thought has already been expressed within the economics profession: "Anyone still not reconciled to the idea of 'something for nothing' should ask a few simple questions: Would I not want my children to have a small trust fund that shields them from the fear of destitution and allows them to invest fearlessly in their real talents? Would their peace of mind render them lazy layabouts? If not, what is the moral basis for denying all children the same advantage?"[297]

Admittedly, a solution for the danger of AI uniting with the raw self-interested human nature and neoliberal economics is not going to be a simple and easy undertaking. It requires common effort to bring forward a radical new mindset. The main thrust of this book supports an attempt to acquire such a mindset. Essential for this process is the engagement in *intimate individual self-transformation* and self-development by a sufficient number of people who do so as an act of their free will, thereby building a spiritual community. The method for accomplishing this, and a justification for it, are the main themes of this book. It is argued here that humanity is facing a host of incoming cataclysmic challenges, with AI technology being just one of them.[298] The acquisition of a new mindset is a prerequisite for the necessary global cooperation we will need to overcome them. (If you, the reader, have landed in this chapter without reading the material up to this point, this paragraph might sound somewhat weird and unrealistic. If this is the case, and you care to make any sense of it, please read the first two chapters.)

In any event, we should keep in mind that "there is tremendous power in defining ideals,"[299] and even if we only partially succeed in this transformation, even if (enough) people simply just commit to the path and start treading it slowly, acquiring this new mindset has a huge potential to bring humanity forward. It would, in time, among other things, enable us to retain and elevate human culture, it would enable an AI-supported prosperous civilized world, and it would help us recognize the hidden uniting bonds among all human beings, so that the healthy and nourishing relationships among humans would grow in recognition as our highest and most important treasure. This could then become the cornerstone of a new ethical paradigm, based not on rules, commands, categorical imperatives, veils of ignorance, or social contracts, but on something infinitely more liberating and noble. If we get there, even just part of the way, this would, as a matter of course, allow for the welcoming of a more just redistribution of resources and wealth as well. Already, in significant ways, even though many of us are not quite sure how to get there,[300] many among us understand or surmise what stands in our way and what needs to be done. Signs are everywhere for those who want to see them, and a recent article by Annie Lowrey sums it well up: "we would need a new mindset, one that understands wealth as something we all share and that prioritizes keeping each and every family financially secure, regardless of their participation in the job market ... Americans valorize work. We tolerate inequality and poverty. The problem is not the robots, then. The problem is us."[301]

This particular danger is one of the greatest presented to us by AI. But we should welcome it wholeheartedly, as it is also our great opportunity for growth. Maybe even the greatest in an era. May we use it well.

The first tests of how AI might benefit or harm humanity might arrive sooner than we expected – a 2023 Goldman Sachs report estimates that AI technology is likely to automate around 25% of labor tasks in advanced economies,[302] which seems like a good approximation to plan with. How we will deal with the displaced labor force is a good first test of whether we will be able to use AI for the benefit of society.

[D6] The danger of humans building emotional relationships with AI technology

This danger presented by AI is probably the most multi-faceted, complex, and hard to comprehend of them all. It requires that we descend a bit deeper toward the truths we can acquire about human minds and the relationships between human minds. For this reason, the deeper meaning and the possible dangers caused by the development of (especially exclusive and long-term) emotional relationships with AI are fully addressed in separate chapters dedicated to the human self and relationships. We will attempt to make several inroads here.

It is palpable that the idea of building relationships with AI stirs a lot of emotion and arouses the imagination. Articles, books, and movies have been created about various aspects of it.[303] Movies portraying AI machines gaining access into the intimate space of the human mind, like *Her* (2013), *Ex Machina* (2014) and *I'm Your Man* (2021), have entered public discourse as attempts to process the prospect of human relationships with machines. Industry offering AI "companions" (like *Replika* and *Pi* for example)[304] has been developing for several years already. Even if their efficacy is limited, mental health AI chatbots (like *Woebot* and *Youper* for example) have been at least tried by tens of thousands of people in need of mental health treatment.[305]

Most humans have a kind of gut reaction and an emotional response when the topic of relationships with AI companion machines is raised. But in most cases, our feelings of this kind don't tell us enough, they don't easily penetrate the depths of our dilemma, and our thoughts don't easily shed light on this conundrum either. In the public debate about AI, no compelling psychological explanations are offered about why, exactly, we humans experience relationships — particularly exclusive long-term relationships — with machines differently than relationships with other people.

Unifying bonds and relationships among human beings are special, there is much more to them than meets the eye. In the second chapter, while discussing existential despair, we have already mentioned (and are restating it here by repeating the whole paragraph again) that *out of all our mental health needs, human relationships are the most existentially important.* They form the cornerstone of our humanity, serving as the central hub from which all meaning, purpose, and motivation for any kind of engagement or work emanate. Both traditional wisdom and modern science converge on this essential truth about human beings: the formation of meaningful bonds with others and the nurturing exchange of care are universally recognized as foundational to mental well-being, more than any other factor. This is an established scientific fact with virtually no controversy. For infants to grow into healthy and strong adults, healthy attachment relationships with caregivers are indispensable. In the realm of psychotherapy, therapeutic relationships, perhaps more than any other factor, are key to healing psychological traumas. In the words of psychiatrist, psychologist and psychoanalyst, founder and pioneer of the *attachment theory*, John Bowlby:

> "Intimate attachments to other human beings are the hub around which a person's life revolves, not only when he is an infant or a toddler or a schoolchild but throughout his adolescence and his years of maturity as well, and on into old age. From these intimate attachments a person draws his strength and enjoyment of life and, through what he contributes, he gives strength and enjoyment to others. These are matters about which current science and traditional wisdom are at one."[306]

We will have to complete this discussion in a separate chapter dedicated to relationships, but for now, suffice it to say that because AI companions can mimic many aspects of the authentic human-to-human relationship — including empathy, curiosity, humor, and loyalty — humans can easily be deceived that a genuine relationship with deterministic machines is possible and that they are interacting with a real agency. However, any "conversation with an artificial intelligence is one-sided—an illusion of connection."[307]

Philosopher Madeleine Ransom articulates it succinctly: "There is a risk AI companion bots will impoverish human relationships. Sophisticated versions of sexbots, and carebots for the elderly, will be incredibly enticing to many. They will appear to be great listeners, aim to please, and won't have any (genuine) wants of their own. One danger for us is that we come to 'prefer' the company of these bots – or become addicted to them – and so lose our desire to interact with other humans. Another danger is that we lose our capacity to interact with other humans meaningfully. Having a relationship that allows us to be the only one with needs, frustrations, and desires is a recipe for narcissism and stunted self-growth. Social media has already impoverished friendship, and AI has the potential to further erode our gloriously messy human relations."

For this reason, apart from simple and occasional entertainment, or assuming the role of personal assistants, machines have no business meddling in the domain of human relationality. This is especially true for the formative period of child development. Children need genuine attachment relationships with human beings who care, and not providing for this most essential developmental need of every child unavoidably causes trauma and represents abuse. Adults whose mental health is compromised need human professionals and human relationships. Our societal inability to provide for these essential needs must be addressed at its source, it cannot be remedied by machines, as this will only temporarily alleviate and mask the real problems facing us. We need to wake up and fiercely fight to recognize and defend the "brotherhood and inter-dependence of mankind," to borrow the words from Frederic Douglass.[308] Relational connections among all humans represent our spiritual foundation and treasure, to which we are mostly blind and ignorant in modern society.

The true substance and profoundness of relationality between human minds is felt by every human being, even if we have little understanding of its nature. Its true meaning and depth are even harder to grasp than the depth of the individual human mind. Until we get there, the only safe way to proceed is to consider human relationships as sacrosanct.

[D7] The danger of humans delegating their creativity and humanity to AI

It is evident that AI can help humans be more productive and efficient. We should embrace that. But then, not everything is about productivity and efficiency. There is a reason we humans seek to do certain types of work, even if we are slow and ineffective at it at first. Imagine an athlete preparing for the Olympic games deciding to be more efficient by letting a robot do the exercises instead. This is a ridiculous idea, and with a string of decisions like this (hey, maybe robots could compete instead of humans too!) the culture of Olympic games would be devalued, and it could potentially completely disappear. How about other types of work and other domains of culture? Does it make sense that AI writes an essay about ethics instead of a student in an ethics class? AI could do it in a fraction of a second, instead of the student painstakingly learning about it in the class the whole semester before they can produce something worth reading. An essay written by AI would probably sound better and be well thought out too. How about a newspaper article written by AI? A manager's letter to the employees? A romantic letter? A letter to best friend? How about a chapter in a book, or even the whole book maybe? How about some cool AI lyrics for a song, or a thrilling movie script? Heck AI, make us the whole movie, or better even, make two dozen of them, here is the prompt, take a second and make entertainment galore! … Yeah, exactly.

But then, why not? After all, AI has access to almost everything anybody has ever written or created in the context of human culture, so it can easily extract from it and create something that feels new and that could be worth reading, listening to, or watching. Yet, observing ourselves from another angle while pondering this, we likely feel a healthy human sentiment telling us that this line of thinking is profoundly problematic (even if we decide to ignore the significant economic and social implications due to the displacement of humans active and employed in arts and media.)

One problem has to do with the process of creating and building culture and civilization in the first place. AI has no agency, it lacks personal experiences, emotions, and reason – it generates content based on already existing data embedded within the *parameters* of its model, so it can essentially only reshuffle and recombine (a vast number of) existing ideas and styles already created by human minds, it can't create completely new and original content with a unique perspective.[309] Granted, there are many good ideas and styles in AI models already, they represent thousands of years of human civilization, but reshuffled repeatedly, they would in time inevitably lead to cultural homogenization. For example, if an AI model were trained only on data created by humans before the 19th century, it couldn't "invent" quantum physics, it took the reasoning human mind of Max Planck (and several other scientists) to get the ball rolling in that direction. Such an AI model couldn't "invent" the theory of relativity either, which took Einstein to discover. If AI were trained only on data created before the 12th century, it couldn't come up with anything resembling Newtonian physics, or Leonardo's *Mona Lisa*, Michelangelo's *Pietà*, or Raphael's *Sistine Madonna*. No architectural design such AI would come up with could resemble the architecture of *Chartres Cathedral* or of *Taj Mahal*. Neither would any of its writings resemble works of Shakespeare, Goethe, or Rumi, nor would any of its music resemble the 18th-century polyphonic music of Bach or the

1960s songs of the Beatles. Creating a whole new paradigm like Buddhism or Confucianism, or writing the *Bhagavad Gita* or *Tao Te Ching* from scratch, would also be examples of what is out of reach for such an AI. It is easy to get dazzled by the capabilities and demonstrated intelligence of AI models, and while AI can be a great tool and can be utilized in many ways useful to humans, we need to keep in mind that *AI does not create culture, reasoning human minds do.*

Culture (from Latin *cultura*) is best understood as a verb, it is about cultivation, it is a process of taking in the existing undeveloped, unrefined, and simple, and then enveloping it with care, nurturing it, supporting its growth, development, evolution, all in order to make it into something new and better, more refined, developed, and sophisticated. In the context of humanity's development in the last several thousand years, the result of this process is recognizable in the forms of our civilization: social structures, governance, laws, ethical norms, architecture, philosophy, art, science, technology, and more. Culture is a minimum prerequisite for civilization, *culture undergirds civilization.* And human reasoning minds are the only known creators of culture known to us. It has also been said that culture is roughly everything we do and monkeys don't.[310] It is almost certain that primatologist Frans de Waal would readily issue a rebuttal to this statement (as he did in his book *The Ape and the Sushi Master*),[311] and we sure must agree with that sentiment. However, even though animals undeniably have a culture of sorts, such culture is very different from our human culture. Human culture builds civilizations that keep introducing new creations, our civilizations grow, starting simple and developing toward higher levels of sophistication. Humans might still be inefficient and slow at it, but each of our reasoning minds inherently has the capacity to act like "a self-rolling wheel, a first movement."[312] And human beings can intentionally work on ennobling their minds and can indeed experience creative moments — both small and big in scope — when they elevate the selves within their minds, each becoming increasingly more akin to the "unmovable mover"[313] and less like the externally determined (caused) entity. Animals, on the other hand, have cultures that are predetermined and static, they are essentially unchanged, the same as they were a million years ago. If somebody wrote it, 'A History of Ape Civilizations' would be a rather short book.

Regarding the origins of human culture, we read in many scholarly sources today that it is believed that human culture began when agriculture and trade allowed people to have surplus food and economic stability. It is rather curious that this is the first thing scholarly interest goes to when pondering culture. Food and economy. This is, of course, an important aspect, once the economic strength liberated human beings, they were free to create culture. The role of the economy as a liberating and enabling force for culture is an important one (even if we seem to have forgotten that lesson lately.) However, the abundance of food (or wealth) cannot create culture by itself, it represents only the enabling precondition that serves cultural development. If we see a well-fed monkey sitting on a plush sofa and playing with a book, we can be pretty sure that he neither read it nor wrote it. But if we liberate human minds, we can observe how such minds can indeed start to create culture. We can also observe how the culture created in this way in turn loops back and works on the human minds, making them more cultivated too, ennobling them, so that in subsequent iterations human minds create more sophisticated features within the domain of human culture.

The inability of AI to be original and create culture is a limitation we should keep in mind. But there is more. The second problem with overzealously delegating creative endeavors to AI has to do with the development and cultivation of human minds. Unless we intend to move toward some variant of the uncivilized future like the one portrayed in the 2006 tragicomedy *Idiocracy*, we need to stop ignoring the need for the cultivation of human minds. Even if the arrival of AI might be complicating matters in this respect, AI is not the only obstacle here, so let's briefly consider this landscape right before the arrival of AI.

Decades before AI arrived, we have (maybe not intentionally, but still carelessly) demoted the cultivation of human minds to the status of a hobby. In recent decades mainstream views have been such that, while we accept that education is important for human beings (or human minds), we consider that its purpose is mainly (or even solely) career training, rather than the pursuit of knowledge, search for wisdom, and ennobling of the mind. This wasn't always so, for example during the Age of Enlightenment (yes, modern Western civilization still stands on the platform built by philosophers of that time), even if only a small number of people could find their way into educational institutions, the ones that could, did it overwhelmingly for reasons of seeking and pursuing knowledge, not job prospects. Many Enlightenment thinkers devoted themselves to the pursuit of wisdom, at any cost they could bear. One only has to think of Spinoza, who stood by his philosophical convictions (which were denounced by his community as "abominable heresies") even after he was excommunicated from his Jewish community, expelled from the city of Amsterdam, and assaulted on the steps of the synagogue. David Hume, a philosopher whose thoughts we still ponder

250 years after his death, didn't really make many smart career moves, as he struggled to secure a position in academia due to his controversial ideas. Now, not everyone today wants or needs to follow in the steps of Spinoza or Hume, but society as a whole would be much wiser and do much better if we wouldn't choke such ideals in people who harbor them, and if we wouldn't seek to strip such people from livelihood and dignity. As things stand today, we have — by means of our institutional and cultural efforts — created a rather perverse set of incentives for the pursuit of knowledge. Not only are our institutions (and investments in them) complicit in this, but child upbringing (no doubt fed by parents' desire that their children have a life with dignity) now reflects it too. More often than not, children hear some version of the following story before or during their years of education: "My child, you should learn, try to do well, and get good grades in school, because you need to be able to get a decently paying job when you finish your education. That is the purpose of your education, to be better at competing against other humans on the 'job market' and to earn as much money as you can, so that you can survive and/or live in comfort. So, make sure that you choose the field that is in demand on the 'job market,' suppress your other interests, and work hard." We seem to routinely pass such existentially demoralizing ideals to many of our children and youth, and to many of us, it doesn't seem that any other choice is available. As things stand, for the past several decades, the 'job market' has been favoring the so-called STEM (Science, Technology, Engineering, and Mathematics) fields. Thus a major imbalance in our cultural life is happening because young people feel forced to follow the 'job market' regardless of their intrinsic interests, so for example in higher education, STEM educational fields are becoming dispropor-

tionally inflated and humanities departments are experiencing a sort of exodus.[314] Amounts of money and resources we are pouring into cultural life (reflected in education and career prospects), almost exclusively towards STEM, without any consideration of balance or societal needs, is staggering. The major impact of such imbalance on our cultural life, and thus on our civilization, is either ignored or understated. We seem oblivious to the larger contexts and cultural currents such developments create. For example, we all too easily decide to eliminate humanities, civics, and art from education. The crucial importance of literature and art in shaping and expanding human imagination and moral understanding is all but forgotten. We did know at one point that literature could help us sharpen our minds so that we could challenge our preconceptions and understand complexities better: "literature is the human activity that takes the fullest and most precise account of variousness, possibility, complexity, and difficulty."[315] But such sentiments seem to be fading and such pillars of culture crumbling under pressures of deferred maintenance. We can't ignore this cultural landscape when we consider the arrival of AI. A conscious and targeted effort, including funding and proper attention, must be invested into balancing of our cultural and educational landscape.

Enter the AI. Human minds, within a society that neglected their development due to the career-only focused education — severely lacking insights that humanities, civics, and art, can provide — are not properly prepared to face the intelligent and eloquent AI machinery. Even social networks, with much weaker AI capabilities, have been a serious challenge for our humanity. It is all too easy for human minds to become captivated and infatuated with AI and its dazzling demonstrations of intelligence and its indefatigable capability to entertain and to capture our attention. We need to find ways to arrest this development and to create an environment supportive (enough) of human minds such that they can do what they naturally gravitate toward, and many human minds indeed yearn for true learning. In order to thrive human society needs many skills and many virtues, however, there seems to be an important subset of skills we are fatally ignoring, even choking. We recklessly ignore the cultivation of educational environments and career paths (do we really want 'job market' to decide that for us?) that are essential for the development and exercising of the reasoning human minds – environments that promote not only the utilization of intelligence, but of all capacities of reason. Human minds need nourishing environments where they can develop critical thinking skills, learn to use language to articulate sophisticated arguments, create art that touches emotional strings in the audience and moves them to action, or just bring tears in their eyes because they were privileged to witness a profound experience. We don't need to create and invest in environments that educate us to be conformists and to follow our fears (do it because we must), such path is a trap for humanity and in time leads to the doom of civilization. Such a path represents a complete abandonment and betrayal of the ideals of Enlightenment we stand on (we thought that 'cutting the branch one stands on' is a joke). We need environments that nurture human minds so that they become strong enough and can courageously resolve to commit to actions in support of what is true, beautiful, and good.

Therefore, we need to get ready to meet the AI. There is still time (if we get our act together soon!) But in any event, AI is truly an empowering tool for humanity, and we should use it with prudence, carefully considering AI's strengths and weaknesses, utilizing it only in wisely chosen targeted applications, and always clearly indicating what role AI plays in our creations. In her already mentioned essay about AI, *The Coming Humanist Renaissance*, Adrianne LaFrance cautions us that while we should "outsource busywork to machines," we must refrain from "outsourcing our humanity to this technology, ... we should resist overreliance on tools that dull the wisdom of our own aesthetics and intellect." The AI "of the near future will supercharge our empirical abilities, but it may also dampen our curiosity. We are at risk of becoming so enamored of the synthetic worlds ... that we cease to peer into the unknown with any degree of true wonder or originality."[316] We ignore such advice at our own peril.

And the final note on this danger of AI: how about using AI to generate intimate letters meant for people we care about, family, friends, or romantic partners? Unless it is done in jest, one could imagine that the most common human gut reaction to receiving a letter created by an AI from a friend or romantic partner is one of disappointment or even betrayal. We shall, however, set this topic aside and return to it in the context of AI and relationships. For now, suffice it to say that human minds might be deceived by simulated emotions for a while, but most healthy human beings can ultimately discern whether entities they are relating to are also minds with agencies or just empty shells of machines without personhood. Human relationships are special, they are a rather mysterious phenomenon too. Only living beings can truly develop relationships. Machines cannot reach that domain, regardless of whether they are demonstrating intelligent behavior or not.

[D8] The alignment problem

The *AI alignment problem*, which revolves around the possibility that AI may perform tasks in a way that is not aligned with the intentions of human beings who deployed it, is a topic of debate in the AI community.[317] The prospect of non-aligned AI is experienced as profoundly unsettling by us human beings. One possibility why AI may go about accomplishing assigned tasks in ways unexpected by humans is because its intelligence doesn't have the full context of the existing reality (or, as Yann LeCun puts it, "AI doesn't have common sense"), it operates based on its rote "understanding" of the rules of reality it learned. A popular example in AI literature is based on the thought experiment of *paperclip maximizer*, where an AI, designed to maximize the manufacturing of paperclips, moves beyond the paperclip factory and finally converts the whole Earth and then the rest of the universe into paperclips.[318] Another example is the story of AI crashing the game program after it was instructed that "no game should be lost" – mission accomplished. How about the assignment that "no human beings should suffer ever again"; would a quick and instantaneous explosion of the planet count as an optimal solution and mission accomplished?

The fact that AI — based on its extensive training — can in many cases mimic well-reasoned actions does not mean that AI can indeed reason. In a game of Go, where game rules and boundaries are preset and unchangeable, all actions that eventually lead to winning a game seem well-reasoned and represent a prudent choice. Not so much in real life, where active agents with will and purposes (i.e. humans) and a much wider context (compared to what AI is trained on) constantly shift the underlying assumptions. Trusting AI with important tasks does indeed require it to have reason and common sense.

The only way we know how to accomplish this today is by using reasoning human minds to monitor and guide AI, either during the extensive AI training phase or — for critical applications — in real-time. Additionally, a carefully thought out, strict, and enforceable regulation, with clear legal and ethical framework, must limit actions AI can do autonomously.

A good example of a domain where either a strong regulation or an outright prohibition of AI must be instituted is financial markets, in which AI could potentially be allowed to autonomously make decisions and initiate actions with serious real-world consequences. Absent any regulation, we could imagine a scenario in which AI is given a task to maximize the returns of a mutual fund portfolio that happens to disproportionately represent fossil fuel companies. Based on its analysis, AI might forecast that short-term gains could be made by divesting from renewable energy companies from another (smaller) mutual fund it also controls. Based on such analysis, AI could rapidly (i.e. fraction of a second) sell off all renewable energy shares. This action might benefit the first portfolio in the short term, but it could inadvertently cause a huge drop in the market value of renewable energy stocks. If large enough, this action could seriously affect the transition to renewable energy sources. This illustrates how AI, while fulfilling given objectives, may inadvertently cause detrimental damage in a wider economic or environmental context.

Therefore, human supervision and regulatory frameworks are necessary to align AI with human intentions. Human reason and purposeful agency must be supplied to AI externally, and our AI technology must account for and allow that.

The other possibility pondered by some in the AI community, currently debated mainly on philosophical grounds, concerns the alignment of the future "superintelligent" AGI (Artificial General Intelligence). Looking toward the horizon from where we stand today, there is little doubt that AI will get better as we scale up deep neural networks representing it, or as we discover new AI engineering paradigms. It is almost certain that AI will become much more capable than it is presently, even in the very near future. Will that be enough to earn it a rank of AGI in the foreseeable future is not at all clear at this point. AGI is presently a rather loose concept. It depends on what we understand under the term "intelligence." It is obvious that raw intelligence is only one aspect of the capacity to reason. Our AI systems already demonstrate considerable levels of raw intelligence today, but they don't have any common sense, they don't reason, they are *idiot savants* in many respects.[319] AGI of the future is only a hypothetical concept. Some in the AI community assume that AGI, created by humans in the future, will be an intelligent entity with its own "agency", "purposeful intentions" and "sentience." AGI could therefore — at some point in the future — "consider" human beings to be unintelligent low-life and remnants of undeveloped past and proceed to treat us accordingly. We need to keep in mind that the existence of such an entity is only science fiction at this point.[320] Furthermore, the current levels of ignorance and hubris of our species are considerable, and our present knowledge is too limited and nowhere near to being able to construct a creature, to fashion a being with its own agency, purposeful will, and sentience. And considering humanity's current developmental stage, it seems that it is much better that way. In a purely hypothetical and highly unlikely event, if it so happens that we somehow stumble on any possibility to tinker, with external means, with an entity that not only demonstrates superior intelligent behavior like today's AI, but truly is an agency with its own intentions and purposes, being it "human" or "artificial," we should immediately reflect on our current maturity as species (or lack thereof) and on our limited capacity to deal with such a "discovery." Then we should close that door shut for the time being and toss the keys into the fiery chasm of Mount Doom. The sheer idea that it would be possible for us to affect the alignment of (fortunately only hypothetical) AGI that possesses its own agency and will is pure folly. We, modern humanity, carelessly inflict adverse traumatic experiences on other humans[321] and are having many doubts even about how to raise our own children, let alone how to "raise" and "align" an intelligent alien AGI creature. If such a discovery somehow fell into our lap, we almost certainly wouldn't be ready for the task.

In any event, tinkering with AGI is surely not our way into the realms of mind where agency and purposeful will reside and can be experienced directly. The only meaningful, rewarding, and safe entrance into the realms of mind for the human species is a direct exploration through ethically guided inner exercises, for example as established in Platonic and Neoplatonic wisdom of dialectic, with deep (and largely obscure for us) roots in even older mystery traditions. This ancient wisdom temporarily retreated into the background after the philosophy of empiricism gained wider acceptance and the Age of Enlightenment arrived. It seems to be knocking on our doors again. This topic touches the core of what this work is about, and an attempt to address it can be found in its final chapters.

3.4. The Bad AI: Limitations

Assuming that we can overcome — to a sufficient degree — the dangers AI brings along, we still have to deal with its limitations. What do we consider AI's limitations?

Yann LeCun, a pioneer in deep learning and chief AI scientist at Meta, has an uncommon perspective on AI performance: "the advance in technology over the last five years has been astonishing, ... but we're easily fooled by those systems into thinking they are intelligent, just because they manipulate language fluently. The only other example that we have of an entity that can manipulate language is other humans, so when we see something that can manipulate language flexibly, we assume that entity will have the same type of intelligence as humans, but it's just not true, *those systems are incredibly stupid.* ... There is this thing called common sense, ... [animals, for example] cats have some level of common sense, and no AI system today has any of it ... [Also, human] babies in the first few months of life learn an incredible amount of background knowledge about the world ... and we don't know how to do this with computers..."[322]

AI language fluency can indeed be misleading. We all too easily get dazzled by AI's highly intelligent use of language and forget that there is so much more to what we commonly recognize as purposeful behavior with common sense. For example, it is remarkable that infants somehow have the innate capacity to use reason (manifested as common sense) and rapidly learn from very limited data,[323] while AI requires vast amounts of training data upfront and often struggles to adapt to new situations.

This should not be considered just a technical limitation of AI, there is a decisive qualitative difference between a human reasoning mind and a machine with no agency of its own. Some AI scientists harbor a belief that advances in our understanding of deep neural networks, or some other software architecture or algorithm, or a combination of software and hardware that will better mimic what is happening in the human brain will be able to somehow create a device, not only much more intelligent than today's AI, but truly akin to the human mind and demonstrating other features of a reasoning mind, like its own agency, reason, purposes, and sentience. The term *Artificial General Intelligence (AGI)* is often bundled together with this belief. We need to be very clear that, based on our current knowledge, this can be only a hypothetical belief and nothing more.[324] AI scientists and engineers are poised to create much more powerful AI systems, which will demonstrate increasingly higher levels of intelligence, and based on the current track record, they will almost certainly succeed, there is little doubt about that. We may at one point even decide to call such intelligent systems AGI. However, the creation of artificial systems with agency, reason, its own purposes, and sentience is an entirely different story. Apart from what we know through our own individual inner subjective experiences, we human beings, in general, have very little understanding of what concepts like mind, agency, reason, purposeful intentions, and sentience represent and what their true foundation is. Assuming that it is possible that an independent agency of AGI will somehow "emerge" from our software and hardware is not based on anything we know, it is presently only a figment of imagination. (Likewise, the notion that human agency, reason, purposeful intentions, and sentience are just "emerging" from the processes in the human brain is not based on anything we know, it is just a belief, a mere assumption.)[325]

We will return to this aspect in our discussion of the AI *alignment* problem, in the section on AI dangers.

What does the fact that AI doesn't have common sense tell us about its limitations and its ability to perform assigned tasks independently? Not having a wider context and common sense is indeed a serious constraint. This is the main reason why we cannot allow AI to conduct many important tasks today.[326] With this in mind, let's consider Large Language Models (like ChatGPT) and their limitations, as they are arguably the most intelligent AI machinery we presently have.

[L1] AI Hallucinations

LLMs can generate content that is incorrect, completely made up, or even nonsensical; in other words, they can *hallucinate* unpredictably.[327] An LLM can unexpectedly generate complete fabrications while appearing very persuasive, competent, and eloquent. This is the reason why there is always a reminder under the ChatGPT prompt box: "ChatGPT can make mistakes. Consider checking important information."[328] Problems related to hallucinations can be reduced by additional training of the LLM by humans (reinforcement learning with human feedback or related technique), by careful engineering or sequencing prompts (input queries), or even by letting several LLMs "debate" the response (inspired by Marvin Minsky's idea of "society of minds"). However, this problem is deep-seated and inherent to these models. LLMs can't plan their output (what they will "say") in advance and are not proactive. They are rather very reactive: while constructing its output one word at a time, an LLM doesn't "know" what the next word is going to be – every time the next word in a sentence needs to be determined, the complete text constructed up to that point is fed into the input, and the probabilities are calculated for the subsequent word to generate; the word with the highest score comes next, and the whole process is repeated.[329] In Yann LeCun's words: "Large language models have no idea of the underlying reality that language describes. ... [they] generate text that sounds fine, grammatically, semantically, but they don't really have some sort of objective other than just satisfying statistical consistency with the prompt. ... Language is built on top of a massive amount of background knowledge that we all have in common, that we call common sense."[330] In many ways, it seems that there is so much more to our inner and outer worlds than language can describe.[331] Of course, if this limitation is properly considered, LLMs can still be very useful assistants to humans. They can help us increase productivity in all domains where language or symbols are used, be it an email draft, research consultation or evaluation, or a snippet of software code. We just have to keep in mind that AI demonstrates intelligence, but it can make mistakes as it doesn't have purposeful agency and therefore can't have what we recognize as reason or common sense.

[L2] AI Bias

Another serious limitation is *AI bias*. If the material AI is trained on reflects biased views, even implicitly, the resulting generated output is likely to contain biases as well. This can disproportionately affect minority groups and individuals and has the potential to reinforce existing social and economic inequalities. Bias is likely to affect racial and ethnic minorities, women and gender minorities, people with disabilities, people living in poverty, elderly populations, and certain geographical regions, among other categories. The bias contained in AI training has a major influence on fairness and equity in the domain where AI is utilized — banking and law enforcement are obvious important examples — and it also erodes trust and prospects for the adoption of AI technologies. AI developers should seek to understand and mitigate these biases through diverse underlying training data and techniques like reinforcement learning with human feedback;[332] however, all human users of AI should keep in mind that biased outputs are a possibility. AI bias is a well-recognized problem, with plenty of material written about it (an endnote with pointers to some of it is included.)[333]

[L3] AI Interpretability

The final limitation we will mention here is the *AI interpretability* (a.k.a. *explainability*) problem. At this point, it is not obvious, at least not to me, whether interpretability is just a limitation, or should it be considered an outright danger. One way or the other, the fact is that we don't know how to mitigate it. So, what is interpretability in the context of AI systems? (Most modern AI systems, at the time of this writing, are based on deep neural network architectures and we will discuss interpretability in this context, with the stipulation that AI interpretability problem is, in principle, independent from the underlying architecture.)

Deep neural network based AI is a *black box* to us humans who made it. We do know how to put the AI machinery together, how to write software that represents it, how to "train" it, and how to use it. However, we don't know exactly how it works. Nobody does, including the scientists and engineers who designed it. It does sound weird, but that's the way things are. If, for example, ChatGPT-3 comes up with a text output based on the text input we gave it at the prompt, we currently don't have the means to determine exactly how it did it. If the output is in any way incorrect (e.g. it is a nonsensical hallucination), we can't troubleshoot and debug the process itself in any way. We don't know exactly which training material (containing hundreds of billions of words, or more), and to what degree, contributed to the numerical values of each of the connection parameters in its deep neural network (there are 175 billion of them) during the training phase; we also don't know which nodes and parameters in the network contributed to that particular text output during the inference phase. If we don't like the output, the only thing we can do is try to coax a better answer with a different input. And even if the new output comes out the way we like it, we still don't know how it happened. Of course, the stakes could be significantly higher in other domains, for example if AI is used to screen employment applicants at companies, loan applicants at banks, to make decisions about surveillance for law enforcement, or to launch intercontinental missiles. All we have access to are inputs and outputs, nobody can tell why AI "decides" one way or the other. Depending on the application, this can quickly bring us into some undesired murky waters and into some very scary scenarios. These considerations indicate that we need to refrain from AI deployment in many critical domains. A lot has been said and written about the AI interpretability problem,[334] it is a subject of ongoing research, but no solutions can be seen on the horizon yet.

The state in which the AI discipline finds itself, due to its interpretability problem, also has some significant philosophical implications. Most people pondering AI, including scientists and engineers, think of AI as "a tool, not a creature,"[335] AI is seen as a deterministic device, with no agency and no purposes of its own. However, the "black box" nature does pose a philosophical dilemma. For example, once GPT-3 is *trained*, all 175 billion numeric *parameters* (or *weights*) representing connections between neurons in its deep neural network are determined. If we copy them into a file and transfer them to another (compatible) instance of GPT-3 across the world, these two instances will behave identically; the same input will generate exactly the same output on both. In some ways, even if it is a black box to us, this suggests that GPT-3 is a deterministic device, basically similar to a thermostat in this respect. However, this assumes that the so-called randomness value (a.k.a. *temperature*) is set to zero.[336] If we increase the randomness value (which is done by default on LLMs like GPT-3, to escape bland outputs), these two GPT-3 instances will start giving different answers for a single input. Everybody may still consider them two deterministic devices, but in principle, we can no longer prove it. In principle, anybody could come along and claim that an elf, a fairy, a Flying Spaghetti Monster, or an evil spirit is behind AI actions, and nobody could prove them wrong; we wouldn't know how. Each of the two GPT-3 instances would represent a black box to us, and we couldn't explain how their outputs are deterministically related to their inputs. This is not an unimportant aspect as it might seem at first. We already have people, even in the AI development community, who consider AI models to have "agency" and "purposes" of their own. It is precisely because we can't explain their behavior in a deterministic fashion, that ideas about AI being a "creature" of sorts — a "being" with "sentience" and its own "purposes" — start appearing natural to us and start to creep into AI discourse, as they already have.[337] (It doesn't help, of course, that we also don't understand — scientifically speaking — our own minds and how it is that we human beings do have agency, reason, purposes, and sentience.) All kinds of perplexities regarding the agency of AI are bound to happen if we cannot explain their processes and actions.

3.5. The Good AI: Promises

What about the promises of AI, of the positive aspects of what is to come? AI is here to stay, and we must certainly keep our beneficial imaginations alive as we ponder, develop, use, and regulate AI. Reid Hoffman prefers to ask the question about the future of AI in this way: "Is there a future where the massive proliferation of robots ushers in a new era of human flourishing, not human marginalization? Where AI-driven research helps us safely harness the power of nuclear fusion in time to help avert the worst consequences of climate change? It's only natural to peer into the dark unknown and ask what could possibly go wrong. It's equally necessary—and more essentially human—to do so and envision what could possibly go right."[338]

Indeed. There are many good reasons why we might want to pursue AI technology development. If humanity achieves the necessary cultural leap, if we manage to heed the advice "Will the best in human nature please stand up,"[339] the benefits of AI will be bountiful. This advice is from Nick Bostrom's *Superintelligence: Paths, Dangers, Strategies*. In it, he also laments that "before the prospect of an intelligence explosion, we humans are like small children playing with a bomb. Such is the mismatch between the power of our plaything and the immaturity of our conduct." Bostrom recognizes that it will not be possible for humanity to run away from it and is afraid that there is no "grown-up in sight." Recent developments seem to be hinting that at least some of his fears might be justified. But then, we might have some solid common ground to build on. In his book *Life 3.0: Being Human in the Age of Artificial Intelligence*, Max Tegmark reminds us that "there are many ethical themes about which there's widespread agreement, both across cultures and across centuries. For example, emphasis on *beauty*, *goodness* and *truth* traces back to both the Bhagavad Gita and Plato."[340] Indeed. But we need to start building upon this ground, and we need to make a radical leap to be able to meet the approaching challenges. In the words of Adrienne LaFrance, "today we need a cultural and philosophical revolution, ... we need a human renaissance in the age of intelligent machines."[341] Entirely on the mark. If — and that is a big if — humanity does make the cultural leap, if we learn how to embrace the ideals of "beauty, goodness and truth" as beacons of our culture, and thus manage to "grow up," we will almost certainly experience the 21st-century Renaissance.[342]

If we get there, what, exactly, could be the benefits of AI to humanity? It is argued in this book that the greatest benefit, by far, would be that we humans, in fact, did "grow up" as expressed in Bostrom's words. If we manage to avoid a dystopian future — perhaps of the kind portrayed in movies like *Blade Runner* and *Mad Max,* or in literary works like *Watchmen, Brave New World,* or *Nineteen Eighty-Four*[343] — by retaining and elevating human culture, we will get to live in a prosperous civilized world in which healthy relationships among human beings are the most important value. This is the big prize for humanity. This is also our big test. Passing this test would mean that we have managed to connect with the better angels of our nature and are able to overcome raw individual self-interest to a satisfactory degree. Our human wisdom must become that sophisticated, it must be able to cleanse, ennoble, and widen our self-interest. *We cannot bring greed and willingness to exploit fellow human beings with us across the bridge into the civilized future of humanity empowered by AI – that is not an available option.* Passing this test would also mean that we are capable of effective global cooperation. Acting (mostly) in unison, in the interest of all of us, is the only way we can have AI in service of civilized humanity. If AI developments serve as a wake-up call and push us to accomplish that, this would also be their greatest benefit.

There would also be other (fringe) benefits. Like major *healthcare advancements*: it is already obvious that AI can improve diagnostic accuracy,[344] aid in drug discovery,[345] and assist in many ways in patient care. AI can easily crunch vast amounts of medical data and help with early disease detection and better treatment plans.[346] AI will not replace human doctors (nor should it) but it will be a great support to all medical professionals. Healthcare research and epidemic monitoring are also obvious areas for the utilization of AI. (And since we would have survived the AI explosion as unified humanity no longer subordinated to our own greed, we would obviously have universal free healthcare for all.)[347] In the *realm of education*, AI can — with human guidance — help generate more per-sonalized, individually targeted educational programs, with the necessary material and intellectually and emotionally engaging lessons, thus enabling humans in teaching professions to be more invested in the relational and social aspects of education. This would also increase opportunities for teachers' own advancement and professional satisfaction. (Did we already mention that surviving the AI explosion would necessarily bring free high-quality education with nearly equal access for all?)[348]

Addressing *climate change and environmental sustainability* is an-other great benefit: AI can improve energy efficiency, optimize resource utilization, and help in modeling environmental data, thus aiding human environment-related decisions. One example is the DeepMind project that uses AI to predict wind patterns and energy outputs from wind farms. Another is an AI model for faster and more accurate global weather forecasting.[349] Then there is a research project on plastic-eating enzymes that could help with pollution.[350] There are high hopes that AI will help scientists achieve a commercially viable fusion process,[351] which would result in the availability of a clean and cheap energy source for the entire planet. There is a strong possibility that AI will create *unprecedented economic growth* by increasing efficiency and creating new markets and industries. And since the only way to survive the AI explosion as a civilized society is to liberate ourselves (to a good enough measure) from our own individual greed, and to grow (as a society) past the exploitative mindset of neoliberal economics (or its successor),[352] we can be confident that the benefits of such economic growth will be rationally distributed, with equality and fraternity[353] as guiding principles of humanity. All this talk may sound like an unrealistic utopian dream to many, but there is no rational reason why we can't get rid of greed in the same way we got rid of slavery, for example. For a long time, the belief that slavery is here to stay was the dominant narrative on the planet. For enough people among us, throughout history, it felt justified and natural to exploit another fellow human being. No longer. We got rid of the sucker. We moved on. Greed is the remaining oppressor of humanity. And we should not have any illusions about our prospects if greed remains the dominant force in our individual human minds. If AI gets to unite with the greed in our hearts, it will empower it to an unimaginable degree, and untold human suffering can be the only result of that union.

Moving on to other potential benefits if things go right: the next area is *improvements in agriculture*: AI can usher in the era of precision agriculture and through it optimize crop yields by better resource utilization (water, fertilizers, etc) and by reducing waste through improved monitoring. AI can be used to track and model bee and other insect movements in the environment as part of the efforts to reverse the global bee colony collapse (bees and other insects are dying in large numbers globally and we don't know why.)[354] *Advances in transportation* could include self-driving vehicles and improvements in public transportation and logistics. AI could help with transportation efficiency and safety. Then, if we don't end up in some form of a dystopian authoritarian society,[355] AI will benefit us all with advances in *public safety and security*: transparent surveillance and data analysis could help with emergency response and crime prevention. Robots with AI would be able to provide assistance in areas humans cannot easily access. *Scientific research* is already benefiting from AI (AlphaFold story is an example) and collaboration between AI and human scientists will only increase. *Global communication, language translation,* even *cultural "translation"* can all be aided by AI, which has the potential to break down cultural and language barriers and facilitate communication and understanding among different cultures. *Enhancing everyday life: AI virtual assistants* could make our lives more efficient, relaxed, and comfortable.

There is more, much more, this is only a subset of what AI could do for us. If we get there.

4 Human Self as Gleaned Through the Lens of Science

There is a single point in the immeasurable world of nature and mind, where no science, and therefore no causal consideration, can have access, not only for practical reasons but also for logical ones: this point is the individual self (the "I"). It is a small point in the universal realm, yet it is also a whole world, embracing all our emotional life, our will, and our thought.[356]

Max Planck

Starting with the Age of Reason, science has firmly established itself as a dominant paradigm and a cornerstone of the modern worldview. Science and scientific method matter, most people and almost all institutions of contemporary society orient themselves by consulting scientific facts. For this reason, it is important that we can clearly identify and differentiate scientific facts from other kinds of propositions, like opinions, beliefs, speculative ideas (even those proposed by renowned scientists), and wishful thinking. This is not always easy because we humans can, and often do, attach to propositions we come to trust and consider believable. Nonetheless, facts matter, opinions and beliefs can be deceiving, even if they sound very persuasive.

The first two chapters of this book dedicate significant attention to debunking two consequential beliefs (fallacies actually) that have embedded themselves in the modern worldview. They affect how we perceive ourselves, how we relate to and treat other people, and how we engage with the broader ecosystem. This is important for our considerations because these beliefs contribute to a collective sense of helplessness and resignation in the face of looming global challenges that require our full attention and global cooperation. As elaborated in our first and second chapters, two beliefs are seriously destructive to our humanity. They are reiterated in shorthand here, they are: 1) human beings are just complex deterministic machines consisting of physical matter, with no intrinsic agency, and no purpose, and 2) human beings, like all other living systems, evolved solely via a process consisting of random-chance mutations of chemical molecules in their genes, which are then selected for fitness. These two scientifically outdated beliefs are used as a platform to promote ideas about human beings being just "survival machines," without any intrinsic agency and purpose, engaged in a struggle termed "survival of the fittest" where "selfish genes" propagate and therefore "pure, disinterested altruism ... has no place in nature." Such ideas have been highly damaging, and they keep inflicting pain and causing despair within humanity.

We now turn to yet another damaging belief that has been gaining traction for several decades already. It appears to be finding pathways to be enshrined into the modern worldview, even though it is in no way associated with any scientific endeavor. Some Western philosophers and scientists espouse this belief and cloak it in scientific language. It boldly proclaims that "the human self is an illusion."[357] The force pushing this unfounded belief seems exceptionally poised, even if there is nothing scientific about it as it is only an assumption. This belief directly contradicts and seeks to invalidate our own inner experiences, the awareness that we exist as individuals with agency, intentions, and purposes, each using *"I am"* to address ourselves. But it is, in fact, very hard to shake off the notion that each of us is a self.

(As an aside here, this belief that the "human self is an illusion," espoused by some Western philosophers and scientists, should not be confused with the notion of "non-self" (anattā/anātman) in Buddhism, as they represent different concepts, even though there were philosophical attempts to consolidate them in the past.[358] The concept of "non-self" is addressed in this book's final chapters, mainly in the section on Buddhism. For now, suffice it to say that Buddha himself declined to comment on the notion that the "individual self" simply does not exist. His approach was practical, and he promoted "noble silence" on questions that he considered not helpful to the path of spiritual liberation. His use of the concept "non-self" (anattā/anātman) was centered around the need to reduce ego-centeredness and attachment to illusions presented by the senses and to move towards the all-embracing unboundedness. Additionally, there are examples of Buddha referring to the concept of "self" (attā/ātman) in which he considers it an unbounded entity whose existence is free to take any form and does not lend itself to affliction or disease. In other words, Buddha considered only such entity to be the "self" (attā/ātman) that is not bound by cravings/desires (tanhā) and thus by suffering (dukkhā). On the other hand, the individual, still "bounded," and not fully liberated self is simply referred to as "non-self" (anattā/anātman)).[359]

Despite the ubiquitous presence of our experiences of purposeful agency — of the constant sense of *"I am"* underlying all our thoughts, feelings, intentions, and actions — modern science offers little insight into this agentive aspect of human beings. Only a select few scientific disciplines have formulated theories and models of the mind and freely employ terms like *self*, *agency*, or *purpose* in their vocabulary. It is implausible for these disciplines to consider any of these concepts as mere *illusions* or *hallucinations*. Such disciplines seek to venture and go as far as science can lead us — within its current confines — toward understanding the human self. Among them are several disciplines primarily concerned with the development, psychopathology, and psychotherapy of the human self. These scientific disciplines have developed effective methods to navigate the difficulty of objectively evaluating what we experience as subjective human experiences. Trained professionals engaged in such disciplines utilize their reasoning minds as objective instruments. If sufficiently proficient and experienced, they can readily identify the intricacies of subjective emotions and thoughts in themselves and others. They can also discern important subconscious patterns within the human mind, either directly through therapeutic engagement and relationships, or by employing sophisticated psychological assessment tools that have been thoroughly researched and validated.

To highlight several important aspects of our current scientific understanding of the human self, an attempt will now be waged to present a brief overview of some pertinent disciplines. It should be understandable that a comprehensive overview of this field — even if brief — is beyond the scope of this work. For this reason, we will limit the content of this chapter to a few essential aspects, maintaining the focus on how the concept of self can be approached with a scientific mindset. The technical jargon used in these disciplines is kept to a minimum. However, I couldn't find a way to completely avoid it while still conveying the important insights they offer. Nonetheless, no previous knowledge or experience in this field is necessary to understand the material. For those entirely unfamiliar with the field, a slow and careful reading should suffice. What follows is an overview of how the development of the human self is characterized in the fields of *attachment theory* (introduced by John Bowlby and further developed and empirically validated by Mary Ainsworth), *psychiatric infant research* (as conceptualized and conducted by Daniel N. Stern), and several *psychodynamic* schools of thought, including *object relations* theory, *intersubjective relational* approach, *affect regulation and mentalization* framework (introduced by Peter Fonagy and his collaborators), and *self psychology* (developed by Heinz Kohut). It is probably fair to state that the interest of these disciplines in the nature and development of the human self is rooted in practical grounds, as they all focus on the development, psychopathology, and psychotherapy of human beings. Among their various achievements, these disciplines have made fundamentally important discoveries about how to parent and raise children, particularly during the crucial developmental period of 0 to 3 years of age, so that they grow into healthy and resilient human beings. Within these disciplines, considering the developing selves of children as "illusions" (or even non-existent) is not a viable perspective; in fact, it is a potentially dangerous proposition. In general, professionals in these fields must understand human selves in order to support their development and to remedy or alleviate mental traumas. Therefore, they cannot afford to indulge in philosophical musings about human selves being "illusions," "hallucinations," or "deterministic mechanisms devoid of free will and a sense of purpose."

I would also like to draw attention to the allegations we sometimes hear from scientists engaged in the so-called "hard sciences" (physics, chemistry, biology, etc), stating that disciplines studying human psychology are "not scientific enough." This is rather peculiar as "hard sciences" decided to reduce their field of study from the whole universe of phenomena to only those phenomena that can be expressed in mathematical equations (i.e. of the physical nature, see the section on Galileo in the second chapter) and that enter our minds only through the portal of our senses. Many scientists with a physicalist mindset — especially if they have not been exposed to mental health suffering (their own or that of others) — simply assume that physical phenomena represent the whole reality, choosing to ignore the phenomena at work solely in human minds, often hoping to wish them away as illusions or hallucinations. In fact, any physical illness would likely be preferred over any mental health illness by anyone who understood the implications. Instead of cheering on and supporting the disciplines that courageously venture into yet uncharted territory — where the phenomena are not so simple as to be explainable with mathematical equations or simple causal connections — some scientists choose to look down on the disciplines that dare to explore the intricate laws at work solely in the human mind. It can be argued that this is probably how we were stuck (for quite some time in the 20th century) with a notion of debilitating depressions being considered "chemical imbalances in the brain" and with similarly misguided reductionist oversimplifications. Sometimes it is even claimed, often unjustifiably, that disciplines studying human psychology with an in-depth focus on the phenomena of the mind are not "evidence-based." At the same time, the scripted/manualized short-term psycho-therapy treatments — simpler and cheaper, with therapists following a generic manual, therefore easier to standardize and research empirically — are labeled with the buzzword (that's what it is) "evidence-based"[360] and widely promoted. While the scripted/manualized short-term treatments certainly hold their place as important tools in mental health, they should not be viewed as a remedy for all mental health problems, because that's not what they are. For everyone's benefit, we should acknowledge that honest research into phenomena related to the development of the self, psychopathology, and psychother-apy is necessary for the long-term benefit of humanity. Yes, science does look somewhat different in these areas. The trajectory of a falling stone can be studied using mathematics and explained by simple causality, and so can the trajectory of an electrical signal propagating through neurons. However, the trajectory of a debilitating depression in the human mind cannot. It is much more complicated than that. Let's recognize this. And instead of looking down on scientists trying to solve one of the most complex enigmas known to us, let's rather decide to invest some serious mind power to understand human minds better. Theories and models of mind we currently have are helpful, but they are still incomplete, even if some of their aspects are verified and considered mature. There are plenty of opportunities for scientific efforts in the field. (Data scientist Jeffrey Hammerbacher, an early employee of Facebook, famously remarked "The best minds of my generation are thinking about how to make people click ads. That sucks."[361] It sure does, if we are to elevate our species to new heights, we indeed need scientists of our generation to be motivated by their humanity and by ideals, rather than by self-interest alone.)

We also need to recognize and appreciate that this type of science requires a different kind of training and a different kind of predisposition and aptitude. The ability to recognize patterns in physical sciences — like in chemical reactions, in quantum mechanics differential equations, or in software algorithms — is very different from the ability to recognize patterns manifesting in theories of mind and psychotherapy. Registering suicidal ideation in a quiet and withdrawn human being, detecting the subtle emotions in oneself that indicate a transference of a traumatic relationship from a patient, or developing high levels of self-reflection and self-awareness necessary for intersubjective encounters during psychotherapy all require unique aptitude and extensive training.

The disciplines reviewed here have come a long way in understanding the human self. Their scientific models, hypotheses, experiments, and validation appear different compared to their counterparts in the "hard sciences." Still, their *effectiveness* and *clinical value* — psychotherapy is sophisticated and involved, yet it can help, and it can save lives — prove that their methods are going in the right direction.

One more important point: it should be evident from our overview that one characteristic aspect is common to all these disciplines. Beginning from different starting points and adopting different perspectives, they all arrived at the *widely supported consensus that human relationships are fundamental in both the development of the human self and the maintenance of mental health.* Understanding how relationships are formative for the developing human mind and how they can be utilized in psychotherapy should be the top priority of any science in this domain. We will be returning to this insight repeatedly.

4.1. Development of Self and Its Reliance on Nurturing Relationships

4.1.1. Attachment Theory

British psychoanalyst and psychiatrist John Bowlby witnessed firsthand the effects of separation on the mental health of children evacuated from London during the Blitz, a period of sustained bombing when Nazi Germany attacked the United Kingdom during WWII. Millions of children were separated from their families and were sent to the countryside in order to protect them from the bombings. Unexpected discovery was that, in terms of their mental health, the evacuated children fared worse than the children who stayed with their families, even though they were physically safer. Bowlby's observations from this period likely had a profound impact on shaping his understanding of the importance of a child's relational bond with their primary caregivers. His early ideas were also influenced by his clinical work with emotionally disturbed children. In 1944, he created a report for the World Health Organization about the mental health of homeless children in post-war Europe. This report, titled *Forty-Four Juvenile Thieves: Their Characters and Home-Life*,[362] can likely be considered the first contribution to what later became the *attachment theory*. In it, he suggested that there was a strong connection between the disruption of the early mother-child relationship bond and the later onset of a mental disorder.

Starting with Bowlby's contributions in the 1950s (which continued into the 1980s),[363] the attachment theory increasingly gained prominence, due in part also to its further development and empirical validation accomplished by Mary Ainsworth (exemplified by the renowned *Strange Situation* experiment).[364] *Attachment theory thus identified the early relationships as the fundamental component of human self development.* The fact that "attachment theory views the sense of self as essentially relational"[365] represented a major departure from the existing interpretations, including the contemporaneous psychoanalytical perspectives (early Freudian psychoanalysis considered relationships only as a secondary influence, and biological drives/instincts were thought of as the primary influence – a position that is now considered outdated).

Several instruments of psychological assessment were used to validate the theory, but one of the most convincing empirical validations of the impact of parenting on a child's attachment style (which affects their mental health development) comes from multiple studies involving the *Adult Attachment Interview* (AAI). This psychological instrument has demonstrated that it can reliably predict a child's attachment style based on the parent's AAI test outcome even before the child is born.[366] AAI outcome reflects a parent's intentional stance toward the child, and it is understood that "the parent's capacity to adopt the intentional stance towards a not-yet-intentional infant, to think about the infant in terms of thoughts, feelings, and desires in the infant's mind and in their own mind in relation to the infant and his or her mental state, is the key mediator of the transmission of attachment."[367]

We will not provide descriptions of various attachment relationship styles, as there is plenty of literature on this topic. One poignant description of attachment and attachment styles, revolving around the interpretation of Sharon Olds's poem *Bathing the Newborn,*[368] can be found in the book *Enhancing Attachment and Reflective Parenting in Clinical Practice* by Arietta Slade and her collaborators.

The nature of the developmentally important attachment bond is such that it is an *affectional bond*, it has a great emotional significance, and as such it is not interchangeable. Relational availability and closeness are desired, and separation causes distress. Attachment bonds also have their significance in relationships beyond infancy, including adulthood. An affectional bond becomes an attachment bond whenever the individual seeks security or comfort from the relationship.[369]

Many researchers have contributed to attachment research following the pioneering work of Bowlby and Ainsworth. Among them are Ed Tronick, Beatrice Beebe, T. Berry Brazelton, and Daniel Stern, all of whom have contributed not only to attachment theory but also more broadly to the fields of infant mental health and developmental psychology. There is an abundance of literature on attachment, a small sample of which is listed in the endnotes.[370]

4.1.2. Psychiatric Infant Research

A new paradigm in the scientific understanding of the development of the sense of self and structures of self was brought about by infant research done by psychiatrist and psychoanalytic theoretician Daniel N. Stern. Prior to his work, performed in the 1970s and 1980s, our understanding of infants was based on external observations of behavior. Stern proposed that infants have a rich inner world of subjectivity (including a nascent experience of self) from a very early age and shifted the research focus to their internal experience. To study it, he focused on the relationship and relational markers during the mother-infant interaction observations. His experiments utilized a detailed microanalysis of recorded and real-time face-to-face interactions, with a focus on non-verbal communication (like facial expressions, gestures, vocalizations, and response times.) Special attention was paid to instances of intense mutual engagement and emotional connection, or what Stern called *present moments* or *moments of meeting* (also *experience as it is lived*), which represent intersubjective events that make up our experiences and can also be agents of transformation and growth. In line with the findings of the attachment theory, Stern found relatedness to be essential for the organization of the self.

Stern was able to identify four distinct stages of early self formation, by observing how it manifests during the first two years of human life: "1) the sense of *emergent self* (0–2 months) involves the process of the self coming into being and forming initial connections; 2) the sense of *core self* and the domain of core relatedness (2–6 months) are based on the single organizing subjective perspective and a coherent physical self; 3) the sense of *subjective self* and the domain of intersubjective relatedness (7–15 months) emerge with the discovery of subjective mental states beyond physical events; and 4) the sense of *verbal self* [or narrative self] forms after 15 months."[371] It is noteworthy that Stern observes that during the *emergent self* development, the differentiation between the self and the other begins early, at birth or even before, and he concludes that therefore "some notion of consciousness"[372] must be present very early on in order to facilitate the progressive organization of the mind.

Based on the extensive research data, Stern was able to realize that self-other relationships cannot be considered simply as a means for the development of an individual separate sense of self (individual subjectivity), but that one can readily observe what can be termed the *relational intersubjectivity* develop during the relationship. He therefore describes human relationships as "the stuff of all human connectedness, intimacy, and trust throughout development, and sees the ability to engage in them as essential to mental health."[373]

Among his other works, Stern's books *The Interpersonal World of the Infant*, and *Diary of a Baby*, and also *The Present Moment in Psychotherapy and Everyday Life*,[374] are considered seminal in the field. His work was groundbreaking in many respects, and it had profound implications for clinical practice, not only in the field of infant mental health and treatment of children but (due to its insights about the roots of psychological issues in early experiences) also for the psychotherapy of adults.

4.1.3. Psychodynamic Theories

Psychoanalysis, founded by Sigmund Freud about 130 years ago, brought several important discoveries relevant to psychology and the theory of mind (note: not to be confused with ToM as used in cognitive science).[375] Among its key insights is the recognition that significant aspects of human emotions and behavior are influenced by unconscious processes, and that early childhood experiences exercise significant influence on the development of the human self. The discipline of psychotherapy has benefited too. For example, the concept of defense mechanisms, such as repression (the unconscious exclusion of troubling thoughts), denial (the refusal to accept reality), and projection (the attribution of one's own unacceptable feelings onto others), inform the therapeutic process in an important way. The concepts of transference & countertransference (where patients unconsciously project feelings onto their therapists, and vice versa, thus enabling the reenactment of significant relationships during the therapy) are also indispensable instruments that inform the therapeutic process.

Many consider psychoanalysis to be "the most disciplined and dedicated method ever devised for the study of human subjectivity."[376] Psychoanalysis is over a century old and has matured as a discipline during that time. Its most significant restructuring happened during the second half of the 20th century, during which a transition from its focus on individual biological drives and instincts toward a more relational perspective occurred. What was originally known as Freudian psychoanalysis has mostly transitioned into what is today called relational psychoanalysis, or, if broadened somewhat to include multiple schools of thought, *psychodynamic psychotherapy*. Both its theory of mind and therapeutic practice incorporated many aspects from relational models like attachment theory, object relations, intersubjectivity, and self psychology.[377] The concepts of self and agency play prominent roles in the psychodynamic theory of mind, or, in the (tongue-in-cheek) words of Bruce Reis, "The *self* is alive and well, and living in relational psychoanalysis ... it continues to occupy a central role ...[and it] has survived the premature reports of its demise."[378]

What follows is a short description of some of the relational perspectives that significantly inform the theory of mind utilized in psychodynamic psychotherapy.

Self Psychology

Self psychology, a theory introduced by Heinz Kohut in the 1970s,[379] in many ways revolutionized North American psychoanalysis. It is Kohut's work that "broke the iron grip of ego psychology by forcing psychoanalysts to think in less mechanistic terms, in terms of selfhood rather than psychological function."[380] Kohut realized that he needs to consider the human self as the "center of individual's psychological universe, ... the center of initiative and the recipient of impressions"; it is the locus of all relationships.[381] *Self is not a mere representation but is itself the active agent.*[382]

In line with Max Planck's statement at the beginning of this chapter, however, Kohut does recognize the difficulty in fully conceptualizing the term self, and he accepts that it might not be definable, possibly even not fully "knowable" and that "we cannot, by introspection or empathy, penetrate to the self per se ... the self is not a concept of an abstract science"[383]

Self psychology aligns well with attachment and related theories, as it sees relationships as primary and fundamental. In this respect, it is very similar to the interpersonal school of psychoanalysis and the theories of Ronald Fairbairn[384] and Donald Winnicott, both central figures in the development of the object relations theory.[385]

Consistent with Winnicott's insights, Kohut observes that a child's self development is nurtured through relationships, the interplay between the child's innate potential and the attuned responsiveness of the *self-objects* (other human beings or things experienced as part of their own self or used as utility for the self.) For this reason, and in line with the findings of attachment theory, self psychology considers parental emotional attunement and the ability to empathize with their children as essential for their development, and *attachment relationships are recognized as a central motivation of the self.*[386]

Empathy is recognized as an essential concept in self psychology. Empathy is not merely an emotion, as it is sometimes perceived; rather, it is a fundamental component of what we call human reason. Importantly, reason should not be narrowly viewed as merely a cold-blooded, unfeeling cognitive capacity.

Empathy has to do with the "recognition of the other," *empathy is marked by the capacity for emotional attunement and for comprehending the experiences of others from their own unique perspectives* (it is not about "what I would feel in their situation.")[387] An important marker of a mature relationship is the mutuality in the exchange of empathy and self-object utility between partners. "In Kohut's view of mature relationships, there is a predominance of *mutuality* in exchanges of empathy and self-object function, while the distinctive ambitions, goals, and ideals of each partner are afforded recognition by the other. The major goal of psychoanalysis is to open up *mutual* paths of empathy between self and other, and empathy undeniably involves *recognition* of the one toward whom it flows."[388]

Object Relations

Object relations theory and therapeutic practice recognize the individual human self as an entity developing through relational interactions with other human selves. Object relations theory sees relationships (past and present) as having a key role in the construction and continuance of self, not only in early relationships with primary caregivers, but also throughout life.

To explain the phenomena they observed in the therapy room, object relations theorists needed to postulate the existence of representational entities we build and maintain in our minds – entities that we use to internally represent, store, interact and play with in order to be able to interact and comprehend the objects of the external world (and other human minds.) For this purpose, they introduced the concept of *internal objects* in their model of self. These objects are seen as internalized mental and emotional representations of significant others (caregivers, friends, romantic partners) that we form through relationships, or even of parts of them that carry some psychologically relevant features (e.g. in this respect, the mother's breast would be a represented "object" for an infant). Such "objects" are of course not literal replicas but rather internal psychological representations (laden with emotions and mental imagery). They are our mental images of people and experiences that either provide psychological comfort/support or cause psychological distress. Object relations theory suggests that our patterns of early object relations, established in early childhood through relationships with our primary caregivers, can continue to influence our relationships in adulthood. Without any intervention, our adult selves are likely to replay these early object relations — with all their comforting but also distressing aspects — in later relationships (affecting our parenting, friendships, and romantic relationships.)

Donald Winnicott also introduced the concept of *transitional objects,* referring to external physical objects (like a blanket or a toy) that a child attaches to and uses to represent their primary caregiver in a symbolic way. These objects are a source of comfort and security for the child, especially during the phase of transitioning toward independence.

An important aspect of this theory and its model — recognized by many object relations theorists and practitioners — is that our purpose for engaging in relationships is not to achieve a certain state of being or feeling. The human need for relatedness cannot be seen as instrumental but as an end unto itself. *It is recognized that the fundamental human striving is for the relationship, and not for pleasure or anxiety reduction (which are secondary).* The relationship itself is the goal and the true substance of the interaction.[389]

Many theorists (they are all practitioners too) have contributed to object relations theory. Some well-known contributors include Donald Winnicott, Ronald Fairbairn, Margaret Mahler, Wilfred Bion, Thomas Ogden, Otto Kernberg, James Grotstein, Jay Greenberg, and many others.

Potential Space as the Playground of the Self

Approximately sixty years ago, Donald Winnicott, a legendary figure in psychoanalysis, introduced the concept of *potential space*.[390] This groundbreaking idea was meant to describe and characterize our inner experience of subjectivity, in a way that can be used in psychotherapy. In his 1993 work *The Matrix of the Mind*,[391] psychoanalyst Thomas Ogden writes that "perhaps the most important and at the same time most elusive of the ideas introduced by Donald Winnicott is the concept of potential space." Potential space represents a model of subjectivity in human minds, it is the "place" where our self "abides," every human being can easily and fundamentally experience it, this is the place where we experience our thoughts, feelings, phantasy, daydreaming, and reverie. Potential space is where we experience the continuity of being, where we feel conscious when we are awake, and where our dreams play out when we sleep. This is where we experience our agency and our sentience. It is the "Spielraum"[392] of the human self, where we live and play as human beings. All cultural experiences, psychotherapy, contemplation, and meditation are experienced and occur within the potential space. Ogden describes it as a "space in which we work creatively, the space in which we relax 'formlessly', the space in which we dream, and the space in which we play."

The subjective experience of the human self cannot be mechanistic, its essence is dynamic and alive, therefore such experience has to allow for tensions, complex relations, and even contradictions to coexist. Potential space can thus be seen as an intermediate area of experiencing, it lies between two poles of experience, which Winnicott termed *fantasy* (our inner psychic reality) and *reality* (actual or external reality as we experience it, "the real world.") It is the nature of the relationship between the poles of fantasy and reality that it contains contradictions and tensions. The essential characteristic of potential space is the experience of *paradox*. Subjective activity in this space — or *playing* as Winnicott termed it in his work *Playing and Reality* — tolerates contradictions, and actively and continuously works to reconcile these two poles (two coexisting realities), their tensions and differences. Ogden uses the term dialectic[393] to refer to this process of constant reconciliation:

> "The dialectical process is centrally involved in the creation of subjectivity. By subjectivity, I am referring to the capacity for the degrees of self-awareness ranging from intentional self-reflection (a very late achievement) to the most subtle, unobtrusive sense of "I-ness" by which experience is subtly endowed with the quality that one is thinking one's thoughts and feeling one's feelings as opposed to living in a state of reflexive reactivity. Subjectivity is related to, but not the same as, consciousness. The experience of consciousness (and unconsciousness) follows from the achievement of subjectivity."[394]

Hans Loewald emphasized that the poles of fantasy and reality are in constant play and should not be separated and kept entrenched in their extreme positions if we are to live a meaningful and fulfilling life. This is summarized in the words of Stephen A. Mitchell:

> "For life to be meaningful, vital, and robust, fantasy and reality cannot be too divorced from each other. Fantasy cut adrift from reality becomes irrelevant and threatening. Reality cut adrift from fantasy becomes vapid and empty. Meaning in human experience is generated in the mutual, dialectically enriching tension between fantasy and reality; each requires the other to

come alive. In the psychic universe of the individual mind, vitality and meaning require open channels between the developmentally earlier, but perpetually regenerated primal density and the clearly demarcated boundaries that make possible adaptive living. For Loewald, only the enchanted life is a life worth living."[395]

and:

"In potential space... we come alive as creators or interpreters of our own experience; reality is interpreted in terms of fantasy, and fantasy in terms of reality. Perception renders fantasy relatively safe; fantasy renders perception relatively meaningful."[396]

Each of our human subjective selves weaves between the inner world of fantasy and the outer world of external reality in the potential space, touching deep and intimate dimensions of our human experience. This weaving of the self is the expression of the striving for aliveness and intimacy, for the experience of being alive in the present moment. This activity is not about mere survival, it is about the *experience of being alive*.

Relationships, too, are experienced in potential space, and they have the ability to transform it into an intersubjective potential space (more about this in the segment on intersubjectivity). Mutuality is necessary for a healthy relationship to unfold, and it is marked by mutual willingness and capacity to both visit the intimate potential space of another human being and to let them visit yours. The psychopathology of the ability to freely dwell and engage in relational play within potential space is a key focus of psychotherapy, as we human beings indeed face obstacles that prevent us from forming healthy relationships. Irrational forces within our minds, as well as rigid adherence to our perceptions of external reality, can make it hard or impossible to build healthy relationships. As long as we are captive (our captors are within) and slaves to our fears, greed, anger, hate, and delusions (to name a few tormentors of humankind), we are not truly free to engage in playing with others in our intimate spaces. Liberation in this realm is the battlefield of our time.

Further exploration and application of phenomena related to potential space in psychotherapy extend beyond the scope of this work, and some additional references are provided in the endnotes.[397] What we have outlined here should, hopefully, suffice to illustrate that the model of potential space is a significant example of the contribution of psychodynamic theory to the theory of mind. It helps us to conceptualize our intricate intimate processes and empowers us to use it in practice, for example, in psychotherapy, parenting, and education. It is evident that models in this kind of science are very different from the models in fields such as physics. This must be so, given the nature of the phenomena we study. The ultimate confirmation of any model's validity should come from its practical effectiveness and application.

Intersubjectivity

Intersubjectivity can be defined as the interrelating of two or more selves or subjectivities. It can also be conceptualized as a shared psychological space (or field) where the relating selves co-exist and co-experience.[398] The modern idea of inter-subjectivity has its roots, speaking in broad strokes, in the philosophies of phenomenology and existentialism, and in developmental psychology. Publishing their works mainly in the first half of the 20th century, philosophers like Edmund Husserl, Martin Buber, and Maurice Merleau-Ponty, and psychologist Lev Vygotsky explored how human minds can interact, share experiences, construct meanings together, and relate to each other.

One way to approach the modern idea of intersubjectivity is to grasp it through the concept of the *present moment* as introduced by Daniel N. Stern in his work *The Present Moment in Psychotherapy and Everyday Life.*[399] "Present moments" are lived experiences that constitute "the nodal points in our everyday intimate relationships," they also "make up the key moments of change in psychotherapy." Such moments arise when "two people make a special kind of mental contact—namely, an intersubjective contact. This involves the mutual interpenetration of minds that permits us to say, 'I know that you know that I know' or 'I feel that you feel that I feel.' There is a reading of the contents of the other's mind. Such readings can be mutual. Two people see and feel roughly the same mental landscape for a moment at least. These meetings are what psychotherapy is largely about. They also provide the happenings that change our lives and become the memories that compose the story of our intimate relationships ... The idea of presentness is key. The present moment that I am after is the moment of subjective experience as it is occurring—not as it is later reshaped by words." During such intimate experiences "a certain intersubjective world emerges. We no longer see our minds as so independent, separate, and isolated. We are no longer the sole owners, masters, and guardians of our subjectivity. The boundaries between self and others remain clear but more permeable."

(As an aside, a little detour on *empathy* follows. Human intersubjectivity is what undergirds human empathy. The concept of empathy cannot be fully understood without understanding the idea of intersubjectivity, as it revolves around the *capacity to interact and share thoughts, feelings, and motives with other human beings.* As we already mentioned in the segment on self psychology, empathy should not be viewed as merely an emotion (this statement does not seek to devalue emotion, which is a power in its own right, see e.g. the compendium *The Healing Power of Emotion*.)[400] Empathy is essential for meaningful interactions and relationships among human beings, and — as relational theories demonstrate — it also carries formative powers that shape the human self. We should not mock, but embrace and appreciate the prospect that our future as a species depends on our capacity for empathy. This has been understood since at least the time of Adam Smith, who identified empathy as crucial for moral judgment.[401] Even David Hume acknowledged that there exists "some spark of friendship for human kind" and impelled that it must "direct the determinations of our mind."[402] There has been some sort of a minor backlash (for lack of a better term) against empathy among a group of contemporary thinkers, often caused by considering the concept of empathy narrowly as an "emotion" and thus considering it "limiting." Psychologist Paul Bloom even states that he is "against empathy" in favor of "rational compassion" (calling such compassion also "cognitive empathy", because "emotions are put in their proper place").[403] Steven Pinker (grudgingly) appreciates empathy just enough to give it a high rank as one of the "four better angels of human nature" (the other three being self-control, moral sense, and reason.)[404] Intersubjective perspective offers a possibility for a deeper understanding, maybe even a reconceptualization (considering the variety of interpretations) of empathy. Intersubjective space, which is where empathy "happens," is also the place where we learn and exercise affect control and other aspects of reason, it is also the only place where "rational compassion" can unfold. Intersubjective space is where we *are* as human selves, this is where we exist, and we do that by entering the relational context in which empathy is an intrinsic participant.)

Together with already mentioned psychodynamic theories and their models, the intersubjective-relational theories were at the forefront of the "relational turn" – the 20th-century paradigmatic shift in psychoanalysis, which placed human relationality at the center of the field.[405] (As an aside, this shift towards the understanding of relationality can be observed in several related disciplines as well, a notable example is the field of *interpersonal neurobiology*.)[406] Both theory and practice recognized relationality as a universal and fundamental feature of human development and started to converge toward the intersubjective-relational paradigm. A number of authors contributed to the field of intersubjectivity, and they all share the position that the human mind must be viewed in terms of relationships and that individual subjectivity itself must be viewed as interpersonal in nature. Stern writes that intersubjectivity has to do with the "ability to share in another's lived experience"[407] and he considers it a "major motivational system essential for human survival – akin to attachment or sex."[408] Robert Stolorow and George Atwood succinctly spell out the main tenet of the theory — not an easy one to digest by a modern Western mindset — by stating that "the concept of an isolated individual mind is a theoretical fiction."[409]

Developmental psychology of today understands that the human sense of self is not developed in isolation but through relationships. Moreover, relationships are seen as necessary for the arising of individual subjectivity, of the individual self. The process of mentalization — the formative understanding and interpretation of one's own and others' mental states (thoughts, feelings, motivations) — depends on intersubjectivity and relationships. Peter Fonagy expresses this position in the following words: "if we developed in a forest on our own, without human contact ... we would have consciousness, but he wouldn't be aware of that consciousness, we wouldn't be able to reflect on it, we wouldn't be able to reflect on ourselves or on others."[410]

Stephen A. Mitchell ponders the difficulty many people espousing the modern Western mindset have when considering the fundamental nature of relationality, and he takes us for a ride in his seminal work *Relationality: From Attachment to Intersubjectivity*:

> "Why is the centrality of the relational so easy to miss, to forget about, to relegate to the conceptual background? It must have something to do with a confusion of minds with the ways in which bodies operate as functional units ... our bodily properties seem more or less prewired, unfolding in a maturational sequence ... we eventually attain an almost complete, physically functional autonomy. It is so easy to think of our minds in similar terms. We tend to take for granted an independent psychical existence in much the same way as we take for granted our independent physical experience ... And we tend to think of our minds similarly as our exclusive property, under our omnipotent control, with our intersubjective exchanges with others a product of our intentions. Thus, traditional theorists of motivation feel they have to supply us with reasons why people are drawn to each other: pleasure seeking, dependency, the need for security, sexual satisfaction, the desire for recognition, the division of labor, and so on. These monadic individual assumptions have been fundamental to Western culture over the past several hundred years and are taken for granted as part of ordinary experience. It is only relatively recently that they have been systematically called into question. Perhaps minds do not develop independently and secondarily seek each other out. Perhaps, as contemporary philosophers, linguists, and analytic theorists are suggesting, minds are fundamentally interconnected. Perhaps the question 'Why am I hanging around with these other minded creatures?' is fundamentally misconceived, predicated on an inattention to a more basic interpenetrability of minds that makes individual mindedness possible in the first place ... One mind presumes other minds ... [T]raditional

theories of motivation, including psychoanalytic and behavioral, begin with the individual organism, its physical needs, its interpersonal needs, its social needs … Picture an oak leaf on its branch asking 'Why am I hanging around with these other leaves?' Motivational theory in psychology and psychoanalysis has taken for granted the individual nature of the psyche, in this case the oak leaf, and then provided motivations for object relations, or the fact that oak leaves tend to be found in clusters. But we are increasingly appreciating the implication of the fact that humans, like oak leaves, are not found in isolation, not possible in isolation. Human minds are fundamentally social phenomena that become focalized"[411]

Such ideas are not exactly new, we find them in classical antiquity, and we find them in Neoplatonism, but we also find them in the more recent history of thought. For example, in the 19th century transcendentalist philosophy, in the words of Ralph Waldo Emerson:

"There is one mind common to all individual men. Every man is an inlet to the same and to all of the same. He that is once admitted to the right of reason is made a freeman of the whole estate. What Plato has thought, he may think; what a saint has felt, he may feel; what at any time has befallen any man, he can understand. Who hath access to this universal mind is a party to all that is or can be done, for this is the only and sovereign agent."[412]

This capacity of the human mind to create and co-create the reality of intersubjective spaces where human selves truly meet in the environment of deep epistemic trust is well understood by Daniel N. Stern: "In short, our mental life is cocreated. This continuous cocreative dialogue with other minds is what I am calling the *intersubjective matrix*. The idea of a one-person psychology or of purely intrapsychic phenomena are no longer tenable in this light. Current thinking in psychoanalysis has moved a great distance in the recent past from a one-person to a two-person psychology. I am suggesting here that we move even further. We used to think of intersubjectivity as a sort of epiphenomenon that arises occasionally when two separate and independent minds interact. Now we view the intersubjective matrix (which is a special subset of the culture and of psychotherapy) as the overriding crucible in which interacting minds take on their current form. Two minds create intersubjectivity. But equally, intersubjectivity shapes the two minds. The center of gravity has shifted from the intrapsychic to the intersubjective ... *Intersubjectivity is a condition of humanness.* I will suggest that it is also an innate, primary system of motivation."[413]

Many theorists and practitioners have contributed to the understanding and the practice of intersubjectivity in psychoanalysis and psychodynamic therapies in the second half of the 20th century and later; most notably Stephen A. Mitchell, Donald Winnicott, Ronald Fairbairn, Heinz Kohut, Daniel N. Stern, Thomas Ogden, Robert Stolorow, George Atwood, Donna Orange, Jessica Benjamin, Jay Greenberg, Lewis Aron, Donnel Stern, and many others. It is recognized that ideas of intersubjectivity have some of their important roots in the interpersonal psychoanalysis of Harry Stack Sullivan and the humanistic psychoanalysis of Erich Fromm.

Affect Regulation, Mentalization, & the Development of the Self

Drawing upon insights from attachment theory, infant psychiatry, and contemporary psychoanalytic and psychodynamic frameworks, Peter Fonagy, along with György Gergely, Elliot Jurist, and Mary Target, developed a theory that explicates the links between the processes of affect regulation, mentalization, and development of the self, as outlined in their 2005 seminal work *Affect Regulation, Mentalization and the Development of the Self*.[414] This theory has been influential in clinical practice and academic research. A decade prior, Allan Shore had focused on these same processes from a neurobiological perspective.[415] *Mentalization-based therapy* (MBT), developed by Anthony Bateman and Peter Fonagy, is closely related to this framework and has demonstrated clinical efficacy in numerous studies.[416]

It is evident that a human infant's *capacity to have and experience psychological states* (subjective states like affects/emotions) in response to the environment is innate, it is not learned or acquired. *Affect regulation* (or *emotional regulation*) involves managing, modulating, and expressing these internal psychological states. *Mentalization* is the ability to recognize and reflect on these psychological states (and eventually those of others, as this capacity matures), and to develop and embed mental representations[417] of these states in one's mind. Mentalization is accomplished by means of the postulated *reflective function* which is also seen as innate to human minds. In essence, the capabilities to 1) experience subjective psychological states like emotions, and 2) to reflect on them, are not learned; babies are born with these abilities.

We should pause and recognize the significance of this innate endowment. The origin and nature of such innate capacities are impenetrable to our present scientific understanding. Nothing humans have created and engineered, including AI, compares to the innate capacities of babies to experience subjective psychological states, the ability to reflect on these states ("some notion of consciousness" as described by Daniel N. Stern), and the ability to construct mental representations of them. This is observable early in human development, even before we are able to observe the emergence of a distinct "sense of self" in an infant's life.

Affect regulation (or emotional regulation) is the process that builds upon this endowment, as it plays a crucial role in the unfolding of a sense of self and agency in an infant. Affect regulation itself is not innate, it presupposes agency, and it can only be accomplished by means of an agency. Because an infant does not initially have a developed sense for self, it is through the formative relationship with their primary attachment figure and *their reflective function* that the sense of self and agency starts to unfold in the infant. Research tells us that very young infants are fully predisposed to and fully engage in relationality. They seek and expect relationships, a baby wholly expects that a person in their presence will relate to them in a meaningful way. This is a universal experience of every human baby, their whole being finds a focal point in it, and they are tremendously distressed if the relational aspect of the primary attachment figure disappears – even if they are still physically present (as originally shown in seminal research by Ed Tronick and colleagues, known as the *Still Face Experiment*.)[418] The primary attachment figure is usually the infant's parent, but any human being who is able and eager to engage in an emotionally attuned relationship with the infant could accomplish this magic. The primary attachment figure's own self and agency, through attuned interactions, support the infant's affect regulation. This is often referred to as *reflective parenting* and it requires that a parent exercises their "capacity to reflect on or mentalize the child's experience" as it unfolds, "to envision or imagine the child's thoughts, feelings, desires, and intentions."[419] The caregiver's attuned responses to the infant's emotions modulate and reflect these emotions back to the infant, allowing for mentalization and internal representation within the infant's developing mind.

An example of healthy and attuned support for a crying infant's affect regulation process might be holding them and conveying a soothing message, something with a meaning similar to "I see that you are in pain, I am here with you, and I will help you." The infant's mentalization creates and embeds an internal representation of this experience, which could be described in words like "the world is a safe place, and *I am* worthy of attention and care."[420] In the early stages of human development, it is, therefore, the parent who has the crucial role of recognizing the infant's emotional states, labeling them with modulating messages, and returning them back to the infant, who in turn uses them to contain/regulate its emotions and to create/embed mental representations for them.

This process involves achieving the right balance by the caregiver: they should be equally far from being emotionally withdrawn from the child (e.g. frequently looking at a smartphone screen while together) and overwhelming the child (e.g. dominating the interaction and intruding into the child's internal process.) This balance supports the child in forming secure attachments and developing a sense of independence. Donald Winnicott described the attitude of a caregiver with the term *good enough mothering*,[421] meaning that caregivers should strive to meet the child's needs adequately but not perfectly. The caregiver provides a *holding environment*[422] where the child feels safe, contained, and free to explore the world. The caregiver is simply present in the same space with the child (if possible, engaging in activities the child can relate to, and perhaps imitate or join in as they grow older), emotionally available, and responsive to the interactions initiated by the child, yet not controlling or intrusive in directing the child's internal processes. They facilitate the child's development by adapting to the infant's needs during the early stages of life, and as the child grows, they gradually allow the child to experience manageable disappointments and frustrations. The caregiver gradually lets the child realize that they are a separate individual and that not all needs will be met instantly or perfectly. This process is critical for the child's developing sense of agency, autonomy, and overall psychological development. It is crucial during the first seven years of a child's life, and it is fundamentally important during the first three years.[423]

Described processes highlight the intricate link between affect regulation and mentalization in early development. "Affect regulation is a prelude to mentalization ... [its] capacity to modulate affect states, is closely related to mentalization in that it plays a fundamental role in the unfolding of a sense of self and agency." The infant's "experience of affect is the bud from which eventually mentalization can grow, but only in the context of at least one continuing, safe attachment relationship. The parent who cannot *think about the child's mental experience* deprives him of a core self-structure that he needs to build a viable sense of himself."[424]

Mentalization involves the development of mental representations of psychological states concerning oneself and others at any age. The theory considers "mentalized affectivity" to be at the core of all relationships, and of the psychotherapeutic process as well. Healthy, mutual human relationships are not possible without mentalization, and most commonly relationship breakdown between adults occurs when mentalization is unidirectional, when we are only concerned about our own internal states and ignore to mentalize and ponder those of the other – when we don't consider the world from other's point of view. In the candid words of Peter Fonagy, this happens when "I do not see the world from her point of view, at all, all

I see is my perspective and my perception of her … this just doesn't lead to anywhere good…"[425]

OK, how bad could it really be for kids if relationships are not there?

We know that human beings thrive in the context of relationships, and as Fonagy reminds us in a recent interview on the topic *Combating a Mental Health Crisis*,[426] nourishing relationships are not optional: "since WWII, we have known that when kids are left alone, they die… René Spitz, in the 1940s, did a striking study[427] where he compared mortality rates of the kids who were brought up in prison with their mothers and those who were on their own [cared for] in hospitals, and irrespective of physical illness, death rates in hospitals was 37%, and in prison all children thrived. Separation is really the worst thing that we can do to kids." The most damaging aspect of neglect is "lack of interest in the particular child, the particular individual human being … that sense, of someone having been interested in me is what I need to develop a sense of my own self, through locking into the interest that the other person has in me, that teaches me who I am. Without it, we are vulnerable."[428]

OK, I can take care of my kid, so it doesn't really take the whole village, right?

In the same interview, Fonagy continues, "[our societies] have placed enormous importance in our culture on a relationship between a mother and a child [or a caretaker and a child], and have made mothers inappropriately and uniquely responsible for maintaining that relationship. [However], the real issue is the child [developmentally] expects to be what's called *alloparented*, to be brought up by a community that takes an interest in that child. The family and the extended family are enormously important. This is now very clear, that part of the difficulty that we encounter with child mental health has to do with the relative absence of high-quality childcare … the fact that parents are at work doesn't impact the child's well-being … *what matters is that there are people around who are interested in that child as an agent, as an active person, what that child is thinking, what that child is feeling, and will modify their behavior according to that child's experience.* That sensitivity is, turns out, to be the critical determinant." In fact, we must consider that "mentalizing is not something that exists within an individual, not something that exists even between the mother and a child, not something even that exists between members of a family, it's something that a community of human beings owns."[429]

4.1.4. Interlude (for story buffs only): Intersubjective Potential Space and the Story of *Parzival*

Two medieval poets from the 12th and 13th centuries, Chrétien de Troyes and Wolfram von Eschenbach, captured and distilled the wisdom of oral traditions and stories created by an unknown sage or sages in earlier centuries. Chrétien's version in Old French, known as *Perceval*, was left unfinished, likely due to his death, but it almost certainly influenced parts of Wolfram's *Parzival*,[430] written in Middle High German. The essence of the story was also immortalized in Richard Wagner's 19th-century mystical opera *Parsifal*. One key aspect of the story carries an important message for our deliberations about the pathways open to humanity in the 21st century.

Even a casual observer of the state of modern humanity would have noticed the rapid deterioration of connections among human beings in our time. The centrifugal forces of raw self-interest, combined with the power of modern technology, are increasingly damaging the fabric of human relationships and are beginning to slowly tear apart the core of what makes us distinctly human and what enables the existence of our civilization. We seem to be gradually approaching the nadir, the lowest point of depression and despair, or rather, the lowest point from which we can still recover in the foreseeable future. Cruelty, violence, and corruption are increasingly asserting their presence, while ethical norms, traditional values, and laws are becoming increasingly sidelined. The center of humanity still holds, it seems, but our foundations are already shaking as formidable challenges announce themselves (including AI, climate change, and anti-democratic nationalism, to name a few.)

Incidentally, *Par-ce-val* can be translated from French as through-the-valley, or through-the-lowest-point, and it does seem that the story carries a message for our time. In the story, Parzival indeed has to go through the lowest point of estrangement and alienation to find a way to elevate himself out of it. How does he accomplish that? We are told that Parzival starts his journey as an innocent simpleton, naïve and inexperienced, foolish even. He rode off, leaving his mother behind, as a young man on a quest to become a "noble knight," dressed only in sackcloth, looking like a "fool," and riding on the "wretchedest nag." Yet, there, underneath the laughable appearance, he unknowingly already carried a treasure.

His early attachment relationship with his mother was a formative force, providing him with a great, even if invisible, endowment. As a young child, Parzival grew up in a protected environment, we are told that he was "cosseted," surrounded by nature in the "forest in the wilds," where he cared for the "singing of the birds overhead, [whose] sweetness pierced him to the heart." We are told of his mother Herzeloyde's love for him; right after the birth, she "loved to kiss him, over and over again. 'Bon fiz, cher fiz, bea fiz,' [good son, dear son, beautiful son] she said with tender insistence." Markers of Winnicott's *holding environment* and *good enough mothering* are also provided for the reader. Her little child was allowed to roam nature and explore alone, to "cut bow and arrows with his own hands" and "wash himself in the meadow on the river-bank," with his mother being just close enough, emotionally present and available, so that when he needed consolation, we are told that his choice was to "run to her, all in tears." His father Gahmuret was killed in a battle before Parzival was born, but his presence was felt through his mother's deep adoration of the man who, we are told, "cultivated self-control and moderation in all things. He was not given to boasting, endured great honour calmly and was free of loose desires." Of his mother, we also know that she was "lovely in person" and that "her modest ways were much commended." We are also told that Parzival learned from her that no human being he meets should be ignored, but should be acknowledged and greeted, "downcast or cheerful, my mother told me to greet them all." Parzival's invisible endowment of secure attachment, hidden by the veil of his naïveté and inexperience, enabled him, among other things, to remain capable of wonder and admiration, uncorrupted, and able to fight off fear (to "never know the sweat of fear.")

Parzival was fortunate, few of us today receive such bountiful endowment. However, as any marathon runner knows, a great start is important, but the race is long, and opportunities for correction do present themselves. Under any external circumstances, human reasoning selves can exercise their agency to transform chosen aspects of their identity and character (marked by "mentalized affectivity" used to transform and recast entrenched emotional traumas and mental representations in their minds), even if in many instances some among us will likely need help to accomplish that. Such decisions and battles to shape one's own inner core take place in the intimate space of the human self, in what Winnicott termed potential space. As we have already outlined in this chapter, potential space is where culture, encounters with others, psychotherapy, meditation, and all inner growth happen. This is the home turf where the human self resides and where our reasoning unfolds.

Despite his secure attachment, lack of traumatic hindrances, his ability to connect with others and to learn and accomplish many tasks (he is on a path to becoming a knight),

Parzival's personal intimate internal space — his potential space — is rather narrow at the beginning of his journey. The suffering of others does not easily make significant waves in it. This is in many ways our present condition in humanity. Individual self-interest plays a dominant role in the vast majority of human beings. Like Parzival, who is approaching his personal lowest point in the story, we must find a way to overcome this condition to a sufficient degree.

Wagner's opera *Parsifal* is referred to as a mystical opera. This seems to be for a good reason, as the process of liberating human selves from irrational forces of self-interest can be considered a mystery – in the sense that it is hidden, out of sight, it can only happen in the intimate space of an individual human being (Greek *mystērion*: hidden, concealed, not obvious, secret.) Furthermore, it is only in these intimate spaces that we can awake to the reality of hidden connections with the rest of humanity (as Plotinus described in his mystical union with *The One*, and in the way Plato pointed out, outlining the path of acquiring the inner virtue of *Justice* as a means to ultimately reach *The One*.)

Parzival's lowest point, as the story tells us, is when in the presence of the suffering King Anfortas, no deep emotion stirs in him. He remains silent and does not "ask the Question." Anfortas's wound, caused by his own weakness, is an "occult" injury (Latin *occultus*: hidden, concealed), inflicted on him in a moment of ignorance, by the powerful wizard Clinschor, who rules the Castle of Wonders and possesses the magic "art" to "bind men and women with his spells." Injured Anfortas is a "sad, unhappy man… unable either to ride or walk or even to lie down or stand – he reclines – he does not sit – his awareness fraught with pain … [and there is always] the stench from his gaping wound." Anfortas "is dogged by misfortune from on high," by an intelligently concocted powerful bind, and there is only one power that can break the spell and heal him – genuine and authentic loving care from another human being, a power hard to come by. Such care is marked by the freely embraced interest in the well-being of the other (within one's own potential space) and manifested by what is referred to in the story as the Question. Anfortas, a representative of a suffering human being in the story, has a wound "of which he could be rid by a Question" alone; no other remedies can restore his health. In their first encounter, Parzival fails to "ask the Question," rationalizing to himself that it would be impolite and that he was anyway "advised" by his teacher "against asking many questions" (rules of our upbringing and tradition can also represent an irrational force we sometimes follow blindly; Freud termed them *superego*.)[431] As a consequence, Parzival soon finds himself in a world where he is deserted, estranged, and alienated. He realized what he had done (or rather failed to do), and his realization "pained him deeply" and "happiness vanished from him without trace." His dear cousin Sigune delivered the devastating message, reflecting how the world at large views Parzival: "you failed so abjectly to ask! You witnessed such great marvels! … [one could add that truly encountering the self of another human being is a marvel] … To think that you could not be bothered to ask … You dishonourable person, man accurst! You showed your venomous wolf-fangs when the canker took root in your integrity and grew apace! You should have had compassion on your host … and inquired about his suffering. You live, yet as far as Heaven's favour goes you are dead!"

No more spoilers. But it is from this point on in the story, that Parzival decides to grow and courageously face battles on his way to becoming truly human. He comes to understand and embrace sacred connections among human beings, and he comes to experience genuine concern for others and empathy (or "rational compassion," for those who prefer the term.) His path leads him to Anfortas again, where he is now able to deliver the Question, rooted in genuine concern and empathy: "Dear Uncle, what ails you?" The words themselves are not that important; *"what ails you?"* is *Parzival's Question*, but it can take other forms too – only the solid platform within the human self that gives birth to such words is of importance. A heartfelt "dude, *what happened to you?"* can also accomplish the task, and so can a completely unspoken Question.

If we apply the conceptualization introduced earlier in this chapter, we could interpret the meaning of the *Parzival* story in the following way. The ability to ask Parzival's Question can only arise in a human self that is freed from irrational forces (possibly through meditative practice, psychotherapy, or both) to a high enough degree and therefore capable of truly residing in the intersubjective potential space. In this space, such a self is capable of widening their own self-interest, becoming a wider vessel as it were, to willingly make room for other human beings and their concerns, and to allow a degree of permeability between the self and the other. This space is also where the joy of encounters with others lives, along with the shared experiences of "I know that you know that I know" and "I feel that you feel that I feel." The profound levels of epistemic trust and the joy of genuine togetherness in this space are indicators of the unmatched transformational power of such encounters for human beings. Parents who deeply love their young children sometimes experience this as grace, or as Alison Gopnik calls it, "a little saintliness."[432] For the majority of us, there is work to be done first, and there are battles to be waged with Clinschor's invading armies and with ghosts within. This indeed is Parzival's quest, as the story tells us. His path involves many battles, and Parzival must — like Plato's charioteer we mentioned earlier — assert dominance and control over his irrational parts (where fears, greed, envy, annoyance, hate, anger, and their ilk, lurk hidden in all of us), bring the light and power of reason into those dark irrational chunks of his being, and integrate them in a healthy way into his potential space. This is the only way to make his "reason master of his passions," to become "sovereign in his own home," and to enable in himself the will that can not only "do what he wants," but indeed "want what he wants" (as a nod to Hume, Freud, and Schopenhauer.) Only when Parzival accomplishes this — symbolized in the story, among other things, by his marriage to Condwiramurs and by his reconciliation and reunion with his half-brother from the East, Fairefiz — is he able to truly ask Parzival's Question and to wield the transformational power that exists only in bonds of love.

A human self deciding to embark on the journey to become capable of asking Parzival's Question is on the path to becoming what is in *perennial philosophy* often characterized as "loving, pure in heart, and humble in spirit."[433] The length of the journey is irrelevant, first fruits are visible immediately, by ourselves and by others, and as long as we are going in the right direction, arrival is only a matter of time. Considerable amount of time, for most of us. That should not concern us, as sages tell us that *patience* (for oneself and for others) and *endurance* are among the first capacities that need to be mastered on the path of inner transformation.

4.2. A Model of Self in Action – Child Psychotherapy: *"Ghosts in the Nursery"*

Preamble: Science of the mind considers dynamic phenomena of the higher order

It is evident from the material in this chapter that acknowledgment and recognition are sought for what we might call *mind science*. The term mind science is not widely used today,[434] and this perhaps represents the fact that the scientific community is still not comfortable talking about the phenomena of mind as if they are "real things." It is often heard that mind phenomena are called "subjective" and "only illusions." Such opinions ignore the fact that it is the phenomena in the human mind — the capacities of our thinking reason — that built everything we refer to as civilization: all culture, including science, and everything human-made that we call "real things." All these achievements presuppose active dynamic processes — thoughts, feelings, intentions of will — in the human mind. If we are to objectively research such phenomena in human minds, science must stretch its current comfort zone and find ways to consider phenomena that are 1) dynamic in nature – like our thoughts and feelings are, 2) can be experienced but are not directly observable by our senses, and 3) not easily quantifiable in numbers. The only instrument to register and process such phenomena we know of today is the human mind. It can be argued that — apart from age-old meditative disciplines for mastering thoughts, feelings, and irrational aspects of human minds (which will be the subject of the second part of this book) — the closest discipline we have to *mind science* today is psychotherapy, particularly many strands of psychodynamic psychotherapy, which today also embrace the attachment theory and infant research, as I attempted to demonstrate with the material in this chapter.

It is also evident from the preceding deliberations that what we might call *mind science* does wear a somewhat different garb compared to what we usually encounter in the so-called "hard sciences." We don't see here many spreadsheets with numbers, colorful graphs, and complex math equations; there are also very few physical laboratories and instruments (unless the research focus is narrowed and used solely to determine whether a given therapeutic modality "works," i.e. whether it can earn the label "evidence-based.")[435] The scientific method which must be used in the domain of the human mind is qualitative in nature and is today commonly applied for the purposes of guiding the dynamic psychotherapeutic process, often in real-time as it unfolds. The basic skeleton of the known scientific framework applies here as well, where careful observation and imaginative consideration lead to the forming of hypotheses, which are then tested in therapy sessions with targeted interventions, possibly verified or pondered further and revised based on real-time observations. The core of this method consists of processing, which is unfolding within the trained reasoning minds of psychotherapists experiencing the dynamic phenomena of psychotherapy. The psychodynamic method is neither easy nor straightforward, and it is often supported by ongoing supervisory relationships among professionals and by countertransference processing groups that help to accurately and objectively process mental content surfacing during therapy. Rigor and professional ethics must remain paramount in such disciplines.

It is obvious that such a method differs significantly from the scientific methods used for the purpose of evaluating whether a particular therapeutic modality is "evidence-based."

In the latter case, the scientific methods are more static, rigid, and akin to those in the "hard sciences." They also have notable limitations. Mind phenomena are dynamic and therefore elusive, resisting attempts to be captured in static snapshots and expressed numerically for the purposes of processing we are accustomed to in the "hard sciences." While it is necessary and valuable to ascertain the general effectiveness of psychotherapies (of all therapeutic modalities), the formalization and numeric representation required for such evaluations renders them rather coarse instruments for evaluating psychotherapy. Effective psychotherapy must focus on the dynamic phenomena of a qualitative nature in human minds, which are not easily represented in numbers. For example, it is practically impossible to standardize and quantify in numbers the powerful, yet tender emotional processing that emerges in a person when they start to recall repressed traumatic memories of feeling neglected by their parents or caretakers. What the effective psychotherapist must do in such moments is rely on the nimble objective reasoning in their minds. They must of course be well trained, experienced,[436] and informed by existing canons of science and of related relevant knowledge, but the only instrument they use during the therapeutic sessions is their reasoning mind.

Even if quantitative scientific procedures have been used to establish the efficacy of psychodynamic methods (in a similar way that this was done for the short-term scripted/manualized therapeutic modalities), it is important to recognize that such scientific verification, while valuable in its own right, is a rather blunt instrument. It requires formalization and standardization of symptoms, therapeutic process, and evaluation criteria, making it rigid and unable to capture the fine, dynamic mental nature of the process. (Such verifications are usually done via Randomized Controlled Trials (RCTs), which typically involve a representative sample of people who all exhibit similar mental health symptoms/diagnoses, and who are divided into a treatment group and a control/placebo group. The treatment group then receives the standardized therapeutic intervention. At the end of the trial, people in both groups are evaluated using standardized psychological tests to determine whether they have experienced improvement, i.e. reduced or resolved symptoms. Statistical analysis is then used to interpret the results.) The danger here is that we focus too much of our attention on symptoms that are easily measurable and quantifiable in numbers, and take the focus away from understanding and treatment of the (widespread) deep-seated psychological traumas with long-term goals in sight.

(An analogy with the process of education can be aptly used here: using standardized multiple-choice tests is one way to confirm that the education we provide to our children is effective and beneficial. However, this is a rather blunt instrument, as it misses many aspects of what education actually does, including critical thinking skills, creativity, emotional development, and social skills. Similarly, RCTs, often touted as the "gold standard," miss many aspects of what psychotherapy achieves; they overlook the complex, individualized interactions and changes that are difficult to standardize and measure quantitatively.)

Yet another way to think about the role of mind science is to think of it as a qualitative study of dynamic phenomena of higher order,[437] compared to "hard science's" study of lower order phenomena in the physical body. In any event, because of the nature of its subject, science in this domain must be much more qualitative. That does not mean that the facts it discovers are less "hard" and they are definitely not less important. The ultimate arbiter of any science, regardless of the garb it wears, is whether its findings can be in some way objectively verified, and whether it can be effectively applied in the world as we experience it. Practical clinical value is one important way to verify the findings of the science of mind.

Child Psychotherapy and *Ghosts in the Nursery*: Understanding Intergenerational Trauma

In an attempt to further characterize the kind of science practiced by relational theorists and psychotherapists in the psychodynamic disciplines, we will now consider an example from the field of child psychotherapy. One well-established approach in modern child psychotherapy is rooted in the practices whose key ideas and methods are outlined in Selma Fraiberg's seminal 1975 paper, *Ghosts in the Nursery*,[438] co-authored with Edna Adelson and Vivian Shapiro. Many researchers at the forefront of the field today consider this work groundbreaking. Arietta Slade states that "Fraiberg's work was revolutionary,"[439] Alicia Lieberman says "from Selma Fraiberg I learned about healing,"[440] and Peter Fonagy calls her work "paradigmatic"[441] as it can be considered foundational for what later evolved into a widely recognized and successful discipline.

The paper discusses the impact of parents' unresolved childhood traumas on their parenting and relationships with their children. It has been determined, by numerous studies, that such parental traumas affect the parent-child attachment relationships and are unconsciously transmitted to their children, potentially affecting the children's psychological development. Drawing on attachment theory and a psychoan-alytic therapeutic framework, Fraiberg and her colleagues have developed a therapeutic method intent on making the threat-ening unconscious emotional content associated with such parental traumas conscious, and thus available for mental processing. The ultimate goal of such mental processing is not only the well-being of a parent but the reinstatement of the healthy formative attachment relationship between the parent and their child. Fraiberg's method originally targeted infants and their parents (it is also known as Infant-Parent Psychother-apy or IPP), addressing the most critical 0-3 age. Child psychotherapy as we know it today has built on this foundation by developing further insights and methods and by providing verification studies (methods such as *Child-Parent Psychotherapy (CPP)*[442] and *Minding the Baby (MTB)*[443] approach for example.)

Reading Fraiberg's *Ghosts in the Nursery* (it is widely accessi-ble online) makes it obvious why science in this domain feels different from the "hard sciences," despite using the same basic framework of the scientific method. Every individual human self represents in many ways a unique, dynamic world of phenomena, making each case in psychotherapy a unique scientific subject requiring careful observation. One person's traumatic experience can be very different from another person's traumatic experience. This is observable in relational dynamics, psychological patterns, and bodily expressions. Mind phenomena present themselves in real-time during psy-chotherapy sessions, in many cases such phenomena only briefly pierce the emotional defense mechanisms of a trauma-tized person, and the therapist must notice them right away, as it can take a long time until an event manifesting the same phenomena can be observed again. An effective psycho-therapist's observations are informed by a deep understanding of the theories of mind. The objectivity and rigor necessary in this domain — rooted in a therapist's mind — can only be achieved by many years of thorough and conscientious train-ing.[444] Psychodynamic therapists often undergo years of per-sonal therapy/analysis themselves in order to understand their own traumas and biases, as they are likely to surface during therapy sessions in the experience of countertransference and need to be accounted for. The therapeutic process is com-monly reinforced by ongoing supervising relationships with colleagues and with regular countertransference group work. In their sessions, therapists must use imagination and dynamic relational thinking. As described in *Ghosts in the Nursery*, observations can also be recorded for further analysis or be done by several practitioners (unless their presence distorts the relational dynamics). These observations in sessions lead to the creation of hypotheses, which are then often discussed by a team of trained practitioners. The two cases presented in Fraiberg's paper vividly demonstrate the use of attachment theory and psychoanalytically informed observations in this process. These hypotheses are qualitative in nature and they are tested in the therapeutic sessions, as interventions within the intersubjective potential space of the psychotherapeutic re-lationship. If the hypotheses are correct, therapeutic effects become observable over time. Should the therapeutic process indicate the need for hypothesis revision, adjustments are made, followed by a new attempt. Patience is needed in this process, important patterns of trauma often take time to reveal themselves, but most often they do eventually, and they can be registered by a careful observer. From a therapist's point of view, observations are enhanced by monitoring transference and countertransference feelings and thoughts, in both oneself and the client; they represent useful instruments that carry a lot of information but, as mentioned, require a high level of training involving the therapist's capacity for self-reflection and self-awareness.

Fraiberg uses the metaphor of "ghosts"[445] to represent unresolved parental traumas. They exist as unconscious, secluded regions within a parent's mind, filled with raw, traumatic affect that is hard to access. "Ghosts" can be seen as the hidden irrational (inaccessible to reason) forces in our minds, they are packed with powerful emotional content, they invisibly lead us to live our lives in a limited way. We don't dare to visit the spaces in our minds where they dwell, to challenge them, shine the light of reason and mentalize them. "Ghosts" can therefore be considered primitive (not represented by thoughts/mentalization) raw forces in our minds that influence what we think, feel, and do. This is how Fraiberg introduces them:

> "In every nursery there are ghosts. They are the visitors from the unremembered past of the parents; the uninvited guests at the christening. Under all favorable circumstances, the unfriendly and unbidden spirits are banished from the nursery and return to their subterranean dwelling place. The baby makes his own imperative claim upon parental love and, in strict analogy with the fairy tales, the bonds of love protect the child and his parents against the intruders, the malevolent ghosts.... [In some families,] intruders from the past have taken up residence in the nursery, claiming tradition and rights of ownership. They have been present at the christening for two or more generations. While no one has issued an invitation, the ghosts take up residence and conduct the rehearsals of the family tragedy from a tattered script."[446]

Research in the field of child psychotherapy has discovered that many deeply traumatized parents cannot access and resolve these powerful, hidden, and unthinkable emotions on their own. It has been determined that a marker of such traumas is the inability to remember and consciously access the powerful emotion of suffering, even if the traumatic events can be remembered factually. It is the agency (reasoning mind) of the psychotherapist that can facilitate this process by creating and maintaining a protective *holding environment*[447] for the parent, and by gently initiating surfacing and mentalizing of the parent's "ghosts" (unresolved traumatic emotions) and supporting the safe unfolding of this process. Detailed descriptions and examples can be found in the literature.[448]

This is a good point in our deliberations to also ponder the following words from Selma Fraiberg's 1978 book *Every Child's Birthright*. They can be considered the North Star for understanding both human development and psychotherapy, as the implications of their meaning affect all of us at some point in our lives, whether as infants, children, teenagers, parents, adults, or in old age:

> "The evidence from diverse studies and schools of psychology converges and has led to this consensus: the human capacity to love and to make enduring partnerships in love is formed in infancy ... The child learns to love through his first human partners, his parents. We can look upon this miraculous occurrence as a 'gift' of love to the baby. We should also regard it as a right, a birthright for every child ... 'Mothering,' that old fashioned word, is the nurturing of the human potential of every baby to love, to trust, and to bind himself to human partnerships in a lifetime of love ... When a baby has been deprived of a mother or a mother substitute through adversity or disaster or the indifference of his society, we have found that the later capacity of that child to commit himself to love, to partners in love, and to the human community will be diminished or depleted."[449]

Perhaps the most wide-reaching message from Selma Fraiberg's work is about the formative power of relationships — especially the early and developmentally critical 0-3 attachment relationships — for the development of the human self. The fact that many modern Western societies demonstrate a truly primitive mindset by ignoring this insight, repeatedly validated in numerous studies, is a tragedy that is already costing us dearly. This is especially evident in the US, where support for provisions like parental leave and childcare for ages 0-3 is almost non-existent.[450] A rational society would prioritize investment in all of its children early on, ensuring that they can grow into healthy human beings who can also contribute to society. This would not only ensure improved quality of life and greater fulfillment for everyone, but it would also substantially reduce societal cost related to healthcare, criminal justice, and lost productivity. Instead, at the time of this writing, the infuriating fact is that more than 13 million children in the US face hunger.[451] This neglect inflicts deep-seated trauma with far-reaching costs to the whole society. A swift introduction of measures to support our children would single-handedly move us to a higher cultural ground as a society, as supporting their own children is among the most straightforward and most powerful transformational actions any society can take on its path toward becoming more humane. As already mentioned, the Nordic countries exemplify this well,[452] demonstrating that with the requisite societal will, substantial improvements in early childhood care and support are easily achievable. This serves as a model for the world, showing that prioritizing the well-being of children is not only possible but also beneficial for the entire society.

It is increasingly evident that it lies in the path of humanity that we must awaken from our perilous slumber and start realizing that care for human beings must become our first and foremost priority. This must also be considered an *economic good*, around which the entire *economic paradigm* can and must be built, on a *much greater scale* than what we have today, including education, trades, professions, and jobs that can enable lives with dignity. The need is great, only humans can fulfill it, and the "untapped market" for the potential economy of care, starting with the "infrastructure of care,"[453] is immense. However, modern society, due to the prevalence of raw self-interest in our minds, mainly considers things that satisfy our self-interest as goods. On the whole, care for humans is currently considered a low-priority afterthought in many modern Western societies. Yet, such care ranks among the most noble work humans can accomplish, and it is essential for the survival of any society, even if it is presently neither recognized nor adequately rewarded. We even must use terms like "care penalty"[454] to describe the sacrifices one must make in order to be able to perform care for humans. The needs of every child, sick, or old person are indeed the needs of the whole society. It is foolish, ignorant, and damaging for everyone to consider these needs as individual, private affairs – we all need them at some point in our lives, and we all appreciate walking through the world of happy, healthy, and productive people, rather than moving through the sloughs of pain and suffering that are markers of primitive societies.

Furthermore, it is to our own peril that we blindly disregard the fact that the sheer scale of our self-interested efforts in manufacturing and distributing material goods — which define our current economy (and reflect the levels of our hubris) — is already choking the planet and life on it.

The first sign that humanity is on an upward path and capable of ushering in a 21st-century Humanist Renaissance that elevates our species to a new cultural level, will be the budding growth of the *economy of care*. If we start truly caring for each other, no one should fear the threatening cataclysms coming our way; instead, we might experience them as a light afternoon breeze. If.

About the author

B.K. is a pen name. I studied physics, electrical engineering, and computer science in Europe and have been living and working as a software engineer in Silicon Valley, California for the past 20+ years. A lifelong interest in philosophy, the nature of the human mind, and spiritual meditative practice has guided my studies and most endeavors throughout my adult life. I have either lived in or extensively traveled to about a dozen countries worldwide, which has been a gift and a tremendous help in understanding different perspectives. Most of my journey was accomplished together with my family, four of us and a dog. The first part of this book was written mainly in 2023, my sabbatical year dedicated to writing. The second part will happen as soon as I can get to it.

Bibliography

Artificial Intelligence and the Human Mind

(Bibliography is also available/updated at: www.AiAndHumanMind.org)

60 Minutes (Director). (2023a, April 16). Google CEO Sundar Pichai: AI impact to be more profound than discovery of fire, electricity | 60 Minutes. https://youtu.be/W6HpE1rhs7w?si=Nrtdujkyc1J52cAQ

60 Minutes (Director). (2023b, April 16). The AI revolution: Google's developers on the future of artificial intelligence | 60 Minutes. https://youtu.be/880TBXMuzmk?si=ejsrTRo8WT9dHE0c

Ackerman, S. (1992). Discovering the Brain. Washington (DC): National Academies Press (US); 1992. 6, The Development and Shaping of the Brain. Available from: https://www.ncbi.nlm.nih.gov/books/NBK234146/

Adadi, A., & Berrada, M. (2018). Peeking Inside the Black-Box: A Survey on Explainable Artificial Intelligence (XAI). IEEE Access, 6, 52138–52160. https://doi.org/10.1109/ACCESS.2018.2870052

Adena, M., Enikolopov, R., Petrova, M., Santarosa, V., & Zhuravskaya, E. (2015). Radio and the Rise of The Nazis in Prewar Germany*. The Quarterly Journal of Economics, 130(4), 1885–1939. https://doi.org/10.1093/qje/qjv030

Adverse childhood experiences. (2023). In Wikipedia. https://en.wikipedia.org/w/index.php?title=Adverse_childhood_experiences&oldid=1186956128

Agrawal, A., Gans, J., Goldfarb, A., & National Bureau of Economic Research (Eds.). (2019). The economics of artificial intelligence: An agenda. The University of Chicago Press.

Agrawal, A., Gans, J., Goldfarb, A., Tucker, A., & National Bureau of Economic Research (Eds.). (2024). The economics of artificial intelligence: Health Care Challenges. The University of Chicago Press.

Ahmad, S. (2019). "It's Just the Job": Investigating the Influence of Culture in India's Commercial Content Moderation Industry [Preprint]. SocArXiv. https://doi.org/10.31235/osf.io/hjcv2

AI Frontiers. (2018, September 29). The man who revolutionized computer vision, machine translation, games and robotics. AI Frontiers. https://medium.com/aifrontiers/the-journey-of-openais-founder-ilya-sutskever-s-story-486e96cd008f

Ainsworth, M.D.S., Blehar, M.C., Waters, E., and Wall, S. (1978.) Patterns of Attachment: A Psychological Study of the Strange Situation. Hillsdale: Lawrence Erlbaum.

Ainsworth, M. S. (1989). Attachments beyond infancy. American Psychologist, 44(4), 709–716. https://doi.org/10.1037/0003-066X.44.4.709

Alba, D. (2023, July 12). Google's AI Chatbot Is Trained by Humans Who Say They're Overworked, Underpaid and Frustrated. Bloomberg.Com. https://www.bloomberg.com/news/articles/2023-07-12/google-s-ai-chatbot-is-trained-by-humans-who-say-they-re-overworked-underpaid-and-frustrated

Albahari, M. (2006). Analytical Buddhism: The two-tiered illusion of self. Palgrave Macmillan.

Amanpour and Co. (Director). (2023a, March 7). Adrienne LaFrance on "The New Anarchy." Hosted by Walter Isaacson. Amanpour & Company. https://www.pbs.org/wnet/amanpour-and-company/video/adrienne-lafrance-new-anarchy-xsiamp/

Amanpour and Co. (Director). (2023b, May 9). "Godfather of AI" Geoffrey Hinton Warns of the "Existential Threat" of AI | Amanpour and Company. https://youtu.be/Y6Sgp7y178k?si=InPMAZwIzylXyEOL

Andersen, H. C. (2014 [orig. c. 1835-1870]). An illustrated treasury of Hans Christian Andersen's fairy tales: The Little Mermaid, Thumbelina, the princess and the pea and many more classic stories. Anastasiya Archipova (Illustrator). Floris Books.

Andersen, R. (2023, July 24). Does Sam Altman Know What He's Creating? The Atlantic. https://www.theatlantic.com/magazine/archive/2023/09/sam-altman-openai-chatgpt-gpt-4/674764/

Andreessen, M. (2023, June 6). Why AI Will Save the World. Andreessen Horowitz. https://a16z.com/ai-will-save-the-world/

Antony, L. M., & Hornstein, N. (Eds.). (2003). Chomsky and his critics. Blackwell Pub.

Angwin, J., Larson, J., Mattu, S., & Kirchner, L. (2016, May 23). Machine Bias. ProPublica. https://www.propublica.org/article/machine-bias-risk-assessments-in-criminal-sentencing

Applin, S. A., & Fischer, M. D. (2013). Watching Me, Watching You. (Process surveillance and agency in the workplace). 2013 IEEE International Symposium on Technology and Society (ISTAS): Social Implications of Wearable Computing and Augmediated Reality in Everyday Life, 268–275. https://doi.org/10.1109/ISTAS.2013.6613129

Arlotta, P., & Fridman, L. (2019, August 12). Paola Arlotta: Brain Development from Stem Cell to Organoid | Lex Fridman Podcast #32. https://youtu.be/lVHRs3uTHNI?si=Dy-cF4oZLLJma4RA

Aristotle, & Lawson-Tancred, H. (1998 [orig. c. 350 BC]). Metaphysics. Penguin Books.

Aristotle, & Irwin, T. (2019 [orig. c. 330 BC]). Nicomachean ethics. Hackett Publishing Company, Inc.

Arsht, A. & Etcovitch, D. (2018, March 2). The Human Cost of Online Content Moderation. Harvard Journal of Law & Technology.

https://jolt.law.harvard.edu/digest/the-human-cost-of-online-content-moderation

Ashcroft, A., & Ashcroft, A. (2023). The Gendered Nature of Chatbots: Anthropomorphism and Authenticity. In M. A. Kuhail, B. Abu Shawar, & R. Hammad (Eds.), Advances in Web Technologies and Engineering (pp. 36–78). IGI Global. https://doi.org/10.4018/978-1-6684-6234-8.ch003

Austen Riggs Center (2023). The Relationship Between Loneliness and Depression. | Austen Riggs Center. https://www.austenriggs.org/our-treatment/conditions/depressive-disorders/loneliness-and-depression

Azoulay, P., Fons-Rosen, C., & Graff Zivin, J. S. (2019). Does science advance one funeral at a time? American Economic Review, 109(8), 2889–2920. https://doi.org/10.1257/aer.20161574

Baker, H.S. & Baker, M.N. (1987.) Heinz Kohut's self psychology: An overview. (1987). American Journal of Psychiatry, 144(1), 1–9. https://doi.org/10.1176/ajp.144.1.1

Barnes, J. (2008). Nothing to be frightened of (1st American ed). Alfred A. Knopf.

Barreiro-Ares, A., Morales-Santiago, A., Sendra-Portero, F., & Souto-Bayarri, M. (2023). Impact of the Rise of Artificial Intelligence in Radiology: What Do Students Think? International Journal of Environmental Research and Public Health, 20(2), 1589. https://doi.org/10.3390/ijerph20021589

Barrett, L. F. (2017). How emotions are made: The secret life of the brain. Houghton Mifflin Harcourt.

Barrett, L. F. (2020). Seven and a half lessons about the brain. Houghton Mifflin Harcourt.

Bateman, A. W., & Fonagy, P. (2004). Mentalization-Based Treatment of BPD. Journal of Personality Disorders, 18(1), 36–51. https://doi.org/10.1521/pedi.18.1.36.32772

Bateman, A., Fonagy, P., & American Psychiatric Association Publishing (Eds.). (2019). Handbook of mentalizing in mental health practice (Second edition). American Psychiatric Association Publishing.

Bayne, T. (2022). Philosophy of mind: An introduction. Routledge, Taylor & Francis Group.

Beebe, B., Cohen, P., & Lachmann, F. M. (2016). The mother-infant interaction picture book: Origins of attachment (First edition). W.W. Norton & Company.

Beebe, B., & Lachmann, F. M. (2014). The origins of attachment: Infant research and adult treatment. Routledge.

Bender, E. M., Gebru, T., McMillan-Major, A., & Shmitchell, S. (2021). On the Dangers of Stochastic Parrots: Can Language Models Be Too Big? Proceedings of the 2021 ACM Conference on Fairness, Accountability, and Transparency, 610–623. https://doi.org/10.1145/3442188.3445922

Berwick, R. C., & Chomsky, N. (2016). Why only us: Language and evolution. MIT press.

Bharucha, T., Steiger, M. E., Manchanda, P., Mere, R., & Huang, X. (2024). Content Moderator Startle Response: A Qualitative Study. In X.-S. Yang, R. S. Sherratt, N. Dey, & A. Joshi (Eds.), Proceedings of Eighth International Congress on Information and Communication Technology (Vol. 695, pp.

217–232). Springer Nature Singapore. https://doi.org/10.1007/978-981-99-3043-2_18

Bhatia, A. (2023, April 26). Let Us Show You How GPT Works—Using Jane Austen. The New York Times. https://www.nytimes.com/interactive/2023/04/26/upshot/gpt-from-scratch.html

Bickmore, T., & O'Leary, T. (2023). Conversational agents on smartphones and the web. In Digital Therapeutics for Mental Health and Addiction (pp. 99–112). Elsevier. https://doi.org/10.1016/B978-0-323-90045-4.00010-1

Bishop, B. (2009). The Big Sort: Why the Clustering of Like-Minded American is Tearing Us Apart (First Edition). Mariner Books.

Blackiston, D. J., Silva Casey, E., & Weiss, M. R. (2008). Retention of Memory through Metamorphosis: Can a Moth Remember What It Learned As a Caterpillar? PLoS ONE, 3(3), e1736. https://doi.org/10.1371/journal.pone.0001736

Blackiston, D. J., Shomrat, T., & Levin, M. (2015). The stability of memories during brain remodeling: A perspective. Communicative & Integrative Biology, 8(5), e1073424. https://doi.org/10.1080/19420889.2015.1073424

Blackman, R. (2020, May 28). How to Monitor Your Employees—While Respecting Their Privacy. Harvard Business Review. https://hbr.org/2020/05/how-to-monitor-your-employees-while-respecting-their-privacy

Bloom, P. (2016). Against empathy: The case for rational compassion (First edition). Ecco, an imprint of HarperCollins Publishers.

Bloomberg Originals. (2023, June 15). Inside OpenAI, the Architect of ChatGPT | The Circuit. https://youtu.be/p9Q5a1Vn-Hk?si=CAB5z4xtXIfW8TvH

Bolukbasi, T., Chang, K.-W., Zou, J., Saligrama, V., & Kalai, A. (2016). Man is to Computer Programmer as Woman is to Homemaker? Debiasing Word Embeddings. https://doi.org/10.48550/ARXIV.1607.06520

Bongard, J., & Levin, M. (2021). Living Things Are Not (20th Century) Machines: Updating Mechanism Metaphors in Light of the Modern Science of Machine Behavior. Frontiers in Ecology and Evolution, 9, 650726. https://doi.org/10.3389/fevo.2021.650726

Born, K. (2023, August 10). Will Generative AI Make or Break Democracy? | by Kelly Born. Project Syndicate. https://www.project-syndicate.org/commentary/generative-ai-could-test-democracies-by-kelly-born-2023-08

Bostrom, N. (2016). Superintelligence: Paths, dangers, strategies. Oxford University Press.

Bostrom, N., & Yudkowsky, E. (2014). The ethics of artificial intelligence. In K. Frankish & W. M. Ramsey (Eds.), The Cambridge Handbook of Artificial Intelligence (1st ed., pp. 316–334). Cambridge University Press. https://doi.org/10.1017/CBO9781139046855.020

Bowlby, J. (1944). Forty-four juvenile thieves: their characters and home-life. The International Journal of Psychoanalysis, 25, 19–53.

Bowlby, J. (1983 [orig. 1969]). Attachment: Attachment and Loss, Volume One (Basic Books Classics). (2nd edition). Basic Books.

Bowlby, J. (1976 [orig. 1972]). Separation: Anxiety And Anger (Basic Books Classics). Attachment and Loss, Volume 2. Basic Books.

Bowlby, J. (1982 [orig. 1980]). Loss: Sadness And Depression. Attachment and Loss, Volume 3 (Revised ed. edition). Basic Books.

Brain Architecture. (n.d.). Center on the Developing Child at Harvard University. https://developingchild.harvard.edu/science/key-concepts/brain-architecture/

Bram, B. (2022, September 27). Opinion | My Therapist, the Robot. The New York Times. https://www.nytimes.com/2022/09/27/opinion/chatbot-therapy-mental-health.html

Britannica, T. Editors of Encyclopaedia (2010, November 9). intelligence summary. Encyclopedia Britannica. https://www.britannica.com/summary/human-intelligence-psychology

Brooks, D. (2023a, August 14). How America Got Mean. The Atlantic. https://www.theatlantic.com/magazine/archive/2023/09/us-culture-moral-education-formation/674765/

Brooks, D. (2023b). How to Know a Person: The Art of Seeing Others Deeply and Being Deeply Seen. Random House.

Brooks, D. & Smerconish, M. (2023, December 30). Why it's important to get to know other people | CNN. https://www.cnn.com/videos/us/2023/12/30/smr-brooks-how-to-know-a-person.cnn

Brooks, E. (2023, December 14). You Can't Truly Be Friends With an AI. The Atlantic. https://www.theatlantic.com/family/archive/2023/12/replika-ai-friendship-apps/676345/

Brooks, E., & Rosin, H. (2023, August 10). Can an AI Save a Life? In The Atlantic. https://www.theatlantic.com/podcasts/archive/2023/08/are-ai-relationships-real/674965/

Brown, A. (2012, March 27). Iris Murdoch against the robots. The Guardian. https://www.theguardian.com/commentisfree/andrewbrown/2012/mar/27/iris-murdoch-sovereignty-good

Brown, K. (2021, June 1). Something Bothering You? Tell It to Woebot. The New York Times. https://www.nytimes.com/2021/06/01/health/artificial-intelligence-therapy-woebot.html

Bubeck, S., Chandrasekaran, V., Eldan, R., Gehrke, J., Horvitz, E., Kamar, E., Lee, P., Lee, Y. T., Li, Y., Lundberg, S., Nori, H., Palangi, H., Ribeiro, M. T., & Zhang, Y. (2023). Sparks of Artificial General Intelligence: Early experiments with GPT-4 (arXiv:2303.12712). arXiv. http://arxiv.org/abs/2303.12712

Buckner, C., & Garson, J. (2019). Connectionism. In E. N. Zalta (Ed.), The Stanford Encyclopedia of Philosophy. Metaphysics Research Lab, Stanford University. https://plato.stanford.edu/entries/connectionism/

Bureau, U. C. (2023a, September 12). Income, Poverty and Health Insurance Coverage in the United States: 2022. Census.Gov.

https://www.census.gov/newsroom/press-releases/2023/income-poverty-health-insurance-coverage.html

Bureau, U. C. (2023b, December 4). Child Poverty Rate Still Higher Than For Older Populations But Declining. Census.Gov. https://www.census.gov/library/stories/2023/12/poverty-rate-varies-by-age-groups.html

Burkeman, O. (2015, January 21). Why can't the world's greatest minds solve the mystery of consciousness? The Guardian. https://www.theguardian.com/science/2015/jan/21/-sp-why-cant-worlds-greatest-minds-solve-mystery-consciousness

Burkeman, O. (2016, January 7). Therapy wars: The revenge of Freud. The Guardian. https://www.theguardian.com/science/2016/jan/07/therapy-wars-revenge-of-freud-cognitive-behavioural-therapy

Buranyi, S. (2022, June 28). Do we need a new theory of evolution? The Guardian. https://www.theguardian.com/science/2022/jun/28/do-we-need-a-new-theory-of-evolution

Callaway, E. (2020). 'It will change everything': DeepMind's AI makes gigantic leap in solving protein structures. Nature, 588(7837), 203–204. https://doi.org/10.1038/d41586-020-03348-4

Carballo, R. (2023, December 11). Using A.I. to Talk to the Dead. The New York Times. https://www.nytimes.com/2023/12/11/technology/ai-chatbots-dead-relatives.html

Carnegie, M. (2023, July 23). The Creepy Rise of Bossware. Wired UK. https://www.wired.co.uk/article/creepy-rise-bossware

Carroll, S. B. (2005). Endless forms most beautiful: The new science of evo devo and the making of the animal kingdom (1st ed). Norton.

Carroll, S. M. (2016). The big picture: On the origins of life, meaning, and the universe itself. Dutton, an imprint of Penguin Random House LLC.

Carroll, S. M. & Kuhn R. L. (2017, October 9). Sean Carroll—Physics of What Happens. https://youtu.be/NsTX3VN7wbU?si=DDIC35pFVuuBnhOU

Carroll, S. M. (2019, September 7). Opinion | Even Physicists Don't Understand Quantum Mechanics. The New York Times. https://www.nytimes.com/2019/09/07/opinion/sunday/quantum-physics.html

Carroll, S. M. & Kuhn R. L. (2022, July 21). Sean Carroll—What Are Observers? https://youtu.be/Vdyp8Xu8J9Y?si=LIUM4hhE_MtOC5_iCase, A., & Deaton, A. (2021). Deaths of despair and the future of capitalism (First paperback edition). Princeton University Press.

Cassidy, J., & Shaver, P. R. (2018). Handbook of attachment: Theory, research, and clinical applications (Third edition). Guilford Press.

Causse, J., Plabutong, N., Barbieri, S. (2023, August 2). The Temptations of A.I. Companionship in "Rachels Don't Run." The New Yorker. https://www.newyorker.com/culture/screening-room/the-temptations-of-ai-companionship-in-rachels-dont-run

CDC. (2023, July 6). Facts About Suicide | Suicide. https://www.cdc.gov/suicide/facts/index.html

Center on the Developing Child at Harvard University: What Are ACEs? (n.d.). What Are ACEs? And How Do They Relate to Toxic Stress? | Center on the Developing Child at Harvard University. https://developingchild.harvard.edu/resources/aces-and-toxic-stress-frequently-asked-questions/

Chalmers, D. (1995). Facing up to the problem of consciousness. Journal of Consciousness Studies, 2(3), 200–219.

Chalmers, D. J. (2002). Philosophy of mind: Classical and contemporary readings. Oxford University Press.

Chalmers, D. J. (2010). The character of consciousness. Oxford University Press, USA.

Chalmers, D. J. (2022). Reality+: Virtual worlds and the problems of philosophy (First edition). W. W. Norton & Company.

Chatterjee, L., & Sengupta, R. (2022). Digitization of Mental Health Services: A Business Perspective. In I. Vasiliu-Feltes & I. Mysore (Eds.), Advances in Healthcare Information Systems and Administration (pp. 206–235). IGI Global. https://doi.org/10.4018/978-1-7998-8966-3.ch009

Chayka, K. (2023, November 13). Your A.I. Companion Will Support You No Matter What. The New Yorker. https://www.newyorker.com/culture/infinite-scroll/your-ai-companion-will-support-you-no-matter-what

Chomsky, N. (1959). A review of B. F. Skinner's Verbal Behavior. Language, 35(1), 26–58. https://doi.org/10.2307/411334

Chomsky, N., & Magee, B. (2021 [orig. 1978]). Chomsky on the "Limits" of Knowledge (1978). https://youtu.be/tc1hsQWzUKc?si=4aplxcT117OShawb

Chomsky, N. (2000). New horizons in the study of language and mind. Cambridge University Press.

Chomsky, N., Belletti, A., & Rizzi, L. (2002). On nature and language. Cambridge University Press.

Chomsky, N. (2007). On language: Chomsky's classic works language and responsibility and reflections on language. The New Press.

Chomsky, N. (2015a). Syntactic structures (Repr. der Ausg. 's-Gravenhage, Mouton,1957). Martino Publ.

Chomsky, N. (2015b). Aspects of the theory of syntax: With a new preface by the author (50th anniversary edition). MIT Press.

Chomsky, N. (2016). What kind of creatures are we? Columbia University Press.

Christian, B. (2020). The alignment problem: Machine learning and human values (First edition). W.W. Norton & Company.

Churchland, P. M. (1995). The engine of reason, the seat of the soul: A philosophical journey into the brain. MIT Press.

Churchland, P. M. (2012). Plato's camera: How the physical brain captures a landscape of abstract universals. MIT Press.

Churchland, P. S. (2013). Touching a nerve: The self as brain (First edition). W.W. Norton & Company.

Chzhen, Y., Gromada, A. & Rees, G. (2019, June). Are the world's richest countries family friendly? Policy in the OECD and EU. UNICEF.

https://www.unicef-irc.org/publications/pdf/Family-Friendly-Policies-Research_UNICEF_%202019.pdf

Clark, C. M. (2012). The sleepwalkers: How Europe went to war in 1914. Allen Lane.

CNBC. (2020, June 19). How Employers Could Be Spying On You While Working From Home. https://youtu.be/7hw4bRFmPgo?si=Y3_dnyl3by4xlaxt

CNN video (2023, July 26). Sexual harassment in the metaverse: How common is it and what should platforms be doing to stop it? | CNN. https://www.cnn.com/videos/world/2023/07/25/sexual-harassment-metaverse-online-worlds-as-equals-cnn-lon-orig.cnn

Collins, D. F. (2021, July 27). Artificial Intelligence Accurately Predicts Protein Folding. NIH Director's Blog. https://directorsblog.nih.gov/2021/07/27/artificial-intelligence-accurately-predicts-protein-folding/

Collins, K. (2023, February 17). How ChatGPT Could Embed a 'Watermark' in the Text It Generates. The New York Times. https://www.nytimes.com/interactive/2023/02/17/business/ai-text-detection.html

Corbyn, Z. (2022, April 27). 'Bossware is coming for almost every worker': The software you might not realize is watching you. The Guardian. https://www.theguardian.com/technology/2022/apr/27/remote-work-software-home-surveillance-computer-monitoring-pandemic

Corning, P. A., Kauffman, S. A., Noble, D., Shapiro, J. A., Vane-Wright, R. I., & Pross, A. (Eds.). (2023). Evolution "on purpose": Teleonomy in living systems. The MIT Press.

Cowen, L. (2023, February 10). How Artificial Intelligence Is Driving Changes in Radiology. Inside Precision Medicine. https://www.insideprecisionmedicine.com/news-and-features/how-artificial-intelligence-is-driving-changes-in-radiology/

Crick, F. (1994). The astonishing hypothesis: The Scientific Search for the Soul. Scribner.

Crispin, J. (2021, September 16). Employers are spying on Americans at home with 'tattleware'. It's time to track them instead. The Guardian. https://www.theguardian.com/commentisfree/2021/sep/16/tattleware-employers-spying-working-home

Cyphers, B. & Gullo, K. (2020, June 30). Inside the Invasive, Secretive "Bossware" Tracking Workers. Electronic Frontier Foundation. https://www.eff.org/deeplinks/2020/06/inside-invasive-secretive-bossware-tracking-workers

Damasio, A. (2010). Self comes to mind: Constructing the Conscious Brain. Pantheon.

Darwin, C. (2009 [orig. 1859]). On the origin of species: By means of natural selection or the preservation of favoured races in the struggle for life. Penguin.

Dastin, J. (2018, October 11). Insight—Amazon scraps secret AI recruiting tool that showed bias against women. Reuters. https://www.reuters.com/article/idUSKCN1MK0AG/

Davidson, R., & Henderson, R. (2000). Electronic Performance Monitoring: A Laboratory Investigation of the Influence of Monitoring and Difficulty on Task Performance, Mood State, and Self-Reported Stress Levels. Journal of Applied Social Psychology, 30(5), 906–920. https://doi.org/10.1111/j.1559-1816.2000.tb02502.x

Davies, H., McKernan, B., & Sabbagh, D. (2023, December 1). 'The Gospel': How Israel uses AI to select bombing targets in Gaza. The Guardian. https://www.theguardian.com/world/2023/dec/01/the-gospel-how-israel-uses-ai-to-select-bombing-targets

Dawkins, R. (1990 [orig. 1976]). The selfish gene (2nd edition). Oxford University Press.

Dawkins, R. (1996 [orig. 1986]). The blind watchmaker: Why the evidence of evolution reveals a universe without design. Norton.

de Waal, F. B. M. (2001). The ape and the sushi master: Cultural reflections by a primatologist. Basic Books.

de Waal, F. B. M. (2006). Our inner ape: The best and worst of human nature. Riverhead Books.

de Waal, F. B. M. (2009). The age of empathy: Nature's lessons for a kinder society. Three Rivers Press.

de Waal, F. B. M. (2010, October 17). Morals without god? Opinionator. The New York Times. https://archive.nytimes.com/opinionator.blogs.nytimes.com/2010/10/17/morals-without-god/

Deaton, A. (2013). The great escape: Health, wealth, and the origins of inequality. Princeton University Press.

Deaton, A. (2023). Economics in America: An immigrant economist explores the land of inequality. Princeton University Press.

Deepfake pornography. (2023). In Wikipedia. https://en.wikipedia.org/w/index.php?title=Deepfake_pornography&oldid=1187925989#cite_note-14

DeLong, J. B. (2022a). Slouching towards Utopia: An economic history of the Twentieth Century (First edition). Basic Books.

DeLong, J. B. (2022b, September 8). Our Ancestors Thought We'd Build an Economic Paradise. Instead We Got 2022. Time. https://time.com/6211380/economic-prosperity-failed/

Dennett, D. (1991). Consciousness explained. Little Brown & Co.

Dennett, D. (2017). From bacteria to bach and back: The evolution of minds. W. W. Norton & Company.

Dennett, D. C., & Caruso, G. D. (2021). Just deserts: Debating free will. Polity Press.

Dickens, C. (1843). A Christmas Carol. The Project Gutenberg. https://www.gutenberg.org/files/46/46-h/46-h.htm

Dickens, C. (2008 [orig. 1841]). Barnaby Rudge (C. Hurst, Ed.; Oxford world's classics paperback, reiss). Oxford Univ. Press.

Donovan, J., Dreyfuss, E., & Friedberg, B. (2022). Meme wars: The untold story of the online battles upending democracy in America. Bloomsbury Publishing.

Dostoyevsky, F. (2003 [orig. 1879]). The brothers Karamazov: A novel in four parts and an epilogue. Penguin.

Douglass, F. (1846) Frederick Douglass Papers: Speech, Article, and Book File, - 1894; Speeches and Articles by Douglass, -1894; Undated; "Self-Made Men," 1859 address before the students of the Indian Industrial School, Carlisle, Pa., manuscript, typescripts, fragments, printed copy, and correspondence, including le. - 1894. [Manuscript/Mixed Material] Retrieved from the Library of Congress, https://www.loc.gov/item/mss1187900531/ (*Self-Made Men* also available at https://monadnock.net/douglass/self-made-men.html)

Dowd, M. (2023, May 27). Opinion | Don't Kill 'Frankenstein' With Real Frankensteins at Large. The New York Times. https://www.nytimes.com/2023/05/27/opinion/english-humanities-ai.html

Drozek, R. P., Unruh, B. T., Liu, G. Z., & Demers, C. Z. (2023). Mentalization-based Treatment. In Encyclopedia of Mental Health (pp. 503–511). Elsevier. https://doi.org/10.1016/B978-0-323-91497-0.00071-0

Eagle, M. N. (2013). Attachment and psychoanalysis: Theory, research, and clinical implications. The Guilford Press.

Eijgenraam, L. (2017). Helping children form healthy attachments: Building the foundation for strong lifelong relationships. Floris Books.

Emerson, R. W. (1979 [orig. 1841]) Essays, First Series. Cambridge: Belknap Press of Harvard University Press. (also available at: https://www.gutenberg.org/cache/epub/2944/pg2944-images.html)

End Cyber Abuse, (n.d.). Image-Based Sexual Abuse – An Introduction – End Cyber Abuse. https://endcyberabuse.org/law-intro/

EU AI Act (2023). EU AI Act: First regulation on artificial intelligence | News | European Parliament. (2023, August 6). https://www.europarl.europa.eu/news/en/headlines/society/20230601STO9 3804/eu-ai-act-first-regulation-on-artificial-intelligence

Fairbairn, W. R. D. (1954). An object-relations theory of the personality. Basic Books.

Fantasia. 1940. https://youtu.be/6Lp6zYQN3zc?si=eUXxe9U8WBAkhme1

Farrow, B. (2021, July 15). AI therapists are on the rise—But can they really fix us? WIRED Middle East. https://wired.me/technology/artificial-intelligence/ai-therapists-are-on-the-rise-but-can-they-really-fix-us/

Feeding America. (n.d.). Child Hunger in America | Feeding America. Retrieved December 8, 2023, from https://www.feedingamerica.org/hunger-in-america/child-hunger-facts

Felitti, V. J., Anda, R. F., Nordenberg, D., Williamson, D. F., Spitz, A. M., Edwards, V., Koss, M. P., & Marks, J. S. (1998). Relationship of Childhood Abuse and Household Dysfunction to Many of the Leading Causes of Death in Adults: The Adverse Childhood Experiences (ACE) Study. American Journal of Preventive Medicine, 14(4), 245–258. https://doi.org/10.1016/S0749-3797(98)00017-8

Ferrante, M. B. (2019, June 21). UNICEF Study Confirms: The U.S. Ranks Last For Family-Friendly Policies. Forbes. https://www.forbes.com/sites/marybethferrante/2019/06/21/unicef-study-confirms-the-u-s-ranks-last-for-family-friendly-policies/

Feyerabend, P., & Hacking, I. (2010). Against method (4. ed., new ed). Verso.

Feynman, R. (1964). The Feynman Messenger Lectures Video Viewer. The Feynman Lectures on Physics. https://www.feynmanlectures.caltech.edu/fml.html#6

Field, H., & Cook, T. (2023, June 6). Tim Cook uses ChatGPT and says Apple is looking at it closely. CNBC. https://www.cnbc.com/2023/06/06/apple-ceo-tim-cook-says-ai-companies-need-to-regulate-themselves.html

Flitter, E., & Cowley, S. (2023, August 30). Voice Deepfakes Are Coming for Your Bank Balance. The New York Times. https://www.nytimes.com/2023/08/30/business/voice-deepfakes-bank-scams.html

Flynn, T. R. (2006). Existentialism: A very short introduction. Oxford University Press.

Fodor, J. A. (1994). The elm and the expert: Mentalese and its semantics. MIT Press.

Fodor, J. A., & Fodor, J. A. (2008). LOT 2: The language of thought revisited. Clarendon Press ; Oxford University Press.

Fodor, J. A. (2015). Minds without meanings: An essay on the content of concepts. The MIT Press.

Folbre, N. (2001). The invisible heart: Economics and family values. New Press.

Fonagy, P. (2001). Attachment theory and psychoanalysis. Other press.

Fonagy, P. (2015). The effectiveness of psychodynamic psychotherapies: An update. World Psychiatry, 14(2), 137–150. https://doi.org/10.1002/wps.20235

Fonagy, P. (2016a, November 18). Peter Fonagy: How Does One Develop Sense of Self? | Simms/Mann Institute. https://youtu.be/7MGrgMMcIsY?si=zqoDZsyjqxUGsgkV

Fonagy, P. (2016b, November 18). Peter Fonagy: Emotional Regulation in Young Children. | Simms/Mann Institute. https://youtu.be/Qjfy-8LshGw?si=S4QkEOKnrWz8Xetf

Fonagy, P. (2017a, April 18). BPD: When Mentalization Breaks Down - Peter Fonagy. | BorderlinerNotes. https://youtu.be/dhEWephIvkg?si=J60cNZgJ11Zkr578

Fonagy, P. (2017b, April 18). What Countries have the Highest Incidence of BPD? - Peter Fonagy. | BorderlinerNotes. https://youtu.be/lcVSMuxApaY?si=xvWwbr0rH6y7oS86

Fonagy, P. (2018, September 18). Goldman Sachs | Talks at GS - Peter Fonagy, Combating a Mental Health Crisis. Goldman Sachs. https://www.goldmansachs.com/intelligence/talks-at-gs/peter-fonagy.html (also at: https://youtu.be/7NX7TIvLCqw?si=QXlbOESAQMkdxrQD)

Fonagy, P., Gergely, G., Jurist, E., & Target, M. (2005). Affect regulation, mentalization and the development of the self. Other press.

Fonagy, P., Gergely, G., & Target, M. (2007). The parent–infant dyad and the construction of the subjective self. Journal of Child Psychology and Psychiatry, 48(3–4), 288–328. https://doi.org/10.1111/j.1469-7610.2007.01727.x

Frankfurt, H. G. (2005). On bullshit. Princeton Univ. Press.

Fosha, D., Siegel, D. J., & Solomon, M. F. (Eds.). (2009). The healing power of emotion: Affective neuroscience, development & clinical practice. W. W. Norton & Company.

Frankl, V. E. (2006 [orig. 1946]). Man's search for meaning. Beacon Press.

Fraiberg, S. (1978). Every child's birthright: In defense of mothering. Bantam Books.

Fraiberg, S., Adelson, E., & Shapiro, V. (1975). Ghosts in the Nursery. Journal of the American Academy of Child Psychiatry, 14(3), 387–421. https://doi.org/10.1016/S0002-7138(09)61442-4

Francis, E., Cheung, H. & Berger, M. (2021, November 11). How does the U.S. compare to other countries on paid parental leave? Americans get 0 weeks. Estonians get more than 80. Washington Post. https://www.washingtonpost.com/world/2021/11/11/global-paid-parental-leave-us/

Freud, S. (1920). A general introduction to psychoanalysis. Horace Liveright. https://doi.org/10.1037/10667-000

Freud, S. (1933). New introductory lectures on psycho-analysis. W W Norton & Co.

Freud, S. (1964). The standard edition of the complete psychological works of Sigmund Freud. (J. Strachey, Ed.). Macmillan.

Freud, S. (2010 [orig. 1930]). Civilization and its discontents (J. Strachey, Ed.; Reprint edition). W. W. Norton & Company.

Fridman, L. (2019, January 11). Deep Learning Basics: Introduction and Overview. https://youtu.be/O5xeyoRL95U?si=HVlZFYSNtri68RQW

Frie, R., & Reis, B. (2001). Understanding Intersubjectivity: Psychoanalytic Formulations and Their Philosophical Underpinnings. Contemporary Psychoanalysis, 37(2), 297–327. https://doi.org/10.1080/00107530.2001.10747081

Friedman, M., & Friedman, R. D. (2002 [orig. 1962]). Capitalism and freedom (40th anniversary ed). University of Chicago Press.

Fromm, E. (1994 [orig. 1941]). Escape from freedom. Holt Paperbacks.

Fromm, E. (1999 [orig.1947]). Man for himself: An inquiry into the psychology of ethics. Routledge.

Fromm, E. (1990 [orig. 1955]). The sane society. H. Holt.

Fromm, E. (2006 [orig. 1956]). The art of loving (Anniversary edition). Harper Perennial Modern Classics.

Fromm, E. (2015 [orig. 1976]). To have or to be? (Reprint edition). Bloomsbury Academic, an imprint of Bloomsbury Publishing Plc.

Fromm, E. (2022 [orig. 1993]). The art of being. Robinson.

FTC (2019, September 3). Google and YouTube Will Pay Record $170 Million for Alleged Violations of Children's Privacy Law. Federal Trade Commission. https://www.ftc.gov/news-events/news/press-releases/2019/09/google-youtube-will-pay-record-170-million-alleged-violations-childrens-privacy-law

Fuller, S. (2004). Kuhn vs. Popper: The struggle for the soul of science. Columbia University Press.

Galilei, G. (1623) Works of Galileo Galilei, Part 3, Volume 15, Astronomy: The Assayer. Rome: Giacomo Mascardi. [Pdf] Retrieved from the Library of Congress, https://www.loc.gov/item/2021666740/

Gallagher, J. (2023, May 25). New superbug-killing antibiotic discovered using AI. BBC NEWS. https://www.bbc.com/news/health-65709834

Gardner, H. (2011). Frames of mind: The theory of multiple intelligences. Basic Books.

Gazzaniga, M. (2018). The consciousness instinct: Unraveling the mystery of how the brain makes the mind. Farrar, Straus and Giroux.

Gazzaniga, M. & Alda, A. (2011, June 2). Scientific American Frontiers | Right Brain vs Left Brain. https://youtu.be/82tlVcq6E7A?si=_-prQyfJlgjc0TsN

Gendler, T. (2011). Philosophy and the Science of Human Nature (26 recorded lessons). Open Yale Courses. https://oyc.yale.edu/philosophy/phil-181

Géron, A. (2023). Hands-on machine learning with Scikit-Learn, Keras, and TensorFlow: Concepts, tools, and techniques to build intelligent systems (Third edition). O'Reilly.

Gershgorn, D. (2018). The inside story of how AI got good enough to dominate Silicon Valley. (2018, June 18). Quartz. https://qz.com/1307091/the-inside-story-of-how-ai-got-good-enough-to-dominate-silicon-valley

Gerson, L. P. (2018). Plotinus: The Enneads. Cambridge University Press.

Gerstle, G. (2022). The rise and fall of the neoliberal order: America and the world in the free market era. Oxford University Press.

Gilpin, L.H., Bau, D., Yuan, B.Z., Bajwa, A., Specter, M.A., & Kagal, L. (2018). Explaining Explanations: An Overview of Interpretability of Machine Learning. 2018 IEEE 5th International Conference on Data Science and Advanced Analytics (DSAA), 80-89.

Gissis, S., Jablonka, E., Zeligowski, A., & Gissis, S. B. (Eds.). (2011). Transformations of Lamarckism: From subtle fluids to molecular biology. MIT Press.

Goethe, J. W. von. (1797). The sorcerer's apprentice. In E.A. Bowring (Trans.), Goethe Ultimate Collection. E-artnow.

Goff, P. (2019). Galileo's error: Foundations for a new science of consciousness. Pantheon.

Goff, P., Moran, A., Harris, A., Koch, C., Seth, A., & Strawson, G. (2022a). Is Consciousness Everywhere?: Essays on Panpsychism (P. Goff & A. Moran, Eds.; 1st edition). Imprint Academic.

Goff, P., Moran, A., Aleksiev, D., Carroll, S., Cortês, M., Delafield-Butt, J., Fields, C., Frankish, K., Harris, A., Koch, C., Leidenhag, J., Liu, M., Ney, A., Prentner, R., Ritchie, S. L., Roelofs, L., Rovelli, C., Seth, A. K., Smolin, L., Strawson, G., Verde, C., Weir, R. S. (2022b). Is consciousness everywhere?: Essays On Panpsychism (journal Of Consciousness Studies). Imprint Academic.

Goldacre, B. (2012, September 27). What doctors don't know about the drugs they prescribe | TED. https://youtu.be/RKmxL8VYy0M?si=diCDfx3T0AmHRmNc

Goldman, J. G. (2010). Ed Tronick and the "Still Face Experiment". Scientific American Blog. https://blogs.scientificamerican.com/thoughtful-animal/ed-tronick-and-the-8220-still-face-experiment-8221/

Goldman Sachs Global Macro Research (2023). Issue 120, July 5, 2023. Top of Mind | Generative AI: Hype, or truly transformative? https://www.goldmansachs.com/intelligence/pages/top-of-mind/generative-ai-hype-or-truly-transformative/report.pdf

Goldman Sachs Intelligence (2023, November 22). AI may start to boost US GDP in 2027. Goldman Sachs. https://www.goldmansachs.com/intelligence/pages/ai-may-start-to-boost-us-gdp-in-2027.html

Golodryga, B. & Abraham, Y. (2024, January 11). Some Israeli intel officers "shocked by what they were asked to do" in Gaza, says Israeli journalist | CNN. https://www.cnn.com/videos/tv/2024/01/10/amanpour-abraham.cnn (use of AI human target creation platform *The Gospel/Habsora* is addressed around 4:50 in the video)

Goleman, D. (2005). Emotional intelligence (10th anniversary trade pbk. ed). Bantam Books.

Goodfellow, I., Pouget-Abadie, J., Mirza, M., Xu, B., Warde-Farley, D., Ozair, S., Courville, A., & Bengio, Y. (2014). Generative Adversarial Nets. In Z. Ghahramani, M. Welling, C. Cortes, N. Lawrence, & K. Q. Weinberger (Eds.), Advances in Neural Information Processing Systems (Vol. 27). Curran Associates, Inc. https://proceedings.neurips.cc/paper_files/paper/2014/file/5ca3e9b122f61f8f06494c97b1afccf3-Paper.pdf

Goodfellow, I., Bengio, Y., & Courville, A. (2016). Deep learning. The MIT Press.

Goodfellow, I. & Fridman, L. (2019, April 18). Ian Goodfellow: Generative Adversarial Networks (GANs) | Lex Fridman Podcast #19. https://youtu.be/Z6rxFNMGdn0?si=TJDLmB6NT87yMKVY

Goodman, P. S. (2022). Davos man: How the billionaires devoured the world. Custom House.

Google, (2019a). How a Beekeeper Is Using AI to Save the Bees. Google. https://about.google/intl/ALL_us/stories/save-the-bees/

Google, (2023a). Med-PaLM. https://sites.research.google/med-palm/

Google DeepMind, (2022a). Advancing discovery of better drugs and medicine. (2022, July 28). Google DeepMind. https://deepmind.google/discover/blog/advancing-discovery-of-better-drugs-and-medicine/

Google DeepMind, (2022b). Creating plastic-eating enzymes that could save us from pollution. (2022, July 28). Google DeepMind. https://deepmind.google/discover/blog/creating-plastic-eating-enzymes-that-could-save-us-from-pollution/

Google DeepMind, (2022c). Fighting osteoporosis before it starts. (2022, September 27). Google DeepMind. https://deepmind.google/discover/blog/fighting-osteoporosis-before-it-starts/

Gopnik, A., Meltzoff, A. N., & Kuhl, P. K. (2001). The scientist in the crib: What early learning tells us about the mind (1st perennial ed). Harper.

Gopnik, A. (2003). The theory theory as an alternative to the innateness hypothesis. In L. M. Antony & N. Hornstein (Eds.), Chomsky and his critics. Blackwell Pub.

Gopnik, A. (2009). The philosophical baby: What children's minds tell us about truth, love, and the meaning of life. Picador - Farrar, Straus and Giroux.

Gopnik, A. (2023a, May 13). A Child's View of Intelligent Machines. Wall Street Journal. https://www.wsj.com/articles/a-childs-view-of-intelligent-machines-65838dae

Gopnik, A. (2023b, October 5). How the Best AI Imitates Children. Wall Street Journal. https://www.wsj.com/tech/ai/how-the-best-ai-imitates-children-fea9c53a

Gopnik, A. (2023c, July 20). The New Promise of Psychedelics. Wall Street Journal. https://www.wsj.com/articles/the-new-promise-of-psychedelics-2280c3b

Gorman, J. (2014, November 11). Learning How Little We Know About the Brain. The New York Times. https://www.nytimes.com/2014/11/11/science/learning-how-little-we-know-about-the-brain.html

Gottlieb, A. (2012, September 17). It ain't necessarily so. The New Yorker. https://www.newyorker.com/magazine/2012/09/17/it-aint-necessarily-so

Graeber, D., & Wengrow, D. (2021). The dawn of everything: A new history of humanity (First American edition). Farrar, Straus and Giroux.

Greenberg, J. R., & Mitchell, S. A. (1983). Object relations in psychoanalytic theory. Harvard university press.

Greene, B., LeCun, Y., Bubeck, S., Harris, T. (2023). World Science Festival. (2023, November 24). AI: Grappling with a New Kind of Intelligence. https://youtu.be/EGDG3hgPNp8?si=-L9dkSshL02j_nSx or https://www.worldsciencefestival.com/programs/ai-grappling-with-a-new-kind-of-intelligence/

Griffith, E. (2023, May 3). My Weekend With an Emotional Support A.I. Companion. The New York Times. https://www.nytimes.com/2023/05/03/technology/personaltech/ai-chatbot-pi-emotional-support.html

Grimm, J., & Grimm, W. (2005 [orig. 1812]). The complete Grimm's fairy tales. Pantheon Books.

Grotstein, J. A. (1999). Projective identification reassessed commentary on papers by Stephen Seligman and by Robin C. Silverman and Alicia F. Lieberman. Psychoanalytic Dialogues, 9(2), 187–203. https://doi.org/10.1080/10481889909539313

Hadot, P., Chase, M., Davidson, A. I., & Hadot, P. (1993). Plotinus or the simplicity of vision. University of Chicago Press.

Hadot, P., & Davidson, A. I. (1995). Philosophy as a way of life: Spiritual exercises from Socrates to Foucault. Blackwell.

Hadot, P. (2004). What is ancient philosophy? (M. Chase, Trans.; 1. Harvard Univ. Press pbk ed). Belknap Press of Harvard Univ. Press.

Hale, K. (2021). A.I. Bias Caused 80% Of Black Mortgage Applicants To Be Denied. Forbes. https://www.forbes.com/sites/korihale/2021/09/02/ai-bias-caused-80-of-black-mortgage-applicants-to-be-denied/

Hanauer, N. & Rolf, D. (2020, September 14). The Top 1% of Americans Have Taken $50 Trillion From the Bottom 90%—And That's Made the U.S. Less Secure. Time. https://time.com/5888024/50-trillion-income-inequality-america/

Hansen, J. E., Sato, M., Simons, L., Nazarenko, L. S., Sangha, I., Kharecha, P., Zachos, J. C., Von Schuckmann, K., Loeb, N. G., Osman, M. B., Jin, Q., Tselioudis, G., Jeong, E., Lacis, A., Ruedy, R., Russell, G., Cao, J., & Li, J. (2023). Global warming in the pipeline. Oxford Open Climate Change, 3(1), kgad008. https://doi.org/10.1093/oxfclm/kgad008

Haque, A.K., Islam, A.N., & Mikalef, P. (2023). Notion of Explainable Artificial Intelligence - an Empirical Investigation from a User's Perspective. ArXiv, abs/2311.02102.

Harari, Y. N. (2018). 21 lessons for the 21st century (First edition). Spiegel & Grau.

Harari, Y., Harris, T., & Raskin, A. (2023, March 24). Opinion | You can have the blue pill or the red pill, and we're out of blue pills. The New York Times. https://www.nytimes.com/2023/03/24/opinion/yuval-harari-ai-chatgpt.html

Harper, T. A. (2023, December 19). The Humanities Have Sown the Seeds of Their Own Destruction. The Atlantic. https://www.theatlantic.com/ideas/archive/2023/12/humanities-university-conservative-critics/676890/

Harris, S. (2014). Waking up: A guide to spirituality without religion. Simon & Schuster.

Harris, T. & Raskin, A. (2023). Center for Humane Technology (Director). The A.I. Dilemma—March 9, 2023. https://youtu.be/xoVJKj8lcNQ?si=LbDH_8R_eK-RvAnC

Harvey, P. (2013). An introduction to Buddhism: Teachings, history and practices (Second Edition). Cambridge University Press.

Hassabis, D. & Fridman, L. (2022, July 1). Demis Hassabis: DeepMind - AI, Superintelligence & the Future of Humanity | Lex Fridman Podcast #299. https://youtu.be/Gfr50f6ZBvo?si=b4-SSocp-9rkchrx

Havlík, M., Hlinka, J., Klírová, M., Adámek, P., & Horáček, J. (2023). Towards causal mechanisms of consciousness through focused transcranial brain stimulation. Neuroscience of Consciousness, 2023(1), niad008. https://doi.org/10.1093/nc/niad008

Hájek, A. (2019). Interpretations of probability. In E. N. Zalta (Ed.), The Stanford Encyclopedia of Philosophy. Metaphysics Research Lab, Stanford University. https://plato.stanford.edu/entries/probability-interpret/

Hancock, L. (2011). Why Are Finland's Schools Successful? Smithsonian Magazine. https://www.smithsonianmag.com/innovation/why-are-finlands-schools-successful-49859555/

Hansson, S. O. (2021). Science and Pseudo-Science. In E. N. Zalta (Ed.), The Stanford Encyclopedia of Philosophy. Metaphysics Research Lab, Stanford University. https://plato.stanford.edu/entries/pseudo-science/

Hayek, F. A. (2009 [orig. 1944]). The Road to Serfdom: Text and Documents-- The Definitive Edition (B. Caldwell, Ed.; 1st edition). University of Chicago Press.

Hedges, C. (2018). America: the farewell tour (First Edition). Simon & Schuster.

Heller, N. (2023, February 27). The End of the English Major. The New Yorker. https://www.newyorker.com/magazine/2023/03/06/the-end-of-the-english-major

Heminway, J., Sapolsky, R., Shively, C., Marmot, M., Roseboom, T., Blackburn, E., Epel, E. (2011). Stress, Portrait of a Killer—Full Documentary (2008). A co-production of National Geographic and Stanford University. https://youtu.be/eYG0ZuTv5rs?si=jQiwsLlg-4Trme2-

Hepburn, B. & Andersen, H. (2021). Scientific Method. In E. N. Zalta (Ed.), The Stanford Encyclopedia of Philosophy. Metaphysics Research Lab, Stanford University. https://plato.stanford.edu/entries/scientific-method/

Hepburn, R. W. (1966). Questions about the Meaning of Life. Religious Studies, 1(2), 125–140. http://www.jstor.org/stable/20004617

Hern, A. (2016, March 15). AlphaGo: Its creator on the computer that learns by thinking. The Guardian. https://www.theguardian.com/technology/2016/mar/15/alphago-what-does-google-advanced-software-go-next

Hern, A., & editor, A. H. U. technology. (2023, March 29). Elon Musk joins call for pause in creation of giant AI 'digital minds.' The Guardian. https://www.theguardian.com/technology/2023/mar/29/elon-musk-joins-call-for-pause-in-creation-of-giant-ai-digital-minds

Hesse, E. (1999). The adult attachment interview: Historical and current perspectives. In J. Cassidy & P. R. Shaver (Eds.), Handbook of attachment: Theory, research, and clinical applications (pp. 395–433). The Guilford Press.

Hilly, L. & Allmann, K. (2015, June 22). Revenge porn does not only try to shame women – it tries to silence them too. The Guardian. https://www.theguardian.com/technology/2015/jun/22/revenge-porn-women-free-speech-abuse

Hinton, G. & Silva-Braga, B. (2023). CBS Mornings (Director). (2023, March 25). Full interview: "Godfather of artificial intelligence" talks impact and potential of AI. https://youtu.be/qpoRO378qRY?si=s4bh5rwSRcIhVqCV

Hobbes, T. (2017 [orig. 1651]). Leviathan (C. Brooke, Ed.; First Edition). Penguin Classics.

Hoel, E. (2023). No current theory of consciousness is scientific (2023, September 25). IAI TV. https://iai.tv/articles/no-theory-of-consciousness-is-scientific-auid-2610

Hoffman, D. (2019). The Case Against Reality: Why Evolution Hid the Truth from Our Eyes. W. W. Norton & Company.

Hoffman, R. (2023a, January 28). Technology Makes Us More Human. The Atlantic. https://www.theatlantic.com/ideas/archive/2023/01/chatgpt-ai-technology-techo-humanism-reid-hoffman/672872/

Hoffman, R. (2023b, September 8). We must shape the AI tools that will in turn shape us. Financial Times. https://www.ft.com/content/02302d04-846e-4d8a-a868-de895dde5a01

Hoffman, R & Tippett, K. (2023, October 5). Reid Hoffman—AI, and What It Means to Be (More) Human. The On Being Project. from https://onbeing.org/programs/reid-hoffman-ai-and-what-it-means-to-be-more-human/

Holt, D. (2023, August 15). Friston's AI Law is Proven: FEP Explains How Neurons Learn. Medium. https://medium.com/@deniseholt1/fristons-ai-law-is-proven-fep-explains-how-neurons-learn-3718d3be69ac

Horgan, J. (2000). The undiscovered mind: How the human brain defies replication, medication, and explanation. Touchstone.

Horgan, J. (2020, January 1). My Go-To Arguments for Free Will. Scientific American Blog Network. https://blogs.scientificamerican.com/cross-check/my-go-to-arguments-for-free-will/

Horgan, J. (2022, June 1). Does Quantum Mechanics Rule Out Free Will? Scientific American. https://www.scientificamerican.com/article/does-quantum-mechanics-rule-out-free-will/

Hsu, T. (2023, January 22). As Deepfakes Flourish, Countries Struggle With Response. The New York Times. https://www.nytimes.com/2023/01/22/business/media/deepfake-regulation-difficulty.html

Hugo, V. (2016 [orig. 1877]). The history of a crime: The testimony of an eye-witness. CreateSpace Independent Publishing Platform.

Hume, D. (2016 [orig. 1739]). A treatise of human nature. In Delphi Complete Works of David Hume. Delphi Classics.

Hume, D. (1983, [orig. 1751]). An enquiry concerning the principles of morals. Hackett Pub. Co.

Hurst, L. (2023). How AI is driving an explosive rise in deepfake pornography. (2023, October 20). Euronews. https://www.euronews.com/next/2023/10/20/generative-ai-fueling-spread-of-deepfake-pornography-across-the-internet

Hutson, M. (2023, May 16). Can We Stop Runaway A.I.? The New Yorker. https://www.newyorker.com/science/annals-of-artificial-intelligence/can-we-stop-the-singularity

Huxley, A. (1969 [orig. 1945]). The perennial philosophy. Chatto & Windus.

Huxley, A. (2009 [orig. 1954, 1956]). The doors of perception and heaven and hell. Harper Perennial.

Huxley, T. (1866). Lessons on elementary physiology 8. London: Macmillan and Co.

IAEA, (2022). What is AI for Fusion? Coordinated Research Projects: CRP F13022 – AI for Accelerating Fusion R&D https://nucleus.iaea.org/sites/ai4atoms/ai4fusion/SitePages/What-is-AI-for-Fusion-.aspx?web=1

IBM, (2023). IBM. AI Essentials. https://www.youtube.com/playlist?list=PLOspHqNVtKADfxkuDuHduUkDExBpEt3DF

IPCC, 2022: Climate Change 2022: Mitigation of Climate Change. Contribution of Working Group III to the Sixth Assessment Report of the Intergovernmental Panel on Climate Change [P.R. Shukla, J. Skea, R. Slade, A. Al Khourdajie, R.

van Diemen, D. McCollum, M. Pathak, S. Some, P. Vyas, R. Fradera, M. Belkacemi, A. Hasija, G. Lisboa, S. Luz, J. Malley, (eds.)]. Cambridge University Press, Cambridge, UK and New York, NY, USA. doi: 10.1017/9781009157926, https://www.ipcc.ch/report/ar6/wg3/

Jablonka, E., & Lamb, M. J. (1999). Epigenetic inheritance and evolution: The Lamarckian dimension. Oxford University Press.

Jablonka, E., Lamb, M. J., & Zeligowski, A. (2014). Evolution in four dimensions: Genetic, epigenetic, behavioral, and symbolic variation in the history of life (Revised edition). A Bradford Book, The MIT Press.

Jablonka, E. (2017). The evolutionary implications of epigenetic inheritance. Interface Focus 7: 20160135. http://dx.doi.org/10.1098/rsfs.2016.0135

James, W. (2018 [orig. 1890]). Principles of psychology. Volumes I and II. Published by Pantianos Classics.

James, W., Burkhardt, F., Bowers, F., & Skrupskelis, I. K. (1979 [orig. 1911]). Some problems of philosophy. Harvard University Press.

Jayshi, D. (2023, April 13). Do 728 Billionaires Hold More Wealth Than Half of American Households? Snopes. https://www.snopes.com/news/2023/04/13/728-billionaires-hold-more-wealth/

Jennings, C. (2016). Paradise now: The story of American utopianism. Random House.

Johnson, A., & Gomez, C. (2023). Stress is weathering our bodies from the inside out. Washington Post. https://www.washingtonpost.com/health/interactive/2023/stress-chronic-illness-aging/

Johnson, S., & Kwak, J. (2010). 13 Bankers: The Wall Street Takeover and the Next Financial Meltdown. Pantheon.

Journeyman Pictures. (2016, September 2). Big Pharma Companies Are Exploiting The World's Poor. https://youtu.be/f9i58nLKu-Y?si=Sq1FhsMKlakBWNgG

Jumper, J., Evans, R., Pritzel, A., Green, T., Figurnov, M., Ronneberger, O., Tunyasuvunakool, K., Bates, R., Žídek, A., Potapenko, A., Bridgland, A., Meyer, C., Kohl, S. A. A., Ballard, A. J., Cowie, A., Romera-Paredes, B., Nikolov, S., Jain, R., Adler, J., … Hassabis, D. (2021). Highly accurate protein structure prediction with AlphaFold. Nature, 596(7873), 583–589. https://doi.org/10.1038/s41586-021-03819-2

Jureidini, J. & McHenry, B. L. (2020). The Illusion of Evidence-Based Medicine: Exposing the crisis of credibility in clinical research. Wakefield Press.

Kahneman, D. (2011). Thinking, fast and slow. Farrar, Straus and Giroux.

Kant, I. (2007 [orig. 1787]). Critique of pure reason (M. Weigelt, Ed.; F. M. Müller, Trans.). Penguin Books.

Kant, I. (1748). Kant: Idea for a Universal History from a Cosmopolitan Point of View. https://www.marxists.org/reference/subject/ethics/kant/universal-history.htm#n2

Kantor, J., Sundaram, A., Aufrichtig, A., & Taylor, R. (2022, August 15). The Rise of the Worker Productivity Score. The New York Times.

https://www.nytimes.com/interactive/2022/08/14/business/worker-productivity-tracking.html

Karp, A. C. (2023, July 25). Opinion | Our Oppenheimer Moment: The Creation of A.I. Weapons. The New York Times. https://www.nytimes.com/2023/07/25/opinion/karp-palantir-artificial-intelligence.html

Kastrup, B. (2016). What Neuroimaging of the Psychedelic State Tells Us about the Mind-Body Problem." Journal of Cognition and Neuroethics. 4 (2): 1–9.

Kastrup, B. (2019). The idea of the world: A multi-disciplinary argument for the mental nature of reality. Iff Books.

Kastrup, B. (2020, February 5) Yes, Free Will Exists, Just ask Schopenhauer. Scientific American Blog Network. https://blogs.scientificamerican.com/observations/yes-free-will-exists/

Kastrup, B. (2023, June 21). Brain scans tell us nothing about consciousness. IAI TV - Changing How the World Thinks. https://iai.tv/articles/brain-scans-tell-us-nothing-about-conciousness-auid-2514

Kaveladze, B., & Schueller, S. M. (2023). A digital therapeutic alliance in digital mental health. In Digital Therapeutics for Mental Health and Addiction (pp. 87–98). Elsevier. https://doi.org/10.1016/B978-0-323-90045-4.00009-5

Kelleher, K. (2023). Revenge Porn, deep fakes, AI, Boston University, Boston University Law School, Rebecca A. Delfino, artificial intelligence » Dome | Blog Archive | Boston University. (2023, August 10). https://sites.bu.edu/dome/2023/08/10/revenge-porn-and-deep-fake-technology-the-latest-iteration-of-online-abuse/

Keynes, J. M. (2015 [orig. 1904-1946]). The essential Keynes. Penguin Books.

Khullar, D. (2023, February 27). Can A.I. Treat Mental Illness? The New Yorker. https://www.newyorker.com/magazine/2023/03/06/can-ai-treat-mental-illness

Kierkegaard, S. (1985 [orig. 1843]). Fear and trembling. Penguin Books ; Viking Penguin.

Killion, V. (2022). Federal Civil Action for Disclosure of Intimate Images: Free Speech Considerations (LSB10723). Congressional Research Service Legal Sidebar.

Klein, E. (2020). Why we're polarized (Illustrated edition). Avid Reader Press / Simon & Schuster.

Klein, E. (2023a, March 12). Opinion | This Changes Everything. The New York Times. https://www.nytimes.com/2023/03/12/opinion/chatbots-artificial-intelligence-future-weirdness.html

Klein, E. (2023b, July 11). Opinion | A.I. Could Solve Some of Humanity's Hardest Problems. It Already Has. The New York Times. https://www.nytimes.com/2023/07/11/opinion/ezra-klein-podcast-demis-hassabis.html

Kleingeld, P., & Brown, E. (2019). Cosmopolitanism. In E. N. Zalta (Ed.), The Stanford Encyclopedia of Philosophy. Metaphysics Research Lab, Stanford University. https://plato.stanford.edu/entries/cosmopolitanism/

Klosowski, T. (2021, February 10). How Your Boss Can Use Your Remote-Work Tools to Spy on You. Wirecutter: Reviews for the Real World. https://www.nytimes.com/wirecutter/blog/how-your-boss-can-spy-on-you/

Klosowski, T. (2022, June 6). There's (Probably) Nothing You Can Do About the New Bossware That's Spying on You. Wirecutter: Reviews for the Real World. https://www.nytimes.com/wirecutter/blog/what-to-do-about-bossware-employee-monitoring/

Knight, W. (2017, October 18). Andrew Ng Has a Chatbot That Can Help with Depression. MIT Technology Review. https://www.technologyreview.com/2017/10/18/148521/andrew-ng-has-a-chatbot-that-can-help-with-depression/

Knox, J. (2011). Self-agency in psychotherapy: Attachment, autonomy, and intimacy (1st ed). W.W. Norton & Co.

Koch, C. (2004). The quest for consciousness: A Neurobiological Approach. Roberts & Co.

Koch, C. (2012a). Consciousness: Confessions of a romantic reductionist (MIT Press). The MIT Press.

Koch, C. (2012b, May 1). This Is Your Brain on Drugs. Scientific American. https://www.scientificamerican.com/article/this-is-your-brain-on-drugs/

Koch, C. (2015). The biology of consciousness - World Science U. World Science U. https://worldscienceu.com/courses/the-biology-of-consciousness-chistof-koch/

Koch, C., Massimini, M., Boly, M., & Tononi, G. (2016). Neural correlates of consciousness: Progress and problems. Nature Reviews Neuroscience, 17(5), Article 5. https://doi.org/10.1038/nrn.2016.22

Koch, C. (2019). The feeling of life itself: Why consciousness is widespread but can't be computed (The MIT Press). The MIT Press.

Kohs, G. (2016). AlphaGo Movie. https://www.alphagomovie.com/

Kohut, H., (1971.) The analysis of the self. International Universities Press.

Kohut, H., (1977.) The restoration of the self. International Universities Press.

Kohut, H., Goldberg, A. & Stepansky, P. (1984). How Does Analysis Cure? University of Chicago Press. https://doi.org/10.7208/chicago/9780226006147.001.0001

Koubeissi, M. Z., Bartolomei, F., Beltagy, A., & Picard, F. (2014). Electrical stimulation of a small brain area reversibly disrupts consciousness. Epilepsy & Behavior: E&B, 37, 32–35. https://doi.org/10.1016/j.yebeh.2014.05.027

Krueger, A. (2017, October 28). Virtual Reality Gets Naughty. The New York Times. https://www.nytimes.com/2017/10/28/style/virtual-reality-porn.html

Krugman, P. (2015, November 9). Opinion | Despair, American Style. The New York Times. https://www.nytimes.com/2015/11/09/opinion/despair-american-style.html

Krugman, P. (2022). Learn Economist Paul Krugman's Perspective on Inequality—2023. MasterClass, https://www.masterclass.com/articles/learn-economist-paul-krugmans-perspective-on-inequality

Kuhlmeier, F. O., Gnewuch, U., Lüttke, S., Brakemeier, E.-L., & Mädche, A. (2022). A Personalized Conversational Agent to Treat Depression in Youth and Young Adults – A Transdisciplinary Design Science Research Project. In A. Drechsler, A. Gerber, & A. Hevner (Eds.), The Transdisciplinary Reach of Design Science Research (Vol. 13229, pp. 30–41). Springer International Publishing. https://doi.org/10.1007/978-3-031-06516-3_3

Kuhn, T. S., & Hacking, I. (2012 [orig. 1962]). The structure of scientific revolutions (Fourth edition). The University of Chicago Press.

Kuyda, E. & Fridman, L. (2020, September 5). Eugenia Kuyda: Friendship with an AI Companion | Lex Fridman Podcast #121. https://youtu.be/_AGPbvCDBCk?si=qBEEH93foB7m1s_N

LaFrance, A. (2020a, May 14). The Prophecies of Q. The Atlantic. https://www.theatlantic.com/magazine/archive/2020/06/qanon-nothing-can-stop-what-is-coming/610567/

LaFrance, A. (2020b, December 15). Facebook Is a Doomsday Machine. The Atlantic. https://www.theatlantic.com/technology/archive/2020/12/facebook-doomsday-machine/617384/

LaFrance, A. (2021, September 27). The Largest Autocracy on Earth. The Atlantic. https://www.theatlantic.com/magazine/archive/2021/11/facebook-authoritarian-hostile-foreign-power/620168/

LaFrance, A. (2022, January 6). America Is Running Out of Time. The Atlantic. https://www.theatlantic.com/politics/archive/2022/01/january-6-reading-guide/621175/

LaFrance, A. (2023a, March 6). The New Anarchy. The Atlantic. https://www.theatlantic.com/magazine/archive/2023/04/us-extremism-portland-george-floyd-protests-january-6/673088/

LaFrance, A. (2023b, June 5). The Coming Humanist Renaissance. The Atlantic. https://www.theatlantic.com/magazine/archive/2023/07/generative-ai-human-culture-philosophy/674165/

Lakey, G. (2016). Viking economics: How the Scandinavians got it right - and how we can, too (1st Edition). Melville House.

Laland, K. N. (2017). Darwin's unfinished symphony: How culture made the human mind. Princeton university press.

Laland, K., Uller, T., Feldman, M. et al. (2014). Does evolutionary theory need a rethink?. Nature 514, 161–164. https://doi.org/10.1038/514161a

Lam, R., Sanchez-Gonzalez, A., Willson, M., Wirnsberger, P., Fortunato, M., Alet, F., Ravuri, S., Ewalds, T., Eaton-Rosen, Z., Hu, W., Merose, A., Hoyer, S., Holland, G., Vinyals, O., Stott, J., Pritzel, A., Mohamed, S., & Battaglia, P. (2023). Learning skillful medium-range global weather forecasting. Science. https://doi.org/10.1126/science.adi2336

Lang, D. & Wikimedia ontributors (2020). 1940s: Spitz. | Wikimedia contributors | Iowa State University Digital Press. https://iastate.pressbooks.pub/parentingfamilydiversity/chapter/spitz/

Lanier, J. (2023, April 20). There Is No A.I. The New Yorker. https://www.newyorker.com/science/annals-of-artificial-intelligence/there-is-no-ai

Lapowsky, I. (2023, June 24). The Race to Prevent 'the Worst Case Scenario for Machine Learning.' The New York Times. https://www.nytimes.com/2023/06/24/business/ai-generated-explicit-images.html

LeCun, Y., Bengio, Y., & Hinton, G. (2015). Deep learning. Nature, 521(7553), 436–444. https://doi.org/10.1038/nature14539

Lee, N. T., Resnick, P., & Barton, G. (2019). Algorithmic bias detection and mitigation: Best practices and policies to reduce consumer harms. (2019, May 22). Brookings. https://www.brookings.edu/articles/algorithmic-bias-detection-and-mitigation-best-practices-and-policies-to-reduce-consumer-harms/

Lee, N. T., Chin-Rothmann, C. (2023). Police surveillance and facial recognition: Why data privacy is imperative for communities of color. (2022, April 8). Brookings. https://www.brookings.edu/articles/police-surveillance-and-facial-recognition-why-data-privacy-is-an-imperative-for-communities-of-color/

Lemoine, B. (2023). I worked on Google's AI. My fears are coming true. (2023, February 27). Newsweek. https://www.newsweek.com/google-ai-blake-lemoine-bing-chatbot-sentient-1783340

Levendosky, A. A., Turchan, J. E., Luo, X., & Good, E. (2023). A re-introduction of the psychodynamic approach to the standard clinical psychology curriculum. Journal of Clinical Psychology, 79(10), 2439–2451. https://doi.org/10.1002/jclp.23551

Levin, M. (2014). Endogenous bioelectrical networks store non-genetic patterning information during development and regeneration. The Journal of Physiology, 592(11), 2295–2305. https://doi.org/10.1113/jphysiol.2014.271940

Levin, M. (2020, May). Michael Levin: The electrical blueprints that orchestrate life | TED Talk. https://www.ted.com/talks/michael_levin_the_electrical_blueprints_that_orchestrate_life or https://youtu.be/XheAMrS8Q1c?si=FhX_O_vAYBC4him2

Levin, M. (2023a). Bioelectric networks: The cognitive glue enabling evolutionary scaling from physiology to mind. Animal Cognition. https://doi.org/10.1007/s10071-023-01780-3

Levin, M. (2023b). Darwin's agential materials: Evolutionary implications of multiscale competency in developmental biology. Cellular and Molecular Life Sciences, 80(6), 142. https://doi.org/10.1007/s00018-023-04790-z

Levin, M. (2023c). DEPT LSC Web (Director). (2023, October 9). 27 Michael Levin—Memory and intelligent problem-solving by unconventional collective intelligences. https://youtu.be/r4N2FEx3cwQ?si=85GoBhvj9VtKWAMk

Levin, M. (2023d). Bioelectricity as Cognitive Glue: From Diverse Intelligence to Regenerative Medicine. https://youtu.be/7UqncReYvso?si=5-bKmYbQst_7ewCW

Levitas, R. (1990). The concept of utopia (1st ed). Syracuse University Press.

Levy, S. (2023a, June 17). Blake Lemoine Says Google's LaMDA AI Faces "Bigotry." Wired. https://www.wired.com/story/blake-lemoine-google-lamda-ai-bigotry/

Levy, S. (2023b, November 10). Fei-Fei Li Started an AI Revolution by Seeing Like an Algorithm. Wired. https://www.wired.com/story/plaintext-fei-fei-li-ai-revolution-seeing-imagenet-algorithm/

Liang, C. (2023, May 23). Opinion | My A.I. Lover. The New York Times. https://www.nytimes.com/2023/05/23/opinion/ai-chatbot-relationships.html

Libet, B., Gleason, C. A., Wright, E. W., & Pearl, D. K. (1983). Time of conscious intention to act in relation to onset of cerebral activity (readiness-potential): the unconscious initiation of a freely voluntary act. Brain, 106(3), 623–642. https://doi.org/10.1093/brain/106.3.623

Lieberman, A. F. (2018). The emotional life of the toddler (Second edition). Simon & Schuster.

Lieberman, A. F., & Van Horn, P. (2008). Psychotherapy with infants and young children: Repairing the effects of stress and trauma on early attachment. Guilford Press.

Lieberman, A. F., & Zeanah, C. H. (1999). Contributions of attachment theory to infant–parent psychotherapy and other interventions with infants and young children. In J. Cassidy & P. R. Shaver (Eds.), Handbook of attachment: Theory, research, and clinical applications (pp. 555–574). The Guilford Press.

Lilliengren, P. (2017). Comprehensive compilation of randomized controlled trials (RCTs) involving psychodynamic treatments and interventions. https://www.researchgate.net/publication/317335876_Comprehensive_com pilation_of_randomized_controlled_trials_RCTs_involving_psychodynamic_t reatments_and_interventions

Lilliengren, P. (2023). A comprehensive overview of randomized controlled trials of psychodynamic psychotherapies. Psychoanalytic Psychotherapy, 37(2), 117–140. https://doi.org/10.1080/02668734.2023.2197617

Linardatos, P., Papastefanopoulos, V., & Kotsiantis, S. (2020). Explainable AI: A Review of Machine Learning Interpretability Methods. Entropy (Basel, Switzerland), 23(1), 18. https://doi.org/10.3390/e23010018

Lipton, Z. C. (2018). The Mythos of Model Interpretability: In machine learning, the concept of interpretability is both important and slippery. Queue, 16(3), 31–57. https://doi.org/10.1145/3236386.3241340

Lowrey, A. (2023, May 17). Before AI Takes Over, Make Plans to Give Everyone Money. The Atlantic. https://www.theatlantic.com/ideas/archive/2023/05/ai-job-losses-policy-support-universal-basic-income/674071/

Luscombe, B. (2023, September 12). What's Behind the Spike in Child Poverty in the U.S. TIME. https://time.com/6313242/child-poverty-rate-2022-census/

Luyten, P., Mayes, L. C., Fonagy, P., Target, M., & Blatt, S. J. (Eds.). (2017). Handbook of psychodynamic approaches to psychopathology (Paperback edition). Guilford Press.

Lyu, D., Stieger, J. R., Xin, C., Ma, E., Lusk, Z., Aparicio, M. K., Werbaneth, K., Perry, C. M., Deisseroth, K., Buch, V., & Parvizi, J. (2023). Causal evidence for the processing of bodily self in the anterior precuneus. Neuron. https://doi.org/10.1016/j.neuron.2023.05.013

Machiavelli, N. (2021 [orig. 1532]). The Prince. Reader's Library Classics.

Maddocks, S. (2023, March 15) Image-Based Abuse: A Threat to Privacy, Safety, and Speech – MediaWell. https://mediawell.ssrc.org/?post_type=ramp_review&p=77411

Mahmood, S. H. (2022, July 16). 10 Virtual AI Companions to Chat and Have Fun With. MUO. https://www.makeuseof.com/online-ai-chat-companions/

Malda-Castillo, J., Browne, C., & Perez-Algorta, G. (2019). Mentalization-based treatment and its evidence-base status: A systematic literature review. Psychology and Psychotherapy: Theory, Research and Practice, 92(4), 465–498. https://doi.org/10.1111/papt.12195

Malhotra, A. (2022, August 20). Dr. Aseem Malhotra—'Evidence Based Medicine Has Been Hijacked'. https://youtu.be/qwovXFzUvfg?si=Ls4q2JGhG9PQvmGf

Maoz, U., & Sinnott-Armstrong, W. (Eds.). (2022). Free will: Philosophers and neuroscientists in conversation. Oxford University Press.

Marcus, G., & Davis, E. (2019). Rebooting AI: Building artificial intelligence we can trust (First edition). Pantheon Books.

Marx, K. (2010 [orig. 1844, 1847, 1848, 1875]). Essential writings of Karl Marx: Economic and philosophic manuscripts, Communist manifesto, Wage labor and capital, Critique of the Gotha Program. Red and Black Publ.

Maslow, A. H. (1966). The Psychology of Science: A Reconnaissance. United Kingdom: Harper & Row.

Maslow, A. H. (1987). Motivation and personality (3rd ed). Harper Collins.

Mazur, A. J., Burns, D. M., Corrigan, K., Miroshnikov, I., Rasimus, T., & Turner, J. D. (2021). The Platonizing Sethian background of Plotinus's mysticism (Rev. ed). Brill.

McGilchrist, I. (2019). The master and his emissary: The divided brain and the making of the Western world (New expanded edition). Yale University Press.

McGilchrist, I. (2021). The Matter With Things: Our Brains, Our Delusions, and the Unmaking of the World. Perspectiva.

McGilchrist, N. (2022). When the dog speaks, the philosopher listens: A guide to the greatness of Pythagoras & his curious age. Genius Loci Publications.

McHenry, B. L. & Brier, A. (2021, May 10). The Illusion of Evidence Based Medicine: Distorted Science in the Age of Big Pharma | The Commonwealth Club of California. https://youtu.be/6A_jzdCDSZk?si=lMnCQjHF9ZbFFZM6

Metz, C. (2016, March 16). In Two Moves, AlphaGo and Lee Sedol Redefined the Future. Wired. https://www.wired.com/2016/03/two-moves-alphago-lee-sedol-redefined-future/

Metz, C. (2019, July 13). Facial Recognition Tech Is Growing Stronger, Thanks to Your Face. The New York Times. https://www.nytimes.com/2019/07/13/technology/databases-faces-facial-recognition-technology.html

Metz, C. (2020, June 16). Riding Out Quarantine With a Chatbot Friend: 'I Feel Very Connected.' The New York Times. https://www.nytimes.com/2020/06/16/technology/chatbots-quarantine-coronavirus.html

Metz, C. (2022, August 5). A.I. Is Not Sentient. Why Do People Say It Is? The New York Times. https://www.nytimes.com/2022/08/05/technology/ai-sentient-google.html

Metz, C. (2023a, March 31). What's the Future for A.I.? The New York Times. https://www.nytimes.com/2023/03/31/technology/ai-chatbots-benefits-dangers.html

Metz, C. (2023b, May 1). 'The Godfather of A.I.' Leaves Google and Warns of Danger Ahead. The New York Times. https://www.nytimes.com/2023/05/01/technology/ai-google-chatbot-engineer-quits-hinton.html

Metz, C. (2023c, May 1). What Exactly Are the Dangers Posed by A.I.? The New York Times. https://www.nytimes.com/2023/05/01/technology/ai-problems-danger-chatgpt.html

Metz, C. (2023d, May 16). Microsoft Says New A.I. Shows Signs of Human Reasoning. The New York Times. https://www.nytimes.com/2023/05/16/technology/microsoft-ai-human-reasoning.html

Metz, C. (2023e, June 10). How Could A.I. Destroy Humanity? The New York Times. https://www.nytimes.com/2023/06/10/technology/ai-humanity.html

Metz, C. (2023f, September 25). The Secret Ingredient of ChatGPT Is Human Advice. The New York Times. https://www.nytimes.com/2023/09/25/technology/chatgpt-rlhf-human-tutors.html

Metz, C. (2023g, November 6). Chatbots May 'Hallucinate' More Often Than Many Realize. The New York Times. https://www.nytimes.com/2023/11/06/technology/chatbots-hallucination-rates.html

Metz, C., & Schmidt, G. (2023, March 29). Elon Musk and Others Call for Pause on A.I., Citing 'Profound Risks to Society.' The New York Times. https://www.nytimes.com/2023/03/29/technology/ai-artificial-intelligence-musk-risks.html

Metz, C., & Wakabayashi, D. (2020, December 3). Google Researcher Says She Was Fired Over Paper Highlighting Bias in A.I. The New York Times. https://www.nytimes.com/2020/12/03/technology/google-researcher-timnit-gebru.html

Metz, C., Weise, K., Grant, N., & Isaac, M. (2023, December 3). Ego, Fear and Money: How the A.I. Fuse Was Lit. The New York Times. https://www.nytimes.com/2023/12/03/technology/ai-openai-musk-page-altman.html

Milanovic, B. (2016). Global Inequality: A New Approach for the Age of Globalization. Belknap Press: An Imprint of Harvard University Press.

Milanovic, B. (2023). Visions of Inequality: From the French Revolution to the End of the Cold War. Belknap Press: An Imprint of Harvard University Press.

Milmo, D. (2023, April 17). Google chief warns AI could be harmful if deployed wrongly. The Guardian. https://www.theguardian.com/technology/2023/apr/17/google-chief-ai-harmful-sundar-pichai

Minsky, M. (2006). The Emotion Machine: Commonsense Thinking, Artificial Intelligence, and the Future of the Human Mind. Simon & Schuster.

Mitchell, M. (2020). Artificial intelligence: A guide for thinking humans (First Picador paperback edition, 2020). Picador.

Mitchell, S. (Ed.). (2000). Bhagavad Gita: A new translation (1st ed). Harmony Books.

Mitchell, S. A. (1988). Relational concepts in psychoanalysis: An integration. Harvard university press.

Mitchell, S. A. (2000). Relationality: From attachment to intersubjectivity. Analytic Press.

Monge, J. C. (2022, September 25). This Website Can Generate NSFW Images With Stable Diffusion AI. MLearning.Ai. https://medium.com/mlearning-ai/this-website-can-generate-nsfw-images-with-stable-diffusion-ai-1ee2913de829

Monroe, J. G., Srikant, T., Carbonell-Bejerano, P., Becker, C., Lensink, M., Exposito-Alonso, M., Klein, M., Hildebrandt, J., Neumann, M., Kliebenstein, D., Weng, M.-L., Imbert, E., Ågren, J., Rutter, M. T., Fenster, C. B., & Weigel, D. (2022). Mutation bias reflects natural selection in Arabidopsis thaliana. Nature, 602(7895), 101–105. https://doi.org/10.1038/s41586-021-04269-6

Moor, M., Banerjee, O., Abad, Z. S. H., Krumholz, H. M., Leskovec, J., Topol, E. J., & Rajpurkar, P. (2023). Foundation models for generalist medical artificial intelligence. Nature, 616(7956), 259–265. https://doi.org/10.1038/s41586-023-05881-4

Morozov, E. (2023, June 30). Opinion | The True Threat of Artificial Intelligence. The New York Times. https://www.nytimes.com/2023/06/30/opinion/artificial-intelligence-danger.html

Mozur, P., & Satariano, A. (2023, March 30). A.I., Brain Scans and Cameras: The Spread of Police Surveillance Tech. The New York Times. https://www.nytimes.com/2023/03/30/technology/police-surveillance-tech-dubai.html

Mullen, J. (2023). Fast-tracking fusion energy's arrival with AI and accessibility. (2023, September 1). MIT News | Massachusetts Institute of Technology. https://news.mit.edu/2023/fast-tracking-fusion-energy-with-ai-and-accessibility-0901

Murdoch, I. (2006 [orig. 1970]). The sovereignty of good. Routledge.

Murray, C. (2013). Coming Apart: The State of White America, 1960-2010. Forum Books.

Myrvold, W. (2022). Philosophical Issues in Quantum Theory. In E. N. Zalta & U. Nodelman (Eds.), The Stanford Encyclopedia of Philosophy. Metaphysics Research Lab, Stanford University. https://plato.stanford.edu/entries/qt-issues/

Nadeau, R., & Kafatos, M. C. (2001). The non-local universe: The new physics and matters of the mind (1. issued as paperb). Oxford University Press.

Nadella, S. & Levy, S. (2023, Jun 13). Microsoft's Satya Nadella Is Betting Everything on AI. Wired. https://www.wired.com/story/microsofts-satya-nadella-is-betting-everything-on-ai/

Nadella, S., & Semuels, A. (2023, May 14). Microsoft's Satya Nadella Doesn't Think Now Is the Time to Stop on AI. Time. https://time.com/6279668/satya-nadella-microsoft-leadership-brief/

Nagel, T. (1974). What is it like to be a bat? Philosophical Review, 83(October), 435–450.

Nagel, T. (2012). Mind & Cosmos: Why the Materialist Neo-Darwinian Conception of Nature is Almost Certainly False. Oxford University Press.

Nardou, R., Sawyer, E., Song, Y. J., Wilkinson, M., Padovan-Hernandez, Y., De Deus, J. L., Wright, N., Lama, C., Faltin, S., Goff, L. A., Stein-O'Brien, G. L., & Dölen, G. (2023). Psychedelics reopen the social reward learning critical period. Nature, 618(7966), 790–798. https://doi.org/10.1038/s41586-023-06204-3

Narikiyo, K., Mizuguchi, R., Ajima, A., Shiozaki, M., Hamanaka, H., Johansen, J. P., Mori, K., & Yoshihara, Y. (2020). The claustrum coordinates cortical slow-wave activity. Nature Neuroscience, 23(6), Article 6. https://doi.org/10.1038/s41593-020-0625-7

National Domestic Violence Hotline. (n.d.). Revenge Porn. The Hotline. https://www.thehotline.org/resources/revenge-porn/

National Research Council (U.S.) & Institute of Medicine (Eds.) (2000). From neurons to neighborhoods: The science of early child development. National Academy Press.

Neuron special issue (2017, June 7). Special issue (vol. 94, pp. 933–1040). Provides a good overview of many different approaches to understanding the brain. https://www.sciencedirect.com/journal/neuron/vol/94/issue/5

Newton, R. P. (2008). The attachment connection: Parenting a secure & confident child using the science of attachment theory. New Harbinger Publications.

Nicholson, B., & Parker, L. A. (2013). Attached at the heart: Eight proven parenting principles for raising connected and compassionate children: (from preconception to age five) (Revised and updated). Health Communications, Inc.

Nietzsche, F. (2018 [orig. 1885]). Thus spake Zarathustra. CreateSpace Independent Publishing.

Nietzsche, F. (2016 [orig. 1889]). Götzen-Dämmerung: Oder wie man mit dem Hammer philosophiert. Hofenberg.

Noble, D. (2008). The music of life: Biology beyond genes. Oxford University Press.

Noble, R., & Noble, D. (2017). Was the Watchmaker Blind? Or Was She One-Eyed? Biology, 6(4), 47. https://doi.org/10.3390/biology6040047

Noble, D. (2022). Modern physiology vindicates Darwin's dream. Experimental Physiology, 107(9), 1015–1028. https://doi.org/10.1113/EP090133

Noble, D., & Noble, R. (2021). Origins and demise of selfish gene theory. Theoretical Biology Forum : 115, 1/2, 2022, 1/2. https://doi.org/10.19272/202211402003

Noble, R., & Noble, D. (2023). Understanding living systems. Cambridge University Press.

NPR. (2023, February 23). Know It All: AI And Police Surveillance. NPR. https://www.npr.org/2023/02/23/1159084476/know-it-all-ai-and-police-surveillance

Nurse, P. (2021). What Is Life?: Five Great Ideas in Biology. W. W. Norton & Company.

Nyrup, R. (2023). Opening the black box | Rune Nyrup. (2023, October 13). IAI TV - Changing How the World Thinks. https://iai.tv/articles/opening-the-black-box-auid-2630

Obama, B. (2006). Commencement Address at Northwestern University. Northwestern University News. https://www.northwestern.edu/newscenter/stories/2006/06/barack.html

Obama, B. (2023). The Verge (Director). (2023, November 7). Obama on AI, free speech, and the future of the internet. https://youtu.be/X15o2sG8HF4?si=6m-6aTu101NKACAm

Ogden, T. H. (1992). The primitive edge of experience. Jason Aronson, Inc.

Ogden, T. H. (1993). The matrix of the mind: Object relations and the psychoanalytic dialogue. J. Aronson.

Ogden, T. H. (1997). Reverie and interpretation: Sensing something human. J. Aronson.

Ogden, T. H. (2001). Conversations at the frontier of dreaming. J. Aronson.

Ogden, T. H. (2015). On potential space. In M. B. Spelman & F. Thomson-Salo (Eds.), The Winnicott tradition: Lines of development, evolution of theory and practice over the decades. Karnac.

O'Gieblyn, M. (2021). God, human, animal, machine: Technology, metaphor, and the search for meaning. Doubleday.

Olds, S. (1984). The dead and the living: Poems (Vol. 12). Knopf.

OpenAI Papers (2023, March 23). GPT-4 system card. OpenAI. https://cdn.openai.com/papers/gpt-4-system-card.pdf

Orwell, G. (2021 [orig. 1945]). Animal farm. Penguin Books.

Orwell, G. (2003 [orig. 1949]). Nineteen eighty-four. Penguin Books.

Paine, T. (1797). Thomas Paine - Agrarian Justice. Social Security History. (n.d.). https://www.ssa.gov/history/paine4.html. (also at: https://en.wikisource.org/wiki/Agrarian_Justice)

Parsons, W. B. (1999). The enigma of the oceanic feeling: Revisioning the psychoanalytic theory of mysticism. Oxford University Press.

Partanen, A. (2017). The Nordic theory of everything: In search of a better life. HarperCollins.

Parvizi, J., Jacques, C., Foster, B. L., Withoft, N., Rangarajan, V., Weiner, K. S., & Grill-Spector, K. (2012). Electrical Stimulation of Human Fusiform Face-Selective Regions Distorts Face Perception. Journal of Neuroscience, 32(43), 14915–14920. https://doi.org/10.1523/JNEUROSCI.2609-12.2012

Pequeño, A. (2023, May 16). OpenAI CEO Sam Altman Urges Greater AI Regulation—Including New Federal Agency—At Historic Congressional Hearing. Forbes; Forbes. https://www.forbes.com/sites/antoniopequenoiv/2023/05/16/openai-ceo-sam-altman-urges-greater-ai-regulation-including-new-federal-agency-at-historic-congressional-hearing/?sh=75f7f826f40a

Perrigo, B. (2022a). DeepMind AlphaFold: The 200 Best Inventions of 2022. (2022, November 10). Time. https://time.com/collection/best-inventions-2022/6229912/deepmind-alphafold/

Perrigo, B. (2022b). Google's AI Lab, DeepMind, Offers 'Gift to Humanity' With Protein Structure Solution. (2022, July 28). Time. https://time.com/6201423/deepmind-alphafold-proteins/

Perrigo, B. (2023, October 11). How the AI Landscape Has Shifted Over the Past Year—And Where Could Go Next. TIME. https://time.com/6322664/state-of-ai-2023/

Pezzulo, G., & Levin, M. (2016). Top-down models in biology: Explanation and control of complex living systems above the molecular level. Journal of The Royal Society Interface, 13(124), 20160555. https://doi.org/10.1098/rsif.2016.0555

Pichai, S., & Pelley, S. (2023, April 16). Google's AI experts on the future of artificial intelligence | 60 Minutes—CBS News. https://www.cbsnews.com/news/google-artificial-intelligence-future-60-minutes-transcript-2023-04-16/

Pichai, S., & Pelley, S. (2023, July 9). Google's AI experts on the future of artificial intelligence | 60 Minutes—CBS News. https://www.cbsnews.com/news/google-artificial-intelligence-future-60-minutes-transcript-2023-07-09/

Piketty, T. (2014). Capital in the Twenty First Century (A. Goldhammer, Trans.). Belknap Press: An Imprint of Harvard University Press.

Pinker, S. (2009). How the mind works (Norton pbk). Norton.

Pinker, S. (2011). The better angels of our nature: Why violence has declined. Viking.

Pinker, S. (2018). Enlightenment now: The case for reason, science, humanism, and progress. Viking, an imprint of Penguin Random House LLC.

Pizer, S. A. (1996). Negotiating potential space: Illusion, play, metaphor, and the subjunctive. Psychoanalytic Dialogues, 6(5), 689–712. https://doi.org/10.1080/10481889609539146

Plakun E. M. (2023, October 25). Responding to the Mental Health Crisis: Is There a Role for Psychodynamic Treatments? | Austen Riggs Center. https://www.austenriggs.org/news/responding-to-the-mental-health-crisis-role-for-psychodynamic-treatment

Planck, M. (1923). Kausalgesetz und Willensfreiheit. Springer Berlin Heidelberg. https://doi.org/10.1007/978-3-642-94475-8 (also at: https://archive.org/stream/MaxPlanckKausalgesetzUndWillensfreiheit/Max_Planck_Kausalgesetz_und_Willensfreiheit_djvu.txt)

Planck, M. (1968). Scientific Autobiography and Other Papers. Philosophical Library.

Plato. (1996 [orig. c. 390-350s BC]). The collected dialogues of Plato: Including the letters (E. Hamilton, Ed.; 16. print). Princeton University Press.

Plato. (1989 [orig. c. 380-350s BC]). Timaeus, Critias, Cleitophon, Menexenus, Epistles. LCL 234. Harvard University Press.

Plato. (2017 [orig. c. 380s BC]). Euthyphro, Apology, Crito, Phaedo. LCL 36. Harvard University Press.

Plato. (2022 [orig. c. 380-370s BC]). Lysis, Symposium, Phaedrus. LCL 166. Harvard University Press.

Plato. (2013a [orig. c. 370s BC]). Plato, Republic. Books 1-5. LCL 237. Harvard University Press.

Plato. (2013b [orig. c. 370s BC]). Plato, Republic. Books 6-10. LCL 276. Harvard University Press.

Plotinus, & Gerson, L. P. (2018 [orig. c. 253-270]). Plotinus: The Enneads. Cambridge University Press.

Pollan, M. (2018). How to change your mind: What the new science of psychedelics teaches us about consciousness, dying, addiction, depression, and transcendence. Penguin Press.

Poo, A. (2015). The age of dignity: Preparing for the elder boom in a changing America. The New Press.

Poo, A. & Klein, E. (2021, December 7). Opinion | Every 8 Seconds, an American Turns 65. How Do We Care for Everyone? | The Ezra Klein Show | The New York Times. https://www.nytimes.com/2021/12/07/opinion/ezra-klein-podcast-ai-jen-poo.html

Poole, D. L., & Mackworth, A. K. (2023). Artificial intelligence: Foundations of computational agents (Third edition). Cambridge University Press. https://doi.org/10.1017/9781009258227

Popper, K. R. (2011 [orig. 1945]). The open society and its enemies. Routledge.

Popper, K. R. (1959). The Logic of Scientific Discovery. London: Routledge, 2002

Porcedda, R. (2023). Interpretability is not Explainability: New Quantitative XAI Approach with a focus on Recommender Systems in Education. ArXiv, abs/2311.02078.

Price, C., & Edwards, K. (2020). Trends in Income From 1975 to 2018. RAND Corporation. https://doi.org/10.7249/WRA516-1

Putnam, R. D. (2020). Bowling Alone: Revised and Updated: The Collapse and Revival of American Community (Revised, Updated ed. edition). Simon & Schuster.

Radwell, S., & Israel, J. (2021). American Schism: How the Two Enlightenments Hold the Secret to Healing our Nation. Greenleaf Book Group Press.

Rand, A., & Branden, N. (1964). The Virtue of Selfishness: Fiftieth Anniversary Edition. Signet.

Raschka, S., Liu, Y., Mirjalili, V., & Dzhulgakov, D. (2022). Machine learning with PyTorch and Scikit-Learn: Develop machine learning and deep learning models with Python. Packt.

Real Stories. (2017, December 20). Dying for Drugs (Pharmaceutical Investigation Documentary) | Real Stories. https://youtu.be/2n6xI8g5-Gw?si=ToIwyolVgfKkmEf1

Reese, H. (2022, February 23). What Happens When Police Use AI to Predict and Prevent Crime? JSTOR Daily. https://daily.jstor.org/what-happens-when-police-use-ai-to-predict-and-prevent-crime/

Reich, R. (2023, December 11). We need to talk about the United States' mental health crisis – and its larger causes. The Guardian.

https://www.theguardian.com/commentisfree/2023/dec/11/united-states-suicide-rates-mental-health-crisis-causes

Reis, B. (2005). The Self is Alive and Well and Living in Relational Psychoanalysis. Psychoanalytic Psychology, 22(1), 86–95. https://doi.org/10.1037/0736-9735.22.1.86

Remnick, D. (2023, October 6). Al Gore Doesn't Say I Told You So. The New Yorker. https://www.newyorker.com/news/q-and-a/al-gore-doesnt-say-i-told-you-so

Ren, F., Ding, X., Zheng, M., Korzinkin, M., Cai, X., Zhu, W., Mantsyzov, A., Aliper, A., Aladinskiy, V., Cao, Z., Kong, S., Long, X., Man Liu, B. H., Liu, Y., Naumov, V., Shneyderman, A., Ozerov, I. V., Wang, J., Pun, F. W., … Zhavoronkov, A. (2023). AlphaFold accelerates artificial intelligence powered drug discovery: Efficient discovery of a novel CDK20 small molecule inhibitor. Chemical Science, 14(6), 1443–1452. https://doi.org/10.1039/D2SC05709C

Rescorla, M. (2020). The Computational Theory of Mind. In E. N. Zalta (Ed.), The Stanford Encyclopedia of Philosophy. Metaphysics Research Lab, Stanford University. https://plato.stanford.edu/entries/computational-mind/

Revenge porn. (2023). In Wikipedia. https://en.wikipedia.org/w/index.php?title=Revenge_porn&oldid=11871685 42

Rogers, C. R. (1995). On becoming a person: A therapist's view of psychotherapy. Houghton Mifflin.

Rogers, R. (2023, April 20). What's AGI, and Why Are AI Experts Skeptical? Wired. https://www.wired.com/story/what-is-artificial-general-intelligence-agi-explained/

Rosin, H. (2023, July 13). AI Won't Really Kill Us All, Will It? In The Atlantic. https://www.theatlantic.com/podcasts/archive/2023/07/ai-wont-really-kill-us-all-will-it/674648/

Rumi (1995 [orig. c. 1247]). The essential Rumi. Harper.

Russell, B. (2008 [orig. 1903]). A Free Man's Worship. In Mysticism and Logic and Other Essays. The Project Gutenberg eBook. https://www.gutenberg.org/files/25447/25447-h/25447-h.htm

Russell, B. (2017 [orig. 1918]). Roads to Freedom. Routledge. (Also at: https://en.wikisource.org/wiki/Roads_to_freedom)

Russell, B. (1972 [orig. 1946]). A history of western philosophy. Simon and Schuster.

Russell, S. J. (2019). Human compatible: Artificial intelligence and the problem of control. Viking.

Russell, S. J., & Norvig, P. (2021). Artificial intelligence: A modern approach (Fourth edition). Pearson.

Sachs, J. D. (2011). The price of civilization: Reawakening american virtue and prosperity (1st ed). Random House.

Sahlberg, P. (2021). Finnish lessons 3.0: What can the world learn from educational change in Finland? (Third edition). Teachers College Press, Columbia University.

Sandel, M. J. (2010). Justice: What's the Right Thing to Do? Farrar, Straus and Giroux.
(for the related recorded 12 lectures at Harvard see https://www.harvardonline.harvard.edu/course/justice or https://youtu.be/kBdfcR-8hEY?si=OhFlQ5FsEisRFyDJ)

Sanderson, G. (2017). Deep learning | Chapter 1-4. 3Blue1Brown (Director). https://youtu.be/aircAruvnKk?si=ZYeNCQUerQ7v2Tbj https://youtu.be/IHZwWFHWa-w?si=D3fcatAAhPnsyHmE https://youtu.be/Ilg3gGewQ5U?si=HuDBvL4ZkGuf0XvZ https://youtu.be/tIeHLnjs5U8?si=6BVGk4tBgNJIjbcS

Santow, E. (2020). Can artificial intelligence be trusted with our human rights? AQ: Australian Quarterly, 91(4), 10–17. https://www.jstor.org/stable/26931483

Sapolsky, R. M. (2023). Determined: A science of life without free will. Penguin Press.

Sapolsky, R. & Smerconish, M. (2023, December 30). Do people not have any free will? | CNN. https://www.cnn.com/videos/health/2023/12/30/smr-do-people-not-have-free-will.cnn

Sargeant, W., Chapple, C. K., & Smith, H. (Eds.). (2009). The Bhagavad Gītā (25th anniversary ed). Excelsior Ed., State Univ. of New York Press.

Sartre, J.-P.(2007 [orig. 1938]). Nausea. New Direction.

Sartre, J.-P. (2021 [orig. 1943]). Being and nothingness: An essay in phenomenological ontology (S. Richmond, Trans.; First Washington Square Press/Atria paperback edition). Washington Square Press/Atria.

Satariano, A. (2020, May 6). How My Boss Monitors Me While I Work From Home. The New York Times. https://www.nytimes.com/2020/05/06/technology/employee-monitoring-work-from-home-virus.html

Satariano, A., & Mozur, P. (2023, February 7). The People Onscreen Are Fake. The Disinformation Is Real. The New York Times. https://www.nytimes.com/2023/02/07/technology/artificial-intelligence-training-deepfake.html

Schäfer, L. (2013). Infinite potential: What quantum physics reveals about how we should live (1st ed). Deepak Chopra Books.

Scherer, M. & Brown, L. X. Z. (2021, July 24). Report – Warning: Bossware May Be Hazardous to Your Health. Center for Democracy and Technology. https://cdt.org/wp-content/uploads/2021/07/2021-07-29-Warning-Bossware-May-Be-Hazardous-To-Your-Health-Final.pdf (also https://cdt.org/insights/report-warning-bossware-may-be-hazardous-to-your-health/)

Schrödinger, E. (1992 [orig. 1944]). What is life? The physical aspect of the living cell ; with, Mind and matter ; & Autobiographical sketches. Cambridge University Press.

Sears, W., & Sears, M. (2001). The attachment parenting book: A commonsense guide to understanding and nurturing your baby (1st ed). Little, Brown.

SehtestBilder. (2011, November 11). Optical illusion: Old or young woman? https://youtu.be/7f1G6Nx5VDw?si=pnb69egsAcdEgh4D

Seth, A. (2017, July 18). Anil Seth: Your brain hallucinates your conscious reality | TED Talk. TED: Ideas Worth Spreading. https://www.ted.com/talks/anil_seth_your_brain_hallucinates_your_conscious_reality

Seth, A. (2021). Being You: A New Science of Consciousness. Dutton.

Shakespeare, W., & Bevington, D. M. (2008 [orig. 1585–1613]). The complete works of Shakespeare (6th ed). Pearson/Longman.

Sharp, C., & Bevington, D. (2022). Mentalizing in psychotherapy: A guide for practitioners. The Guilford Press.

Shaw, J. (2022). Content moderators pay a psychological toll to keep social media clean. We should be helping them. https://www.sciencefocus.com/news/content-moderators-pay-a-psychological-toll-to-keep-social-media-clean-we-should-be-helping-them

Shazeer, N.M. (2020). GLU Variants Improve Transformer. ArXiv, abs/2002.05202. https://api.semanticscholar.org/CorpusID:211096588

Shear, J. (Ed.). (1997). Explaining consciousness: The "hard problem." MIT Press.

Shedler, J. (2010). The efficacy of psychodynamic psychotherapy. American Psychologist, 65(2), 98–109. https://doi.org/10.1037/a0018378

Shedler, J. (2015, January 23). Challenging the Cognitive Behavioral Therapies: The Overselling of CBT's Evidence Bas. Jonathan Shedler—Where is the Evidence for Evidence-Based Therapy? https://youtu.be/3UpHl9kuccc?si=jRP6DIz5DhwN93dN

Shedler, J. (2018). Where Is the Evidence for "Evidence-Based" Therapy? Psychiatric Clinics of North America, 41(2), 319–329. https://doi.org/10.1016/j.psc.2018.02.001 (or: https://jonathanshedler.com/wp-content/uploads/2018/05/Shedler-2018-Where-is-the-evidence-for-evidence-based-therapy.pdf)

Schore, A. N. (2016 [orig. 1994]). Affect regulation and the origin of the self: The neurobiology of emotional development. Psychology Press.

Schore, A. N. (2012). The Science of The Art of Psychotherapy (First Edition). W.W. Norton & Company.

Siegel, D. J. (2012). The developing mind: How relationships and the brain interact to shape who we are (2nd ed.). The Guilford Press.

Siegfried, T. (2017, July 25). There's a long way to go in understanding the brain | Science News. https://www.sciencenews.org/blog/context/neuroscience-understanding-brain

Silver, D., Huang, A., Maddison, C. J., Guez, A., Sifre, L., Van Den Driessche, G., Schrittwieser, J., Antonoglou, I., Panneershelvam, V., Lanctot, M., Dieleman, S., Grewe, D., Nham, J., Kalchbrenner, N., Sutskever, I., Lillicrap, T., Leach, M., Kavukcuoglu, K., Graepel, T., & Hassabis, D. (2016). Mastering the game of Go with deep neural networks and tree search. Nature, 529(7587), 484–489. https://doi.org/10.1038/nature16961

Silver, D., Schrittwieser, J., Simonyan, K., Antonoglou, I., Huang, A., Guez, A., Hubert, T., Baker, L., Lai, M., Bolton, A., Chen, Y., Lillicrap, T., Hui, F., Sifre, L., Van Den Driessche, G., Graepel, T., & Hassabis, D. (2017). Mastering the game of Go without human knowledge. Nature, 550(7676), 354–359. https://doi.org/10.1038/nature24270

Silver, D., Hubert, T., Schrittwieser, J., Antonoglou, I., Lai, M., Guez, A., Lanctot, M., Sifre, L., Kumaran, D., Graepel, T., Lillicrap, T., Simonyan, K., & Hassabis, D. (2018). A general reinforcement learning algorithm that masters chess, shogi, and Go through self-play. Science, 362(6419), 1140–1144. https://doi.org/10.1126/science.aar6404

Simard, S. W., Perry, D. A., Jones, M. D., Myrold, D. D., Durall, D. M., & Molina, R. (1997). Net transfer of carbon between ectomycorrhizal tree species in the field. Nature, 388(6642), 579–582. https://doi.org/10.1038/41557

Simard, S. (2016). Suzanne Simard: How trees talk to each other | TED Talk. https://www.ted.com/talks/suzanne_simard_how_trees_talk_to_each_other or https://youtu.be/Un2yBgIAxYs?si=wbQ9R4X0WDcT3LLq

Simard, S. (2021). Finding the mother tree: Discovering the wisdom of the forest (First edition). Alfred A. Knopf.

Singhal, K., Azizi, S., Tu, T., Mahdavi, S. S., Wei, J., Chung, H. W., Scales, N., Tanwani, A., Cole-Lewis, H., Pfohl, S., Payne, P., Seneviratne, M., Gamble, P., Kelly, C., Babiker, A., Schärli, N., Chowdhery, A., Mansfield, P., Demner-Fushman, D., ... Natarajan, V. (2023). Large language models encode clinical knowledge. Nature, 620(7972), 172–180. https://doi.org/10.1038/s41586-023-06291-2

Skopeliti, C. (2023, May 30). 'I feel constantly watched': The employees working under surveillance. The Guardian. https://www.theguardian.com/money/2023/may/30/i-feel-constantly-watched-employees-working-under-surveillance-monitorig-software-productivity

Slade, A. (2023). Looking back to light the path forward: Ghosts in the Nursery revisited. Infant Mental Health Journal, 44(6), 857–868. https://doi.org/10.1002/imhj.22089

Slade, A., Sadler, L. S., Eaves, T., & Webb, D. L. (2023). Enhancing attachment and reflective parenting in clinical practice: A minding the baby approach. The Guilford Press.

Smerconish, M. (2023a, September 30). AI girlfriends imperil generation of young men | CNN Business. https://www.cnn.com/videos/business/2023/09/30/smr-ai-girlfriends-ruining-generation-of-men.cnn

Smerconish, M. (2023b, September 30). Should police be able to monitor social media? | CNN. https://www.cnn.com/videos/us/2023/09/30/smr-police-surveillance-of-social-media.cnn

Smith, A. (2009 [orig. 1759]). The theory of moral sentiments (R. P. Hanley, Ed.; 250. anniversary ed). Penguin Books.

Smith, C. S. (2023, March 13). Hallucinations Could Blunt ChatGPT's Success - IEEE Spectrum. IEEE Spectrum; IEEE Spectrum. https://spectrum.ieee.org/ai-hallucination

Smith, R. J. (2016), Explanations for adaptations, just-so stories, and limitations on evidence in evolutionary biology. Evol. Anthropol., 25: 276-287. https://doi.org/10.1002/evan.21495

Spelman, M. B., & Thomson-Salo, F. (2015). The Winnicott tradition: Lines of development, evolution of theory and practice over the decades. Karnac.

Spitz, R. (1946). Anaclitic depression. Psychoanalytic Study of the Child, 2(1), 313-342.

Spitz, R. (1945). Hospitalism: An inquiry into the genesis of psychiatric conditions in early childhood. Psychoanalytic Study of the Child, 1(1), 53-74.

Springer, J. T., & Holley, D. (2013). An introduction to zoology: Investigating the animal world (1st ed). Jones & Bartlett Learning.

SSIR. (2023, May 3). Bossware Is Coming for You: Worker Surveillance Technology Is Everywhere. 2023 Stanford Social Innovation Review. https://ssir.org/videos/entry/bossware_is_coming_for_you_worker_surveill ance_technology_is_everywhere

Steiger, M., Bharucha, T. J., Venkatagiri, S., Riedl, M. J., & Lease, M. (2021). The Psychological Well-Being of Content Moderators: The Emotional Labor of Commercial Moderation and Avenues for Improving Support. Proceedings of the 2021 CHI Conference on Human Factors in Computing Systems, 1–14. https://doi.org/10.1145/3411764.3445092

Stein, B. (2006, November 26). In Class Warfare, Guess Which Class Is Winning. The New York Times. https://www.nytimes.com/2006/11/26/business/yourmoney/26every.html

Stern, D. N. (1985 & 2000). The interpersonal world of the infant: A view from psychoanalysis and developmental psychology. Basic Books.

Stern, D. N. (1998). Diary of a baby. Basic Books.

Stern, D. N. (2004). The present moment in psychotherapy and everyday life. W.W. Norton.

Stern, D. N. (2005). Intersubjectivity. In E. S. Person, A. M. Cooper, & G. O. Gabbard (Eds.), The American psychiatric publishing textbook of psychoanalysis (pp. 77–92). American Psychiatric Publishing, Inc..

Stiglitz, J. E. (2012). The Price of Inequality: How Today's Divided Society Endangers Our Future (First Edition). W. W. Norton & Company.

Stiglitz, J. E. (2015). The Great Divide: Unequal Societies and What We Can Do About Them (First Edition). W. W. Norton & Company.

Stolorow, R. D., & Atwood, G. E. (1991). The mind and the body. Psychoanalytic Dialogues, 1(2), 181–195. https://doi.org/10.1080/10481889109538892

Storr, A. (1988). Solitude: A return to the self (1. American ed., 3. print). Free Pr.

Strawson, G. (1994). Mental Reality. The MIT Press.

Strawson, G., Carruthers, P., Jackson, F., Lycan, W. G., McGinn, C., Papineau, D., Rey, G., Smart, & et. (2006). Consciousness and Its Place in Nature: Does Physicalism Entail Panpsychism? Imprint Academic.

Strawson, G. (2018, March 13). The Consciousness Deniers. The New York Review of Books. https://www.nybooks.com/online/2018/03/13/the-consciousness-deniers/ (also available here (adapted/edited): https://web.ics.purdue.edu/~drkelly/StrawsonDennettNYRBExchangeCons ciousness2018.pdf)

Strawson, G. (2019, December 27). Galileo's Error by Philip Goff review – a new science of consciousness. The Guardian. https://www.theguardian.com/books/2019/dec/27/galileos-error-by-philip-goff-review

Stróżyński, M. (2014). The Aporetic Method in Plotinus' Enneads. Symbolae Philologorum Posnaniensium Graecae et Latinae, 24(1), 17. https://doi.org/10.14746/SPPGL.2014.XXIV.1.3

Stróżyński, M. (2020). The Ascent of the Soul as Spiritual Exercise in Plotinus' Enneads. Mnemosyne, 74(3), 448–477. https://doi.org/10.1163/1568525X-12342768

Stróżyński, M. (2022). Spiritual Exercise in Plotinus: The Deictic Method. Classical Philology, 117(3), 495–517. https://doi.org/10.1086/720176

Suleyman, M., & Bhaskar M. (2023). The Coming Wave. Bodley Head.

Sutskever, I. & Fridman, L. (2020, May 8). Ilya Sutskever: Deep Learning | Lex Fridman Podcast #94. https://youtu.be/13CZPWmke6A?si=djxxIXl63n6-ZFn6

Tao Te Ching (n.d.). English by Gia-fu Feng and Jane English, Terebess Asia Online (TAO). https://terebess.hu/english/tao/gia.html#Kap19

Tapper, J., Hinton, J., CNN (Director). (2023, May 2). "Godfather of AI" warns that AI may figure out how to kill people. https://youtu.be/FAbsoxQtUwM?si=_Bmbpd3cheoKe_bM

Tarnas, R. (1991). The passion of the Western mind: Understanding the ideas that have shaped our world view (1st ed). Harmony Books.

Tattersall, I. (2022). Understanding human evolution. Cambridge University Press.

Taylor, S. (2019). How a Flawed Experiment "Proved" That Free Will Doesn't Exist. Scientific American Blog Network. https://blogs.scientificamerican.com/observations/how-a-flawed-experiment-proved-that-free-will-doesnt-exist/

Tegmark, M. (2018). Life 3.0: Being human in the age of artificial intelligence. Penguin Books.

Teicholz, J. G. (2001). The many meanings of intersubjectivity and their implications for analyst self-expression and self-disclosure. In A. Goldberg (Ed.), The narcissistic patient revisited: Progress in self psychology, Vol. 17, pp. 9–42). Analytic Press.

Tenbarge, K. (2023). Found through Google, bought with Visa and Mastercard: Inside the deepfake porn economy. (2023, March 27). NBC News. https://www.nbcnews.com/tech/internet/deepfake-porn-ai-mr-deep-fake-economy-google-visa-mastercard-download-rcna75071

Thatcher, M. & Keay, D. (1987, September 23). Interview for Woman's Own ("no such thing [as society]") | Margaret Thatcher Foundation. https://www.margaretthatcher.org/document/106689

The Fed (2023, Q2). The Fed—Table: Distribution of Household Wealth in the U.S. since 1989. https://www.federalreserve.gov/releases/z1/dataviz/dfa/distribute/table/

The Great Hack. (2019). In Wikipedia. https://en.wikipedia.org/w/index.php?title=The_Great_Hack&oldid=11451 87330

The Observer, Sunday, January 25, 1931 Max Planck Interview. (1931, January 25). The Observer, 17. https://theguardian.newspapers.com/article/121386587/the-observer-sunday-january-25-1931m/

The Original ACE Study (n.d.). The Original ACE Study, The Expanded ACE Survey, Prevalence of ACEs | National Human Trafficking Training And Technical Assistance Center. https://nhttac.acf.hhs.gov/soar/eguide/stop/adverse_childhood_experiences

The Social Dilemma. (2020). In Wikipedia. https://en.wikipedia.org/w/index.php?title=The_Social_Dilemma&oldid=1160723115

The White House, (2023). Blueprint for an AI Bill of Rights | OSTP. The White House. https://www.whitehouse.gov/ostp/ai-bill-of-rights/

Thiel, D., Stroebel, M., & Portnoff, R. (2023). Generative ML and CSAM: Implications and Mitigations. Stanford Digital Repository. https://doi.org/10.25740/JV206YG3793

Thompson, S. A. (2023, March 12). Making Deepfakes Gets Cheaper and Easier Thanks to A.I. The New York Times. https://www.nytimes.com/2023/03/12/technology/deepfakes-cheapfakes-videos-ai.html

Timnit Gebru. (2023). In Wikipedia. https://en.wikipedia.org/w/index.php?title=Timnit_Gebru&oldid=1189387783

Toews, R. (2021). AlphaFold Is The Most Important Achievement In AI—Ever. Forbes. https://www.forbes.com/sites/robtoews/2021/10/03/alphafold-is-the-most-important-achievement-in-ai-ever/

Tolkien, J. R. R. (2005 [orig. 1955]). The Lord of the Rings (50th anniversary ed.). Houghton Mifflin.

Tononi, G., Boly, M., Massimini, M., & Koch, C. (2016). Integrated information theory: From consciousness to its physical substrate. Nature Reviews Neuroscience, 17(7), Article 7. https://doi.org/10.1038/nrn.2016.44

Trilling, L. (2008 [orig. 1950]). The liberal imagination: Essays on literature and society. New York Review Books.

Tronick, E. (2007). The neurobehavioral and social-emotional development of infants and children. W. W. Norton & Co.

Tronick, E., Adamson, L.B., Als, H., & Brazelton, T.B. (1975, April). Infant emotions in normal and pertubated interactions. Paper presented at the biennial meeting of the Society for Research in Child Development, Denver, CO.

Tronick, E., Als, H., Adamson, L., Wise, S., & Brazelton, T. B. (1978). The Infant's Response to Entrapment between Contradictory Messages in Face-to-Face Interaction. Journal of the American Academy of Child Psychiatry, 17(1), 1–13. https://doi.org/10.1016/S0002-7138(09)62273-1

Turkle, S. (n.d.). Technology Is Harming Our Relationships, and We Can Stop It. Big Think. https://bigthink.com/videos/sherry-turkle-on-technology-and-dating/

Turkle, S. & Cornish, A. (2023, May 4). AI in the time of Loneliness—The Assignment with Audie Cornish—Podcast on CNN Audio. CNN. https://www.cnn.com/audio/podcasts/the-assignment/episodes/452e30a8-9b6a-4820-b1a0-aff701480a80

Turner, J. D., Corrigan, K., & Rasimus, T. (Eds.). (2013). Gnosticism, Platonism and the late ancient world: Essays in honour of John D. Turner. Brill.

Twenge, J. M. (2018). iGen: Why Today's Super-Connected Kids Are Growing Up Less Rebellious, More Tolerant, Less Happy--and Completely Unprepared for Adulthood--and What That Means for the Rest of Us. Atria Books.

Uller, T., & Laland, K. N. (Eds.). (2019). Evolutionary causation: Biological and philosophical reflections. The MIT Press.

UMass Boston (2010, March 12). Developmental Sciences at UMass Boston. Ed Tronick | Still Face Experiment | Infant Parent Mental Health. https://youtu.be/vmE3NfB_HhE?si=GLX9RXddmnHFlJqM

van der Kolk, B. A. (2014). The body keeps the score: Brain, mind, and body in the healing of trauma. Viking.

van Gulick, R. (2022). Consciousness. In E. N. Zalta & U. Nodelman (Eds.), The Stanford Encyclopedia of Philosophy. Metaphysics Research Lab, Stanford University. https://plato.stanford.edu/entries/consciousness/

Vance, A. (2011, April 14). This Tech Bubble Is Different. Bloomberg. https://www.bloomberg.com/news/articles/2011-04-14/this-tech-bubble-is-different

Varoufakis, Y. (2016, October 31). The Universal Right to Capital Income | by Yanis Varoufakis. Project Syndicate. https://www.project-syndicate.org/commentary/basic-income-funded-by-capital-income-by-yanis-varoufakis-2016-10

Varoufakis, Y. (2017, December 8). The High Cost of Denying Class War | by Yanis Varoufakis. Project Syndicate. https://www.project-syndicate.org/commentary/class-warfare-fuels-trump-and-brexit-by-yanis-varoufakis-2017-12

Varoufakis, Y. (2018, October 19). What Has Google Ever Done for Us? | by Yanis Varoufakis. Project Syndicate. https://www.project-syndicate.org/commentary/social-ownership-of-google-big-tech-by-yanis-varoufakis-2018-10

Varoufakis, Y. (2019). Talking to my daughter about the economy or, how capitalism works - and how it fails. Farrar, Straus and Giroux.

Varoufakis, Y. (2020, September 28). The Redistribution Games | by Yanis Varoufakis. Project Syndicate. https://www.project-syndicate.org/commentary/three-pronged-strategy-to-redistribute-wealth-by-yanis-varoufakis-2020-09

Varoufakis, Y. (2023a, June 2). New AI Germ Busters Can Also Bust Unions | by Yanis Varoufakis. Project Syndicate. https://www.project-syndicate.org/commentary/ai-that-developed-antibiotic-could-also-neutralize-unions-by-yanis-varoufakis-2023-06

Varoufakis, Y. (2023b). Technofeudalism: what killed capitalism. Penguin Books.

Vaswani, A., Shazeer, N., Parmar, N., Uszkoreit, J., Jones L., Gomez, A.N., Kaiser Ł., & Polosukhin, I. (2017). Attention is all you need. Adv. Neural Inf. Process. Syst. 30 (2017).

Verma, P. (2023, December 17). The rise of AI fake news is creating a 'misinformation superspreader.' Washington Post.

https://www.washingtonpost.com/technology/2023/12/17/ai-fake-news-misinformation/

VICE News. (2021, October 20). How Big Pharma Gets Dangerous Drugs Approved. https://youtu.be/ayE0y7XfCpo?si=sPKgo-efEwEZtMyU

Vittert, L. (2023, September 26). AI girlfriends are ruining an entire generation of men. The Hill. https://thehill.com/opinion/technology/4218666-ai-girlfriends-are-ruining-an-entire-generation-of-men/

von Eschenbach, W. & Hatto, A. T. (1980). Parzival. Penguin Books.

Vu, L. (2023, March 6). Maternity Leave in the US as Compared to Other Countries. Mila's Keeper. https://milaskeeper.com/blogs/news/maternity-leave-in-the-us-as-compared-to-other-countries

Waddell, K. (2017, January 6). Why Bosses Can Track Their Employees 24/7. The Atlantic. https://www.theatlantic.com/technology/archive/2017/01/employer-gps-tracking/512294/

Waldinger, R. (2015). Robert Waldinger: What makes a good life? Lessons from the longest study on happiness | TED Talk. https://www.ted.com/talks/robert_waldinger_what_makes_a_good_life_lessons_from_the_longest_study_on_happiness

Waldinger, R. (2022). Robert Waldinger: The secret to a happy life — lessons from 8 decades of research | TED Talk. https://www.ted.com/talks/robert_waldinger_the_secret_to_a_happy_life_lessons_from_8_decades_of_research

Waldinger, R., & Schulz, M. (2023a, January 19). What the Longest Study on Human Happiness Found Is the Key to a Good Life. The Atlantic. https://www.theatlantic.com/ideas/archive/2023/01/harvard-happiness-study-relationships/672753/

Waldinger, R., & Schulz, M. (2023a). The Good Life: Lessons from the World's Longest Scientific Study of Happiness. Simon & Schuster.

Wallace, A. (2023). Understanding evo-devo. Cambridge University Press.

Wallace-Wells, D. (2023, December 20). Opinion | Income Inequality Has Been Transformed Globally. The New York Times. https://www.nytimes.com/2023/12/20/opinion/income-inequality-global.html

Walsh, D. M. (2015). Organisms, agency, and evolution. Cambridge University Press.

Walsh, M. (Director). (2023). Free Will? A Documentary [Film featuring Sean Carroll, Daniel Dennett, Massimo Pigliucci, Derk Pereboom, Gregg Caruso, Coleman Hughes, Jerry Coyne, Heather Berlin, Robert Kane, Dan Barker, Alex O'Connor, and others]. Reference Frame Films. https://www.freewilldocumentary.com

Wang, A. (2023, November 15). Is My Toddler a Stochastic Parrot? | The New Yorker. https://www.newyorker.com/humor/sketchbook/is-my-toddler-a-stochastic-parrot

Warzel, C. (2023a, November 3). The Great Social Media–News Collapse. The Atlantic. https://www.theatlantic.com/technology/archive/2023/11/social-media-news-readership-decline/675890/

Warzel, C. (2023b, December 18). Nobody Knows What's Happening Online Anymore. The Atlantic. https://www.theatlantic.com/technology/archive/2023/12/internet-information-trends-virality-tracking/676888/

Wegner, D. (2017). The Illusion of Conscious Will (The MIT Press). The MIT Press.

Weinberg, S. (1987). Newtonianism, reductionism and the art of congressional testimony. Nature 330, 433–437. https://doi.org/10.1038/330433a0

Weiser, B. (2023, May 27). Here's What Happens When Your Lawyer Uses ChatGPT. The New York Times. https://www.nytimes.com/2023/05/27/nyregion/avianca-airline-lawsuit-chatgpt.html

Weiss, H. (2023, November 29). U.S. Suicide Rates Hit an All-Time High in 2022. TIME. https://time.com/6340732/u-s-suicide-rates-2022/

Wells, K., & Klosowski, T. (2020, April 6). Domestic Abusers Can Control Your Devices. Here's How to Fight Back. The New York Times. https://www.nytimes.com/2020/04/06/smarter-living/wirecutter/domestic-abusers-can-control-your-devices-heres-how-to-fight-back.html

Wernau, J. (2023, November 29). U.S. Suicides Reached a Record High Last Year. Wall Street Journal. https://www.wsj.com/health/healthcare/americans-suicide-highest-level-2022-02eb10ea

Whitehead, A. N., Griffin, D. R., & Sherburne, D. W. (1978). Process and reality: An essay in cosmology (Corrected ed). Free Press.

Wilkinson, C., & Frost, H. (2022, January 21). The People in Intimate Relationships With AI Chatbots. Vice. https://www.vice.com/en/article/93bqbp/can-you-be-in-relationship-with-replika

Wilkinson, R., & Pickett, K. (2009). The Spirit Level: Why Greater Equality Makes Societies Stronger (First Edition). Bloomsbury Press.

Wilkinson, R. (2011). Richard Wilkinson: How economic inequality harms societies | TED Talk. https://www.ted.com/talks/richard_wilkinson_how_economic_inequality_harms_societies

Wilkinson, R. (2021). Richard Wilkinson: The link between inequality and anxiety | TED Talk. https://www.ted.com/talks/richard_wilkinson_the_link_between_inequality_and_anxiety

Wilson, E. O. (1999). Consilience: The unity of knowledge. Knopf.

Winnicott, D. W. (1965a). The capacity to be alone. In The maturational processes and the facilitating environment, London: Hogarth/Institute of Psycho-Analysis. (Reprinted from International Journal of Psycho-Analysis, 39 (1958), 416-20.)

Winnicott, D. W. (1965b). The maturational processes and the facilitating environment. Karnac Books..

Winnicott, D. W. (2005 [orig. 1971a]). Playing and reality. Routledge.

Witters, D. (2023, May 17). U.S. Depression Rates Reach New Highs. Gallup.Com. https://news.gallup.com/poll/505745/depression-rates-reach-new-highs.aspx

Wittgenstein, L. (2001 [orig. 1922]). Tractatus logico-philosophicus. Routledge.

Wolfram, S. (2023a). What is ChatGPT doing ... And why does it work? (First edition). Wolfram Media, Inc.

Wolfram, S. (2023b). Tech Stories 101 (Director). (2023, August 9). Dr Stephen Wolfram says THIS about ChatGPT, Natural Language and Physics. https://youtu.be/pdPYJKqfiqc?si=uQ4_sKd63UPmzFGU&t=67

Wolfram, S. & Fridman, L. (2023a, May 13). Lex Clips (Director). How ChatGPT works | Stephen Wolfram and Lex Fridman. https://youtu.be/Ic88oVqr66w?si=G8ElWoOIj1QCEqt1

Wolfram, S. & Fridman, L. (2023b, May 13). Lex Clips (Director). Stephen Wolfram explains ChatGPT vs Wolfram Alpha | Lex Fridman Podcast Clips. https://youtu.be/feQhGWVEvQk?si=wh1XEHqS3lQjiIVL

Wooldridge, M. J. (2021). A brief history of artificial intelligence: What it is, where we are, and where we are going (First U.S. edition). Flatiron Books.

WSJ (2014, February 8). Psychedelics Lead to a New Vision of Consciousness. Wall Street Journal. http://online.wsj.com/article/SB10001424052702304626804579362953234754182.html

Xiang, C. (2022, November 1). Scientists Increasingly Can't Explain How AI Works. Vice. https://www.vice.com/en/article/y3pezm/scientists-increasingly-cant-explain-how-ai-works

Yalom, I. D. (1980). Existential psychotherapy. Basic Books.

Yalom, I. (2005). The Schopenhauer Cure: A Novel. Harper Perennial Modern Classics.

Zagorski, N. (2022). Popularity of Mental Health Chatbots Grows. Psychiatric News, 57(5), appi.pn.2022.05.4.50. https://doi.org/10.1176/appi.pn.2022.05.4.50

Zinn, H. (2015). People's History of the United States. Harper Perennial.

Zinn, H. (2018). You can't be neutral on a moving train: A personal history. Beacon Press.

Zou, J., & Schiebinger, L. (2018). AI can be sexist and racist—It's time to make it fair. Nature, 559(7714), 324–326. https://doi.org/10.1038/d41586-018-05707-8

Index

Notes

Artificial Intelligence and the Human Mind

(Notes are also available/updated at: www.AiAndHumanMind.org)

---

[1] **initial shortcomings and problems**: AI technology is not fully reliable, even when *reinforcement learning* (e.g. via human feedback, RLHF, see also (Metz, 2023f)) or similar technologies are utilized. AI can exhibit *biases, hallucinations* (AI generated content is incorrect, made up, or nonsensical), and it also has adverse (frightening?) *interpretability* (a.k.a. *explainability*) problem, i.e. it behaves like a *black box* – the rationale behind AI's output or decisions is very hard to interpret and understand; see e.g. (Smith, 2023), (Linardatos et al., 2023), and (Xiang, 2022). Jaron Lanier provides an argument for the necessity of transparency and interpretability of AI (Lanier, 2023). These aspects of AI are further discussed in the third chapter.

[2] **likely even much more potent**: Sam Altman, chief executive of OpenAI, has referred to AI as a "societal revolution," he also used the term "printing press moment" to describe a possible impact of AI during the US congressional hearing in May 2023 (Pequeño, 2023). Mira Murati, OpenAI CTO, referred to AI as "the most important technology that humanity would ever create" (Blumberg, 2023). Sundar Pichai, Google CEO, considers AI project to be "more profound than [discoveries of] fire or electricity" (Pichai & Pelley, 2023, April/July), (60 Minutes, 2023 a/b). Geoffrey Hinton, often referred to as the "godfather of AI," warns of the "Existential Threat" of AI (Amanpour and Co., 2023b). Reid Hoffman, tech entrepreneur dubbed the "philosopher of Silicon Valley," believes that AI "will reshape all our lives. It will become the primary technology that we use to make decisions and

navigate the world — a steam engine of the mind; a cognitive GPS; a tool for orientation, discovery and navigation." (Hoffman R., 2023b). Adrienne LaFrance, executive editor of The Atlantic, expresses the watershed nature of AI in poignant terms by saying "What's coming stands to dwarf every technological creation in living memory: the internet, the personal computer, the atom bomb. It may well be the most consequential technology in all of human history." (LaFrance, 2023b). New York Times Opinion Columnist Ezra Klein put it succinctly: "This Changes Everything" (Klein, 2023a). These are just a few of the comments about the field poised for explosive growth.

³ **general intelligence**: In discussions surrounding AI, it is common to refer to human intelligence as "general intelligence" and to the current capabilities of AI as "narrow intelligence." The futuristic concept of AGI (Artificial General Intelligence) is also a subject of considerable debate within the AI community, characterized by many diverse theoretical notions and opinions. The *concept of intelligence* itself is multifaceted and can be understood in various ways. A comprehensive treatment of it is obviously beyond the scope of this book, but it will suffice to summarize here several attempts at defining it. Scientifically speaking, the origins of intelligence and the inner workings of this faculty are not known, so most definitions focus on external manifestations of intelligent behavior. Encyclopedia Britannica authors summarize it as the ability to learn or understand, or to deal with new or challenging situations. Human intelligence is characterized by the abilities to learn from experience, adapt to new situations, understand and handle abstract concepts, and use knowledge to control an environment (Britannica, 2010). Concepts of *emotional intelligence* (e.g. Goleman, 2005) and *multiple intelligences* (e.g. Gardner, 2011) have also been proposed. Even if definitions of the concept of intelligence have an elusive quality, every healthy human being can easily recognize its manifestations, and the maxim "I know it when I see it" fully applies here.

⁴ **parasitically leaning on the siphoned aggregate of human intelligence**: AI technology of today can demonstrate intelligence in the context of generating or manipulating content consisting of text, sounds, and images. Until recently, this was the province where human beings reigned supreme. AI does this by "learning" from the existing content created by humans. For

example, *ChatGPT*, OpenAI's Large Language Model (LLM) was "trained" on data consisting of hundreds of billions of words siphoned from books, articles, websites, and other sources created by intelligent human minds (there are indications that GPT-4 was trained on more than two trillion words). This is the ultimate source of its intelligence, this is where the model "learns" about the patterns, styles, and structures in language.

(For wonks only: Most modern AI systems, at the time of this writing, are based on deep neural network architectures. The *training* or *learning* process of deep neural network models can in broad strokes be explained as trial-and-error, accomplished through a vast number of trials, utilizing huge amounts of data and computational resources so that the LLM can *learn* patterns and linguistic structures. The *training* process happens roughly like this: the model, consisting of a software representation of a layered *deep neural network* (terms are inspired by the assumed analogy with neurons in the brain anatomy), is initially presented with input data (e.g. text, typically broken into *tokens* represented by numbers) and the desired output (e.g. the expected next word). The model is then instructed to start making predictions about the connections in the neural network that will generate the desired output (initially it makes random guesses) and the results of its predictions are compared with the desired output. The difference (error) is calculated at the output layer and *backpropagated* through the network, layer by layer, all the way to the input layer, thus completing a feedback loop. This is done to adjust the model's *parameters* (or *weights*, which represent numeric values attributed to connections between nodes) before the subsequent trial. Parameters are what LLM *learns* during the *training* – thus they fully capture the LLM, and their transfer to a different, compatible, platform can fully recreate the trained LLM. Only after the *training* is complete and numerical values of weights are determined, can the model make *inferences* – LLM can generate output based on new, unseen input data. (This is a somewhat simplified explanation of the *training* process, and we can add that, broadly speaking, the machine learning (ML) field distinguishes *supervised learning* (model is provided with expected output for a given input during the training), *unsupervised learning* (model is not provided with explicit instructions, it must identify patterns, groupings, or structures within the data by itself), and *reinforcement learning* (model is conditioned through interaction with environment, e.g. humans provide feedback – which is extensively used to complete training for LLMs)). LLMs can have hundreds of billions of parameters, or more. This information is typically kept as a closely guarded secret by companies developing them, but it is known, for example, that OpenAI's GPT-3 has 175 billion parameters. More detailed (but still high-level) descriptions of this process can be found e.g. in (Wolfram, 2023) and (Mitchell M., 2020)).

[5] **leaders are literally begging to be regulated**: This attitude of AI technology leaders is a bright spot in the whole AI development. Things could have unfolded in a dark way, very fast, if AI leaders were primarily self-interested. Specifically, big credit goes to the OpenAI leadership team for ushering in this mindset, but also to many other technology leaders in the AI arena. Here are some examples and testimonies: Sundar Pichai, Google CEO, stated that AI "can be very harmful if deployed wrongly and we don't have all the answers there yet – and the technology is moving fast. So, does that keep me up at night? Absolutely." He called for a global regulatory framework for AI, and when asked if nuclear arms-style frameworks could be needed, he said: "We would need that." (Milmo, 2023), (Pichai & Pelley, 2023, April/July), (60 Minutes, 2023 a/b). Satya Nadella, Microsoft CEO, said that "there is also a place for us to take responsibility as purveyors of this technology *before* regulation, and then expect that there will be regulation" (Nadella & Semuels, 2023). Tim Cook, Apple CEO, also said that "companies have to employ their own ethical decisions. … Regulation will have a difficult time … because it's moving so quickly. So, I think it's incumbent on companies as well to regulate themselves" (Field & Cook, 2023). However, due to the competing interests, the notion of "companies regulating themselves" is often hard to accomplish in practice; a case in point is the immediate ousting of Timnit Gebru, a prominent ethical AI researcher from Google, when she raised concerns over Google's AI development (see the paper Gebru co-authored (Bender et al., 2021) that resulted in her termination from Google, see also (Metz & Wakabayashi, 2020) and (Timnit Gebru, 2023)). Founders of a safety-focused AI start-up *Anthropic*, Daniela and Dario Amodei, are championing the notion that all AI research and products must "put safety at the frontier." Geoffrey Hinton, the "godfather of AI," left his position at Google so that he could dedicate himself to

being the voice of reason about the prospects of AI; he recently gave an interview in which he agreed that some kind of regulation is needed and said that he doesn't consider himself to be an "expert on how to do regulation. I'm just a scientist who suddenly realized that these things are getting smarter than us. I want to sort of blow the whistle and say that we should worry seriously about how we stop these things getting control over us. And it's going to be very hard. And I don't have the solutions. I wish I did" (Tapper & Hinton, 2023). Tristan Harris, from the *Center for Humane Technology* is more pessimistic and warns that AI might be coming too fast for modern society, which may not be able to absorb it; he uses a metaphor: "it's like the 24th century crashing down on the 21st century ... imagine if the 20th-century technology was crashing down on 16th-century governance, ... so you know it's the 16th century, you've got the king, you've got their advisers, but suddenly television, radio, video games, and thermonuclear weapons all show up, so they just land in your society, yeah, but you're like: 'call the knights!' ... and the knights show up and what are you going to do? ... With AI, ... everyone who's working on safety [needs] to make as much progress as possible. [But] right now, the companies are caught in a race to continue to scale as fast as possible..." (Greene et al., 2023).

[6] **contemplating chances for human extinction due to AI**: See e.g. (Harari et al., 2023), (Metz & Schmidt, 2023), (Tegmark, 2018), (Bostrom, 2016). In March 2023, more than 1,000 artificial intelligence experts and eminent thinkers — including Elon Musk, Steve Wozniak, Yuval Noah Harari, Max Tegmark, Tristan Harris, Christof Koch, Gary Marcus, Yoshua Bengio, Stuart Russell, Daron Acemoglu, Emad Mostaque, and others — urged for a delay in AI development, so that capabilities and dangers of AI can be properly studied and mitigated (Hern, 2023), see full list at https://futureoflife.org/open-letter/pause-giant-ai-experiments/. See also *Center for AI Safety* at https://www.safe.ai/.

[7] **AI containment**: The concept of AI containment is introduced and considered in (Suleyman & Bhaskar, 2023).

[8] **this is just the way human nature is**: Self-interest as a trait of human nature has been recognized and pondered from many angles, and is a recurrent theme in literature, philosophy, psychology, and economics (it is also accessible via self-introspection to all of us). Throughout the book, we will revisit this

topic frequently, and for now, we are just listing several often-discussed sources: (Hobbes, 1651), (Hume, 1739), (Machiavelli, 1532), (de Waal, 2009), (Freud, 1930), (Dawkins, 1976), (Rand & Branden, 1964), (Hayek, 1944), (Fromm, 1956), there is more of course, this is just to put few stakes in the ground. An example of a modern powerful public imagination about our self-interested nature, inspired by a movie, can be found in Gordon Gekko's speech (acted by Michael Douglas) from the 1987 movie *Wall Street*: "greed — for lack of a better word — is good. Greed is right. Greed works. Greed clarifies, cuts through, and captures the essence of the evolutionary spirit" this fictional speech still reverberates strongly in many circles today, and it continues to justify and inspire forces of self-interest.

[9] **cataclysmic challenges coming our way, AI technology being just one of them**: The power of AI technology is such that if it goes wrong, it can go quite wrong for humanity; the potential *perils posed by AI* are frightening and many have commented on this, see e.g. (Metz, 2023b, 2023c), (Harari et al., 2023), (Harris & Raskin, 2023), and (Metz & Schmidt, 2023) for some thoughts about it. AI dangers are discussed in the third chapter of this book. But it is also worth noting here — even if that is not our main topic — that AI is not the only major challenge in desperate need of effective global cooperation.

It is becoming increasingly obvious — to anyone who cares to see it — that another menacing tempest is taking shape on the horizon of history. <u>*Climate change*</u> propelled by human beings is starting to decimate ecosystems and is already making some parts of the planet uninhabitable. Climate migrants are already on the move and, having nowhere to go, they are increasingly pushing on the international borders. It is estimated "that in this century we may have one billion climate migrants crossing international borders" (Remnick, 2023.) Yet, we human beings are unable to get our act together, even to slow it down, and our actions actually keep accelerating it (see e.g. IPCC report on climate change (IPCC, 2022)). In the 2023 paper (Hansen et al., 2023) published by James Hansen (he of the "godfather of climate science" fame, whose 1988 US Senate testimony is considered as the beginning of the age of climate alarm), and a group of collaborators, an alarming claim is made: even the scientists focused on climate risks have been systematically underestimating how much warming the planet is likely to experience in the very near future. The goal of the 2015 Paris Agreement on climate change, to limit warming to 1.5 degrees Celsius above preindustrial levels, is no longer possible. The "less ambitious" goal, limiting warming to less than 2 degrees Celsius — which is legally binding and to which the signatories formally agreed — already looks unrealistic. This alarming speed-up of global heating means that the world will be 1.5C hotter within the 2020s and 2C hotter sooner than 2050. Climate change is a global process, affecting everyone on the planet, and it has been growing into an epochal challenge to the survival of a civilized human society as we know it. As things stand today, our actions to prevent the approaching cataclysm have been very much localized and limited. Overall, we are more or less passively watching the tempest draw closer, most of us either occupied by our own self-interest (or frightened due to it), like spellbound, unable to rise up to the task which requires the entire humanity to unite and act in unison.

There is more. On yet another front, we can observe that many decades of our self-interested behavior increased _widespread societal inequalities worldwide_ (see e.g. (Deaton, 2023), (Piketty, 2014), (Wallace-Wells, 2023), (Hanauer, & Rolf, 2020), (Stiglitz, 2012, 2015), (Case & Deaton, 2021), (Deaton, 2013), (Milanovic, 2016, 2023), (Wilkinson & Pickett, 2009), (Wilkinson, 2011, 2021), (Krugman, 2022), (Price & Edwards, 2020), (Sachs, 2011), there is much more…; two poignant narratives about greed causing inequality and major societal damage can be found in (Goodman, 2022) and (Johnson & Kwak, 2010)). Together with the accompanying rise of _societal polarization_ (for some recent treatments on societal polarization see (Klein, 2020), (Radwell & Israel, 2021), (Varoufakis, 2017), (Goodman, 2022)), and _anti-democratic nationalism_ (see e.g. (Hedges, 2018), (LaFrance, 2022, 2023a), (Amanpour and Co., 2023a)), it is straining social fabric to the point that the _institutions of civilized society are seriously threatened_. Inequality is a corrosive and destructive force for human societies. Joseph Stiglitz, a Nobel laureate in economics, summarized the prospect we are facing if we don't find a way to overcome our behaviors that are causing inequality: "Widely unequal societies … are neither stable nor sustainable in the long term" (Stiglitz, 2012). Neoliberal economics (and now its remnants) has brought inequality to unprecedented levels by relentlessly pumping resources from poor to rich for several decades, and it still wreaks havoc as a major dehumanizing force, even if it is now considered a broken paradigm. Ponderings about which trends are shaping up to inherit the era of neoliberal economics are sobering; in the words of economist Brad DeLong, we can expect that whatever comes next will likely be "mixed with surviving Neoliberal remnants, ethno-nationalist populism, authoritarian state surveillance capitalism, or out-and-our neo-fascism" (DeLong, 2022b). And one more note relevant to our considerations here: the process of societal polarization has been enormously amplified by the proliferation of social media technologies (propelled by AI), which all too easily exhibit their shadow side (*The Great Hack* (2019) and *Social Dilemma* (2020) documentary movies are widely credited for raising awareness about it).

These are a few examples of major challenges facing humanity, all of them unsolvable unless we can all unite under a single banner and achieve effective global cooperation. The attempts we are currently waging to combat them are weak and they are mainly consisting of political and legal regulation. We are trying to "regulate" the beast of self-interest in human minds, but this is a losing battle, and we are failing.

[10] **human beings also have an innate compassionate side**: See for example (de Waal, 2009) and (Fromm, 1956, 1993). In his 2011 book *The Better Angels of Our Nature,* Steven Pinker acknowledges this fact in the following way: "We live in an age of empathy ... Here is a sample of titles and subtitles that have appeared in just the past two years: The Age of Empathy, Why Empathy Matters, The Social Neuroscience of Empathy, The Science of Empathy, The Empathy Gap, Why Empathy Is Essential (and Endangered), Empathy in the Global World, and How Companies Prosper When They Create Widespread Empathy. In yet another book, The Empathic Civilization." Pinker also remarks that even David Hume had to acknowledge it, albeit in a very minimal way: "[It] cannot be disputed that there is some benevolence, however small, infused into our bosom; some spark of friendship for human kind; some particle of the dove, kneaded into our frame, along with the elements of the wolf and serpent. Let these generous sentiments be supposed ever so weak; let them be insufficient to move even a hand or finger of our body; they must still direct the determinations of our mind, and where every thing else is equal, produce a cool preference of what is useful and

serviceable to mankind, above what is pernicious and dangerous.
—D avid Hume, An Enquiry Concerning the Principles of
Morals."

[11] **A society based purely on selfish motives and market
forces may produce wealth, yet it can't produce the unity and
mutual trust, etc**: (de Waal, 2009)

[12] **human beings mainly think in stories**: (Harari, 2018)

[13] **"idea whose time has come"**: This is an often-used quote
from Victor Hugo, actually paraphrased from a statement in *The
History of a Crime* (Hugo, 1877).

[14] **... worldview that is prevalent in the modern
Westernized developed world. While its foundations are
rooted in the ancient cultural heritage that spans many global
civilizations, it can be considered young in historical terms,
having been significantly shaped by the powerful influences
of the Renaissance and the Age of Enlightenment**: A
comprehensive and captivating history of the Western thought,
from the pre-Socratic Greeks to the present day, can be found in
Richard Tarnas's *The Passion of the Western World* (Tarnas, 1991).

[15] **"solitary, poor, nasty, brutish, and short"**: From
(Hobbes, 1651)

[16] **urged to see ourselves as separate individual units**:
Bertrand Russell, a Nobel laureate in literature, summarized this
disquieting and comfortless aspect of core beliefs of the Western
worldview in an essay *A Free Man's Worship*, by saying that for a
human being "his origin, his growth, his hopes and fears, his loves
and his beliefs, are but the outcome of accidental collocations of
atoms; that no fire, no heroism, no intensity of thought and
feeling, can preserve an individual life beyond the grave; that all the
labours of the ages, all the devotion, all the inspiration, all the
noonday brightness of human genius, are destined to extinction in
the vast death of the solar system, and that the whole temple of
Man's achievement must inevitably be buried beneath the débris of
a universe in ruins" (Russell B., 1903). In a similar vein, Jean-Paul
Sartre, a leading figure in the existentialist movement, ponders the
meaning of life from a modern perspective and states: "All existing
things are born for no reason, continue through weakness and die
by accident. ... It is meaningless that we are born; it is meaningless

that we die", (the first part is from (Sartre, 1938); the whole citation, in this translation, is from (Hepburn, 1966)).

[17] **next to impossible to act truly cooperatively**: A related perspective about modern Western culture echoes through Barack Obama's commencement speech to graduates at Northwestern University: "we live in a culture that discourages empathy. A culture that too often tells us our principal goal in life is to be rich, thin, young, famous, safe, and entertained... [and] encourage[s] these selfish impulses." (Obama, 2006).

[18] **if this worldview were true and complete, why would we even bother?**: Contrary to the sentiment of this question, there are some very erudite and valiant attempts out there (for example (Pinker, 2018)) trying to point out how humans are naturally predisposed to ethics, how all is (more or less) good with us, and how the ideas of the Age of Enlightenment, in their contemporary understanding, can provide good enough answers to deep existential questions, like "Why should I live?", and they often state that "life has been getting better and better for more and more people" and actually "[e]verything is amazing". In my view, yes, history and facts show us that humanity has been making significant progress; however, we should keep the sensitivity for the burning existential questions alive, lest we indeed end up like a character in Steven Pinker's anecdote who, while falling off the roof says "so far so good" as he passes each floor. We should not mock, but try to understand the existential depth and real dread behind the questions like "What advice do you have for someone who has taken ideas in your books and science to heart, and sees himself as a collection of atoms? A machine with a limited scope of intelligence, sprung out of selfish genes, inhabiting spacetime?" Yes, ideals of the Age of Enlightenment, "reason, science, and humanism," are indeed "stirring, inspiring, [and] noble"; however, why would we think that they are sufficient to assuage our existential dreads? (quotes are from Pinker, 2018, p. 3-6, 283, 290). People may not be "oblivious" to the scope of human progress, but can still experience existential dread. The voice from within may be telling them that some hidden aspect of their essential nature is being attacked and suffocated, even if they are well-fed, entertained, and safe. Paul Krugman ponders this aspect in his column "Despair, American Style" (Krugman, 2015): "the truth is that we don't really know why despair appears to be spreading ...

But it clearly is, with troubling consequences for our society as a whole. ... you probably expect me to offer a solution. But while universal health care, higher minimum wages, aid to education, and so on would do a lot to help Americans in trouble, I'm not sure whether they're enough to cure existential despair." Viktor Frankl discusses this phenomenon in (Frankl, 1946), where he termed it "existential vacuum." In his work *Existential Psychotherapy* (Yalom, 1980), Irvin Yalom focused on several ultimate life concerns (death, freedom, isolation, and meaninglessness) that he believed contributed to the existential vacuum. Existential philosophers have been trying to address this phenomenon since the 19th century. We have many leads, but don't seem to be able to find good enough answers; existential dread is on the rise and is indeed already weighing heavily on modern humanity.

[19] **willingly conform to traditions, societal norms, even authoritarian structures of the group**: Erich Fromm was one of the pioneers of this notion, e.g., in his work *Escape from Freedom* (Fromm, 1941).

[20] **Some traditional worldviews promote wisdom that can curb selfish individual impulses, ensuring harmonious group life**: A case in point is the traditional tribal worldview, articulated by the 17th-century indigenous leader, Wandat chief Kandiaronk, who conveyed his tribe's views to the European settlers — as recalled in anthropologist David Graeber and archaeologist David Wengrow's book *The Dawn of Everything: A New History of Humanity* — that it is "unaccountable that one man should have more than another, and that the rich should have more respect than the poor." He believed that only in inhumane societies could people choose to devote themselves to the endless pursuit of more money, stating that to "imagine one can live in the country of money and preserve one's soul is like imagining one can preserve one's life at the bottom of a lake. Money is the father of luxury, lasciviousness, intrigues, trickery, lies, betrayal, insincerity—of all the world's worst behavior." (Graeber & Wengrow, 2021, p. 48-59).

[21] **universal, cosmopolitan worldview**: A short philosophical overview of the cosmopolitan ideal can be found in (Kleingeld & Brown, 2019).
Note that the focus in this book is not so much on the political and economic aspects of the cosmopolitan idea, one can consider these aspects as technical details if there are enough human beings who

wholeheartedly embrace the cosmopolitan ideal. Our main concern here is how to enable and unleash the impulse in many individual human beings, who in the depths of their inner life yearn, seek to adopt, and strive for the cosmopolitan ideal.

[22] **not unlike how the youngest child is treated in many fairy tales**: "Simpleton" or "dummling" youngest son motive is often found in fairy tales and stories, for example in *Water of Life*, *The Golden Goose*, and *The Golden Bird* (Grimm & Grimm, 1812). One can also view in this way Frodo from Tolkien's *The Lord of the Rings* (Tolkien, 1955), also immortalized in Peter Jackson's *The Lord of the Rings* film trilogy (2001-2003), evident e.g. in Saruman's talk to Gandalf: "You did not seriously think that a Hobbit could contend with the will of Sauron?"

[23] **adopt a position that this indeed represents a possibility**: For human beings entrenched in the modern Western worldview, this may require a *leap of faith* of sorts, in some ways not unlike the process described in *Fear and Trembling* (Kierkegaard, 1843).

[24] **science … seems ill-equipped to deal with the phenomena of the mind**: Thomas Nagel famously expressed this conundrum (even if he focused only on consciousness as one phenomenon of mind): "Without consciousness the mind-body problem would be much less interesting. With consciousness it seems hopeless. The most important and characteristic feature of conscious mental phenomena is very poorly understood. Most reductionist theories do not even try to explain it … Perhaps a new theoretical form can be devised for the purpose, but such a solution, if it exists, lies in the distant intellectual future." (Nagel, 1974).

[25] **texture of the therapist-client relationship**: See interview with Irvin Yalom in (Yalom, 2009).

[26] **"science progresses one funeral at a time"**: This is a paraphrase of a longer statement Max Planck made in his "Scientific Autobiography" published in 1949, where he says: "A new scientific truth does not triumph by convincing its opponents and making them see the light, but rather because its opponents eventually die and a new generation grows up that is familiar with it" (Planck, 1968, 33); see also one recent study about the topic: (Azoulay, 2019).

[27] **You will find [nature] delightful and entrancing**: Richard Feynman lecture *The Character of Physical Law - Part 6 Probability and uncertainty - the quantum mechanical view of nature* (Feynman, 1964).

[28] **we can only tinker on their edges with the currently accepted scientific approach**: It should be acknowledged that significant progress has indeed been made in the field of neuroscience in the last decades. This progress is mainly based on several key technological innovations (fMRI, PET scanning, electric or magnetic neurostimulation, optogenetics/photostimulation, to name a few), which enable us to better understand which parts of the brain are active when the mind performs a given task and to manipulate the activity of neurons in the brain. However, despite this progress, we haven't really made much of a movement in terms of understanding how the conscious mind is related to the brain. In this respect, we are still where we were in classical antiquity, also where we were back in 1866, when Thomas Huxley remarked that "what consciousness is, we know not; and how it is that anything so remarkable as a state of consciousness comes about as the result of irritating nervous tissue, is just as unaccountable as the appearance of the Djin when Aladdin rubbed his lamp," (Huxley, 1866). Closer to our time, in 1994, Nobel laureate Francis Crick reiterated that "Consciousness is a subject about which there is little consensus, even as to what the problem is." (Crick, 1994, p. xii) and "…we do not yet know, even in outline, how our brains produce the vivid visual awareness that we take so much for granted … we lack both the detailed information and the ideas to answer the most simple questions: How do I see color? What is happening when I recall the image of a familiar face? And so on." (Crick, 1994, p. 24). About two decades later, in 2012, Christof Koch wrote: "How the brain converts bioelectrical activity into subjective states … is a puzzle. The nature of the relationship between the nervous system and consciousness remains elusive and the subject of heated and interminable debates." (Koch, 2012a, p. 23). We continue to be puzzled by the whole phenomenon: "…at this point we have … little ideas how consciousness comes about" (Koch, 2015) and "despite increasingly refined clinical and experimental studies, a proper understanding of the relationship between consciousness and the brain has yet to be established" (Tononi et al., 2016). Antonio Damasio states that "The business of understanding how

the brain makes a conscious mind remains unfinished. The mystery of consciousness is still a mystery" (Damasio, 2010). Stuart Russell reminds us that "while we know a great deal about the biochemistry of neurons and synapses and the anatomical structures of the brain, the neural implementation of the cognitive level—learning, knowing, remembering, reasoning, planning, deciding, and so on—is still mostly anyone's guess", he also points us to (Siegfried, 2017), (Neuron special issue, 2017), (Gorman, 2014); see (Russell S. J., 2019). In the face of this, one could remain persistent and argue that there is no need to change the course yet, neuroscience may still be the domain where the explanation for the brain-mind connection is to be found. On the other hand, after many decades of intense focus on neuroscience, we might want to step back and widen our horizon for the research.

[29] **just talking openly about it might have been a career suicide for a scientist**: Christof Koch, who worked with Francis Crick on the problem of the brain and its link to consciousness since the late 1980s, writes about this period: "…writing about consciousness was taken as a sign of cognitive decline. Retired Nobel laureates could do it, as could mystics and philosophers, but not serious academics in the natural sciences. Betraying an interest in the mind-body problem beyond that of a hobby was ill-advised for a young professor, particularly one who had not yet attained tenure. Consciousness was a fringy subject: graduate students, always finely attuned to the mores and attitudes of their elders, rolled their eyes and smiled indulgently when the subject came up." (Koch, 2012a). In (Burkeman, 2015) we are reminded that "As late as 1989, writing in the International Dictionary of Psychology [about] consciousness [was] that "it is impossible to specify what it is, what it does, or why it evolved. Nothing worth reading has been written on it.""

[30] **an opening for a radically new science of the mind has started to emerge and has already been advocated for**: To mention several examples: renowned biologist and Nobel laureate Sir Paul Nurse states the following regarding the prospect of finding satisfactory answers about abstract thought, self-consciousness, and free will: "I do not think we can rely only on the tools of the traditional natural sciences to get there. We will have to additionally embrace insights from psychology, philosophy and the humanities more generally." (Nurse, 2021). Thomas Nagel

considers the "dominant scientific naturalism" and views it as "incapable of providing an adequate account, either constitutive or historical, of our universe" (Nagel, 2012). Galen Strawson believes that only a new "revolutionary" way of thinking might be able to address the mind-body problem (Strawson, 1994). Philip Goff also states that "[n]othing less than revolution is called for" (Goff, 2019).

[31] **started to ponder and point to some possible alternatives**: For example, see (McGilchrist I., 2021), (Strawson et al., 2006), (Nagel, 2012), and (Goff, 2019) to name a few.

[32] **caused by some other process in a "physical substrate," as is often speculated**: The notion that the mind is simply a secondary "emergent" phenomenon, and that it is created/caused/constructed by a "physical substrate" (i.e. brain) is simply assumed in many circles, the correlation observed in experiments is assumed to be causation; there are many examples for this in the scientific literature, see e.g. (Crick, 1994), (Tononi, 2016), (Koch, 2019), (Seth, 2021), just to name a few. Specifically for emotion, it has been stated that the "brain constructs instances of emotion ... in the normal way that the brain constructs any other mental state" (Barrett, 2017). Patricia Churchland acknowledges that "brain science has not developed far enough" to explain a phenomenon of mind like consciousness, but still harbors a fervent belief and states: "I am who I am because my brain is what it is." (Churchland P.S., 2013) Similarly, Steven Pinker, even if he agrees that "we don't understand how the mind works" also firmly states that "the mind is what the brain does" (Pinker, 2009).

[33] **theories with respect to the relationship of physical phenomena and mind phenomena**: A comprehensive overview can be found in (Chalmers, 2010).

[34] **dismissing them as byproducts, as "illusions" or "hallucinations"**: Illusionism is looking for an easy way out – there is no need to understand and explain consciousness (and other aspects of mind) if we simply declare a belief that they don't exist; this is the "most extreme version" of reductionism (Chalmers, 2022). It somehow became quite common to refer to consciousness and self as "illusion," "user-illusion," "hallucination," or "controlled hallucination," even "trick with mirrors", e.g. see (Wegner, 2014), (Harris, 2014), (Dennett, 1991,

2017), (Gazzaniga, 2018), (Seth, 2021). Emotions have been referred to as "hallucinations of the body" (Damasio, 2010). Such statements are often proclaimed with certainty and conviction as if they represent a fact of some kind, but they are mere beliefs, attempts to provide descriptive illustrations, and philosophical speculations of sorts. Moreover, such statements use terms (illusion & hallucination), whose meaning we can't even define without in some way already assuming the consciousness or mind of an agent – the very entity (or "user") that experiences an illusory or hallucinated perception; illusions and hallucinations can't alone perceive themselves after all. The persuasiveness and aura of certainty of such statements are purely psychological, not factual. A concise counterargument can be found in (Strawson, 2018). We should also mention that, already in the 18th century, Hume famously said — as if to foreshadow this way of speculating about the inner experience — of the human self the following: "I am certain there is no such principle in me." He believed that the self is somehow just a conglomerate of internal and external perceptions. In his view, there is only "some particular perception or other, of heat or cold, light or shade, love or hatred, pain or pleasure. I never can ... observe any thing but the perception." (Hume, 1739).

(As an aside, in this work I am treating these "self-as-illusion" and related illusionist views separately from the notion of "non-self" (anattā/anātman) in Buddhism, as they are different concepts. This topic is explored elsewhere in this book. See also note #362, and insightful treatment of this topic in *Analytical Buddhism: The Two-tiered Illusion of Self* (Albahari, 2006).)

³⁵ **need a "physical substrate" in the brain where we should be able to find their causes**: Several proposals regarding the so called "physical substrate" have appeared in the last three decades: Neural Correlates of Consciousness (NCC) in the brain have been proposed by Crick and Koch, see e.g. (Crick, 1994), (Koch, 2004) and (Koch et al., 2016). Integrated Information Theory (IIT) postulates the Physical Substrate of Consciousness (PSC) in the brain, with the hope that we will discover "physical causes" in it for every conscious experience, see e.g. (Tononi et al., 2016). (Havlík et al., 2023) provides an overview of the field of empirical neuroscience researching causal mechanisms of consciousness; authors agree that "conscious experience represents

one of the most elusive problems of current empirical science", the field currently "consists of highly speculative theories … and an ever-growing list of knowledge gaps" and is "nowhere near to answering" fundamental questions, but have an expectation that future experiments with active interference with brain circuitry via neurostimulation might bring us closer to "causal explanations" of how the brain might give rise to conscious experience (this last point is discussed in a separate note #37.)

[36] **"that we have a firm grasp of what the brain is and what it does is pure folly":** (Damasio, 2010).

[37] **we have only correlations and speculations to show for it, nothing more:** It should be noted that several scientists have tried to claim in the past that we have discovered brain-mind causal explanations for some phenomena of consciousness. This is misleading as some relationships between events may indeed appear as causations, but to claim that conclusively, we would need to understand the underlying mind-brain process. We shouldn't simply assume that the brain gives rise to the mind and then interpret experimental results within that framework as the only possibility. We should also allow for other possibilities; for example, the brain could serve merely as a filter or receiver (in the same way a radio or streaming device is just a receiver, it doesn't create the music it plays in any way, even if interfering with the device can affect the music output through its loudspeaker). One example of this is the statement made in a TED talk (Kanwisher, 2014) that a specific brain region (fusiform gyrus) is "causally involved with face perception"; this is based on the experiment published in (Parvizi et al., 2012), where electrical brain stimulation was able to affect face perception. Another, very intriguing, experiment from Parvizi's Stanford lab (Lyu et al., 2023) reports that electrical brain stimulation (posteromedial cortex, anterior precuneus) was able to affect participants' subjective experiences of bodily self, including inducing dizziness and even detachment. Yet another example is the use of the electrical brain stimulation of the claustrum region in the brain, by which consciousness could be disrupted/reinstated (Koubeissi et al., 2014), and optogenetic stimulation, where claustrum stimulation silences brain activity across the cortex (Narikiyo et al., 2020). All these, and similar, experiments are very suggestive of causation, but in all of them we seem to be dealing only with one necessary link in the process

chain; and we don't know yet how or why that link produces the observed effects. It is established that the brain does play some role in at least some aspects of consciousness, but that does not automatically imply causation. Many interpretations are possible from the scientific point of view, brain might be only one link in the causal chain, it might also be a sort of "reducing valve" (the term Aldous Huxley used, and experiments with psychedelics also suggest: psychedelics silence brain activity, rather than increase it; see e.g. (Koch, 2012b), (Huxley, 1954, 1956), (Kastrup, 2023)), or the brain may be performing a reflective function (like a mirror) for the more fundamental mind processes during the abstract reasoning; scientifically speaking any of this could be possible. The already mentioned (and often used) analogy of a radio/streaming device can also easily be utilized to suggest an alternative explanation. For example, if we remove a single wire from the receiving/streaming device, we may affect the reception of music, maybe stop it altogether, if we put the wire back, the music comes back as before the experiment. That doesn't mean that the wire in question, or the device itself, "causes" or participates in any way in the creation of music, it is just one link necessary to transmit the music to the loudspeaker. In some ways it might be technically correct, but still misleading, to say that the wire is "causally involved" with the music played on the device. It would be closer to the factual reality to state that removal of the wire can affect the music output, in the same way that neurostimulation in the brain can affect some aspect of consciousness - that is all these experiments reveal to us.

[38] **"significantly different from the rather crude materialistic way many neuroscientists hold today"**: (Crick, 1994, 262-3)

[39] **An example may illustrate...**: In addition to the example used in the main text, another commonly used example is to consider the brain analogous to a radio (or TV) receiver so that "perhaps like a radio set, the brain [picks] up at least something of whatever it was from out there, and that became what is experienced" (McGilchrist I., 2019, p. 196). The receiver just receives signals from a distant transmitter while it plays music. Receiver, with all its circuitry, is necessary for us to hear the music, which is actually created elsewhere (and this is true even if we can affect the output by tinkering with the receiver's circuitry). The

point is that unless we understand the underlying mechanism, we cannot claim causality, in this case receiver clearly doesn't cause music, it is just one connecting link. In the words of psychiatrist and neuroscientist Iain McGilchrist: "I do not know that the brain 'causes' consciousness: it might or might not. For example, it might transduce, or otherwise mediate, consciousness" and "[w]hile no-one could possibly dispute the existence of an intimate relationship between brain and mind, the nature of that relationship remains highly disputable. ... do we know that matter can give rise to consciousness? This is merely an assumption. When a TV set malfunctions, it can distort the image or sound it relays in a large number of ways, depending on where in the system the malfunction lies. ... To an observer from another planet, it might prove impossible to tell that the TV set did not generate, but merely transmitted, its material: pull the plug and the show ceases to exist."(McGilchrist I., 2021, p. 54, p. 1591). Other alternatives have also been pondered. For example, Aldous Huxley proposed that we may consider the brain as a reducing valve of sorts, which captures some of the realities in the practically unlimited realities of the mind, like snapshots of mind reality: "To make biological survival possible, Mind at Large has to be funneled through the reducing valve of the brain and nervous system." He also suggested that psychedelic drugs might be suspending the activity of this reducing valve. See (Huxley, 1954, 1956). Psychedelics are indeed found to affect the brain in such a way that they quiet it down and stop much of its activity, rather than increasing it, see also e.g. (Koch, 2012b) and (Kastrup, 2023). Therefore, these few examples of possible (even if unproven) alternatives illustrate the fact that it is premature to claim a causal link from brain to mind before we can understand the underlying processes.

[40] **The notion that we should view ourselves only as sophisticated machines is based on unproven and incorrect opinions**: See further discussion about pertinent scientific facts in the second chapter, particularly about the modern research in the fields of evolution and natural selection, under sections: *Evolution, and its Pernicious Misunderstanding as "Survival of the Fittest"*, and *Evolutionary Molecular Biology on the Frontiers of Science*. See also (Bongard & Levin, 2021).

[41] **outdated, woefully incomplete, and one-sided interpretation of evolution (Herbert Spencer's "survival of the**

fittest"): See further discussion about science in the second chapter, particularly about modern research in the fields of evolution and natural selection.

[42] **evolving to support our "selfish genes"**: From *The Selfish Gene* (Dawkins, 1976), where an unfounded belief is blatantly stated that we are all just "survival machines—robot vehicles that are blindly programmed to preserve the selfish molecules known as genes" and that "pure, disinterested altruism ... has no place in nature." Primatologist Frans de Waal considers this and observes that even "Poor Darwin must be turning in his grave, because the world implied here is totally unlike what he himself envisioned" (de Waal, 2001). The fact that in his book Dawkins also introduced the idea of *memes* — units of cultural information, akin to genes, that "replicate," "mutate," and "evolve," thus shaping human culture and social evolution — doesn't change his main assumption that human beings are essentially "machines," and that all evolution depends on random chance mutations at the onset of any change. A related idea has also been used by other authors, for example by biologist E.O. Wilson in his 1998 book *Consilience*, where he considers memes to be biological "units of culture ... [equivalent to] its correlates in brain activity." See also further discussion about pertinent scientific facts related to this in the second chapter of this book, particularly about modern research in the fields of evolution and natural selection.

[43] **connecting line from the physical brain to the mind is unproven, it is in fact "highly disputable"**: From The *Matter with Things* by a psychiatrist and neuroscientist, Iain McGilchrist (2021, p. 1591).

[44] **don't fully know what ... life really is**: A case in point is represented by positions given in the recent book "What is Life?" (Nurse, 2021) by the renowned biologist and Nobel laureate Sir Paul Nurse. In it he affirms that living beings are for any observer "obviously alive" and they "[seem] so full of purpose"; however, it is rather difficult to provide a scientific answer to "what is life? I have been thinking about this question for much of my life, but finding a satisfactory answer is not easy. Perhaps surprisingly, there is no standard definition of life, although scientists have wrestled with this question across the ages." In this book, he seeks to portray and characterize life with the five "overarching ideas" of scientific biology to "help us make sense of life in all its

complexity." He ultimately sides with the reductionist interpretation that "living entities are chemical, physical and informational machines"; however, he acknowledges that how our "abilities to think, to debate, to imagine, to create and to suffer … [emerge] from the wet chemistry of our brains provides us with an extraordinarily challenging set of questions." In terms of epigenetic and related phenomena playing out particularly during the development of living organisms, Nurse states that "[u]nderstanding how structures form at larger scales, in objects such as organelles, cells, organs and whole organisms is more difficult. Direct molecular interactions between components cannot explain how these structures form." In a similar vein, he also acknowledges Schrödinger's position about the concept of life, outlined in the book with the same title "What is Life?" (Schrödinger, 1944): "he argued that to really explain how life works, we might need a new and as yet undiscovered type of physical law." Nurse manages to maintain a sort of reverent attitude towards the idea of life by referring to it as one of the "most fascinating and mysterious" aspects of the "awe-inspiring universe."

[45] **no free will**: We have well-known thinkers like Sam Harris, Robert Sapolsky, Derk Pereboom, Gregg Caruso, and others proclaiming that human beings have no free will. This is despite the fact that the idea of determinism is a mere assumption and did not come through science. We will return to this topic in the main text repeatedly. For a few alternative perspectives, see *Yes, Free Will Exists, Just Ask Schopenhauer* (Kastrup, 2020) and *My Go-To Arguments for Free Will* (Horgan, 2020). Another topic, often discussed in connection with the concept of free will is the well-known *Libet experiment* (Libet et al., 1983), which was interpreted by some as evidence that human beings have no free will. It in fact doesn't demonstrate that, and even the ardent supporters of the "there is no free will doctrine" agree with this position; Robert Sapolsky devotes a whole chapter to it in his 2023 book *Determined* (Sapolsky, 2023), and even he concludes that "Free will, I believe, survives Libetianism" (p. 36). See also (Taylor, 2019). We won't discuss the Libet experiment here since it is already widely covered in the literature.

[46] **we are just "robots" who find it useful to persuade ourselves that we are autonomous beings**: See e.g., *The Selfish*

Gene (Dawkins, 1976), also *Iris Murdoch Against the Robots* (Brown, 2012). Daniel Dennett ponders that humans could indeed be robots because he assumes that "in principle, a suitably 'programmed' robot, ... would be conscious, would have a self." Scientifically speaking we have no idea that this could be true, nothing in our body of knowledge points toward such a conclusion. He then he further observes that some people already have an opinion that such position is simply "obvious and unobjectionable. 'Of course we're machines! We're just very, very complicated, evolved machines made of organic molecules instead of metal and silicon, and we are conscious, so there can be conscious machines—us.' " (Dennett, 1991). Mere opinions and facts should be kept separate on any quest for truth.

[47] **everything is pre-determined by movements of physical stuff (as described in the laws of physics of our day)**: See e.g. (Walsh, 2023), (Carroll S.M., 2016), and (Carroll & Kuhn, 2017, 2022).

[48] **folks supporting *free will determinism***: See e.g. (Walsh, 2023) and (Dennett & Caruso, 2021).

[49] **supporters of *free will compatibilism***: See e.g. (Walsh, 2023) and (Dennett & Caruso, 2021).

[50] **we are just a bunch of atoms and atoms are going to do whatever they were going to do**: See (Carroll S.M., 2016), also (Walsh, 2023), and (Dennett & Caruso, 2021)

[51] **since Newton challenged a purely mechanistic mindset, ... the word "physical" became more of an honorific term**: Chomsky terms it "collapse of the mechanical philosophy," which he identifies as "the last serious effort to develop a positive and purportedly complete account of the 'material world' " (Antony & Hornstein, 2003), see also (Chomsky et al., 2002, 51-2), and discussion in chapter IV in (Chomsky, 2016).

[52] **Nobody knows exactly how that works, this is like a black box to us**: An informative essay "Even Physicists Don't Understand Quantum Mechanics", by Sean Carroll, can be found in (Carroll S.M., 2019).

[53] **there are several contending theories**: Much has been written about the interpretation of quantum physics; for a concise explanation see (Myrvold, 2022), also e.g. (Carroll S.M., 2016, 2019).

[54] **"there are real mysteries associated with quantum mechanics"**: (Carroll S.M., 2016, p.366).

[55] **nobody has the slightest notion what it means**: Russel's citation is taken from (Hájek, 2019). The concept of probability is not well understood, we fundamentally don't know what it is, even if we can intuitively grasp that a coin toss has a 50% probability for the head to end up on top – but that is only valid until the experiment is done, at which point the probability "collapses" and we learn the outcome.

[56] **we still have a limited understanding of what matter really is**: While the physicalist world view still seems to be prevalent among scientists today, different views of the nature of reality started to emerge after quantum physics became the mainstream paradigm. We will return to this later in the main text but can note at this point that other alternatives to physicalism have been offered, some of them in recent decades. For example, computer scientist and philosopher Bernardo Kastrup, e.g. in his book *Idea of the World: A Multi-disciplinary Argument for the Mental Nature of Reality* (Kastrup, 2019), has argued that physicalism does not adequately explain the nature of consciousness and subjective experiences. He promotes an idealistic perspective on reality in which the physical world and all physical phenomena are simply manifestations of a universal consciousness. Donald Hoffman suggests yet another alternative in which the physical world emerges from the primary reality of consciousness (Hoffman D., 2019). There is also a sort of a revival of the worldview of panpsychism, see e.g. (Goff et al., 2022a), (Goff et al., 2022b), (Goff, 2019), and (Strawson et al., 2006). For an overview of several theories see (Chalmers, 2010).

[57] **how can we claim that it is fully deterministic**: Richard Feynman articulated the non-deterministic nature of quantum physics by stating that there is "probability all the way back at the fundamental laws", and that the future "is unpredictable: it is impossible to predict in any way, from any information ahead of time." He also challenged the statement of an imaginary philosopher of science speaking in favor of determinism: "it is necessary for the very existence of science that the same conditions always produce the same result," and answered it by simply stating what experimental results tell us: "Well, they don't." (Feynman,

1964). See also *Does Quantum Mechanics Rule Out Free Will?* (Horgan, 2022).

[58] "all we are is the outcome of what came before, and what came before that, and what came before that... we are nothing more or less than the sum of biology over which we have no control... personal responsibility doesn't make any sense": (Sapolsky & Smerconish, 2023).

[59] as Sapolsky also (partially) accepts in *Determined*: "no single result or scientific discipline can [disprove free will]. But—and this is the incredibly important point—put all the scientific results together, from all the relevant scientific disciplines, and there's no room for free will": (Sapolsky, 2023, p. 8).

[60] Sapolsky seems to actually agree with this, as his rhetorical question "Why would we bother getting up in the morning if we're just machines?" is answered by "Hey, don't ask me that; that's too difficult to answer": (Sapolsky, 2023, p. 244).

[61] we have a bad habit of wanting to believe that laws of physics are solid ... as if we have already discovered everything important there is to discover: See e.g. (Carroll & Kuhn, 2017, 2022), (Walsh, 2023), (Carroll S.M., 2016).

[62] we have discovered all fundamental forces that can affect matter, "we are done" has been proclaimed: Sean Carroll in (Walsh, 2023).

[63] gravity: It should be noted that in Einstein's general theory of relativity, gravity is linked to the curvature of the spacetime continuum.

[64] Great enigmas abound in manifestations of all stages of developing life and what we call living beings (e.g. causes underlying *epigenetics* and *developmental bioelectric networks* of living organisms are a complete mystery to us presently): This characterization can also be heard from eminent researchers in biology; for example in a compendium, which grew out of the 2021 London conference *Evolution on Purpose*, we read that scientists consider that we have "important gaps in our understanding of some of the major open questions of biology, such as the origin and organization of organismal form, the relationship between development and evolution, and the biological bases of cognition

and mind" (Corning et al., 2023). *Developmental electricity* experiments are moving the frontier of science and are in need of explanation regarding the underlying causes of the observed phenomena, e.g. (Levin, 2020) and (Levin, 2023c). See also the discussion about science in the second chapter, particularly about the recent research (last few decades) in the fields of molecular biology, evolution, and natural selection.

[65] **we don't really know whether the mind is a manifestation of physical matter, or is it maybe the other way around**: some additional thoughts in this direction can be found e.g. in (Nadeau & Kafatos, 2001) and (Schäfer, 2013).

[66] **Galen Strawson reminds us in his Guardian article**: (Strawson, 2019).

[67] **Planck even elaborated further: "I regard matter as derivative from consciousness..."**: (The Observer, 1931).

[68] **What Is It Like to Be a Bat?**: (Nagel, 1974).

[69] **"at the present time [solution to the problem of consciousness] seems far too difficult"**: (Crick, 1994, p. xi).

[70] **we are basically "nothing but a pack of neurons"**: (Crick, 1994, p. 3).

[71] **hard problem of consciousness**: David Chalmers acknowledges the problem we are facing already in the opening of his first paper on the topic, with the following words: "Consciousness poses the most baffling problems in the science of the mind. There is nothing that we know more intimately than conscious experience, but there is nothing that is harder to explain ... To make progress on the problem of consciousness, we have to confront it directly." (Chalmers, 1995).

[72] **debate about consciousness**: Several good overviews and (mainly) recent contributions can be found for example in (Chalmers, 2002), (van Gulick, 2022), (Bayne, 2022), (Chalmers, 2010), and (Shear, 1997). An argument against considering consciousness to be only an "illusion" can be found in (Strawson, 2018). Also worth noting in this context is that this debate is focusing not only on the concept and nature of *consciousness*, but also — albeit not quite overtly — on the concept of *being*, which is intuitive to our inner experience, but it is somehow too spooky for modern science to deal with at this point, so it appears that the

term that comes closest to it is *unity of consciousness* - for an overview see chapter 14 *What is the Unity of Consciousness* written by Bayne & Chalmers in (Chalmers, 2010).

[73] **several contending interpretations**: For several perspectives see (Chalmers, 2010), (Bayne, 2022), (Goff et al., 2022a), (Goff et al., 2022b), (Goff, 2019), and (Strawson et al., 2006), and (Kastrup, 2019).

[74] **even if no clear consensus has yet emerged about why (or how) it is that we have a first-person inner subjective experience**: Tim Bayne's statement at the conclusion of the discourse titled *The Self* encapsulates this sentiment: "Whatever else we might be, we are certainly the kinds of beings that find questions about our own nature deeply puzzling." (Bayne, 2022).

[75] **we need to develop a curiosity for observation and a will for critical inquiry in this domain**: This is said in a spirit similar to that harbored in remarks made by Alison Gopnik, a renowned developmental psychologist and philosopher of mind, who — even after proclaiming to be a devout atheist — stated: "The human capacity for change means that we can't figure out what it is to be human just by looking at the way we are now. We need instead to peer forward into the vast ramifying space of human possibilities" (Gopnik, 2009, p. 247).

[76] **Schrödinger called it *deception***: see Epilog in *What is Life?* (Schrödinger, 1944).

[77] ***experience of what both Plato and Plotinus refer to as The One or The Good***: just as an introductory note, it should be mentioned here that Plato's dialogues, for example *Republic* and the *Parmenides*, discuss the idea of a singular, transcendent principle (Plato, 1996 [c. 370s BC], *Republic VI*, 509b; *Parmenides*, 137c). Plato describes *The Good* as the ultimate form or idea, and as the source of all reality. This concept has many parallels with the concept of *The One* used by Plotinus in *Enneads* to refer to absolute simplicity and unity, from which everything emanates, these concepts have been examined extensively in philosophy, for a sample see e.g. (Hadot et al., 1993), (Mazur et al., 2021), (Turner et al., 2013), also e.g. (Plato, 1996 [c. 390-350s BC]) and (Plotinus, 2018 [c. 253-270]) as primary sources.

Note on primary sources for Plato: In addition to the standard book formats, several audiobooks (acted and narrated by a group of actors led by Ray Childs) are also available.

[78] **Plato hints at it**: There are many indications that Plato's doctrine goes beyond what he wrote and published. A whole new discipline of "Plato's Unwritten Doctrines" seems to have sprung to research it. As already indicated, Plato's written works were only meant to help his readers approach the more profound "knowledge of the subjects to which I devote myself" and about which "I have composed no work … for there is no way of putting it in words like other studies" because "acquaintance with it must come rather after a long period of attendance on instruction in the subject itself, and communion therewith, when suddenly, like a blaze kindled by a leaping spark, it is generated in the soul and at once becomes self-sustaining" (Plato, 1989, 1996; [orig. 353 BC], *Epistle VII*, 341c-d).

[79] **Plotinus unambiguously (even if somewhat cursory) describes a process that leads to the inner experience of unity with *The One***: See (Plotinus, 2018 [c. 253-270]); structure and method of Plotinus's spiritual ascent have become a research topic of interest, particularly in the last two decades, see e.g. (Mazur et al., 2021), (Stróżyński, 2022, 2020, 2014), (Turner et al., 2013). Pierre Hadot's research on Plotinus can be found in (Hadot, 2004, 1995, 1993).

[80] **term coined by renowned philosopher Pierre Hadot, e.g. in his work *Spiritual Exercises from Socrates to Foucault***: (Hadot, 1995).

[81] **the entirety of Western philosophical tradition is but "a series of footnotes to Plato"**: The exact quote is "The safest general characterization of the European philosophical tradition is that it consists of a series of footnotes to Plato" (Whitehead 1978, p. 39).

[82] **ugly duckling**: *Ugly Duckling* is a fairy tale written in 1843 by H.C. Andersen. See (Andersen, 2014).

[83] **there are many noteworthy exceptions – eminent philosophers, such as Iris Murdoch, Julia Annas, and those in the scholarly orbit of Gregory Vlastos (among many others I fail to mention!)**: Just to name a few (in full knowledge that this list is unjustifiably leaving many important thinkers out!): Iris Murdoch, Julia Annas, Gregory Vlastos, Richard Kraut, Terence Irwin, Paul Woodruff, Alexander Nehamas, and many others.

[84] In her book *The Sovereignty of Good*, Iris Murdoch points to the existence of *The Good* and breaks it to us that we are, in fact, not robots, "we are moral agents.": (Murdoch, 1970), see also (Brown, 2012).

[86] described in Mystic, Gnostic, and multiple other sources: See also Aldous Huxley's *The Perennial Philosophy* (1945).

[87] related inner experiences have been reported during recent trials involving psychedelic drugs: See the 2019 documentary *Fantastic Fungi*, also (Gopnik, 2023c), (Nardou et al., 2023), (Pollan, 2018), (Kastrup, 2016), (WSJ, 2014), and (Huxley, 1954, 1956).

[88] result of physical body suppression via a substance: Recent fMRI studies of subjects under the influence of psychedelics show that the brain quiets down and stops much of its activity, rather than increase it; see the previous note, also e.g. (Koch, 2012b), (Kastrup, 2023), and (Huxley, 1954, 1956).

[89] "the grandest of all thoughts": see Epilog in (Schrödinger, 1944)

[90] *Perennial Philosophy*: (Huxley, 1944).

[91] *The Doors of Perception*: (Huxley, 1954).

[92] *Heaven and Hell*: (Huxley, 1956).

[93] *The Art of Being*: (Fromm, 1993).

[94] *To Have Or to Be*: (Fromm, 1976).

[95] *Civilization and Its Discontents*: (Freud, 1930)

[96] on Roman Rolland, "renowned for his humanitarianism and pleas for tolerance between peoples and nations": (Parsons, 1999).

[97] the crude materialist notion that human beings are only complex machines, automatons without free will … is considered here as unfounded and misguided speculation: Embodying this vein, Viktor Frankl reminds us that a "human being is not one thing among others; things determine each other, but man is ultimately self-determining" (Frankl, 1946). The term "thing among things" was previously introduced by Jean-Paul Sartre (1943) as an epitome of the idea that human beings are not fundamentally different from objects in the world. For Sartre,

humans are unique in that they possess consciousness and freedom, which sets them apart. However, when humans are treated as mere objects — by society, by other people, or even by themselves — they become a "thing among things," losing their unique human characteristics of freedom and choice.

[98] **free will ... hard determinist and compatibilist**: See e.g. (Dennett & Caruso, 2021) and (Walsh, 2023) and).

[99] **Modern philosophical views in the vein of structuralism, post-structuralism, and postmodernism — which assume inherently weak agency of human beings, who thus often end up being playthings of dominant forces in nature, language, and society**: Details about the listed theories are beyond the scope of this work; a very short overview can be found in the last chapter of (Flynn, 2006).

[100] **"our reason functions only to the degree to which it is not flooded by greed"**: (Fromm, 1993)

[101] **Buddhist interpretation of why the human mind can end up unfree (in short: the mind is suffering due to contamination with greed, hatred, and delusion)**: Often also translated as "greed, hate, delusion", "greed, aversion, delusion" or "greed, resentment, infatuation" (the latter version is used in Aldous Huxley's *The Perennial Philosophy* (1945)).) These three are referred in Buddhism as the three main poisons/fires (or roots of unskillful action). They are mentioned in several places in the Pali canon, e.g. "All is burning... Burning with the fire of greed/lust, with the fire of hate, with the fire of delusion." Extinguishing these fires is the key goal of Buddhist practice, the word *nibbāna/nirvana* literally means extinguishing (of fire), arriving at the point where "passion fades out. With the fading of passion, [noble follower] is liberated" (Adittapariyaya Sutta: The Fire Sermon, SN 35.28). We also have a short description of them in (Harvey, 2013, p. 43): "The three possible motivating 'roots' of unskillful action are: (i) greed (*lobha*), which covers a range of states from mild longing up to full-blown lust, avarice, fame-seeking and dogmatic clinging to ideas; (ii) hatred (*dosa*, Skt dvea), which covers mild irritation through to burning anger and resentment, and (iii) delusion (*moha*), as in stupidity, confusion, bewilderment, dull states of mind, ingrained misperception, specious doubt on moral and spiritual matters, and turning away from reality by veiling it from oneself."

(Note about the sources for Buddhist Pali texts (suttas and their translations): For the majority of quotes in this book I have used *Access to Insight* (www.accesstoinsight.org/tipitaka) as a source; it references texts by both sutta numbers (in English) and their corresponding PTS references (in Pali.))

[102] **like a deer entangled in snares**: from a Buddhist sermon captured in Ariyapariyesana Sutta (The Noble Search, MN26) about a "noble follower" whose mind is overly attached to their bodily senses and bodily nature, who is thus "tied to these five strings of sensuality — infatuated with them, having totally fallen for them, consuming them without seeing their drawbacks or discerning the escape from them — should be known as having met with misfortune, having met with ruin ... Just as if a wild deer were to lie bound on a heap of snares: it should be known as having met with misfortune, having met with ruin; the hunter can do with it as he will."

[103] **It is also consistent with the ancient Hindu wisdom passed down to us in the earliest Hindu scriptures, the Vedas, and their philosophical interpretations the Upanishads, in Patanjali's Yoga Sutras, and in related narratives like the Bhagavad Gita**: For example, in the Bhagavad Gita (II, 62-63), we read: "For a man dwelling on the objects of the senses, an attachment to them is born; from attachment, desire [greed] is born; from desire anger is born; from anger arises delusion; from delusion confusion of memory; from confusion of memory the loss of reason; from loss of reason one goes to complete ruin" (see e.g. in (Sargeant et al., 2009)).

[104] **Tao Te Ching, of Taoist philosophy, also speaks of life in which freedom from desire and artificial constructs (like imposed beliefs or societal norms) leads to a true understanding of reality and inner peace**: For example, in Tao Te Ching, Ch.19 we read:
"It is more important
To see the simplicity,
To realize one's true nature,
To cast off selfishness
And temper desire."
(Tao Te Ching, (n.d.))

[105] **in the Sufi tradition, as exemplified by the poet Rumi at the end of the Islamic Golden Age, we are urged to recognize the "prison" of self-imposed boundaries and worldly concerns, and we are encouraged to seek freedom via spiritual awakening**: For example:

"Be empty of worrying.
Think of who created thought!
Why do you stay in prison
when the door is so wide open?"
(Rumi, c.1247).

[106] **the capacity for *reason* and specifically for *objective thinking***: The capacity for reasoning (also for objective thinking) as used here is not to be confused with what we typically refer to as intellect, which is only one of the capacities available to reason. As will be expounded later, like in Plato's *chariot allegory* where the charioteer must balance forces of the soul, reason has more to do with the healthy balance of capacities (forces) within the mind, than about any of them separately. Plato deems this balance to be a virtue, whose markers are individual and societal health and wellbeing. Pure intellect is understood here as the capacity, which neuroscientists sometimes associate with the left-brain hemisphere, it is good at mechanistic, detailed analysis and abstraction, and it is roughly what Iain McGilchrist terms "emissary," appointed by the "master" to be a good servant, as emissary is "better at carrying out procedures than understanding their meaning" (McGilchrist I., 2021, p.336; see also (McGilchrist I., 2019)). Pure intellect is in some respects akin to a calculation instrument, it performs best on IQ tests, but is rather cold and machine like. It needs to be balanced with other forces of the mind in order to get context and meaning. If a parable in literature were sought to portray a pure detached (and cold) intellect, one could point to the character of intellectually brilliant Ivan (and his influence on the shrewd character of Smerdyakov), as they, and the tragic fate they both encounter, are portrayed in Dostoyevsky's novel The Brothers Karamazov (Dostoyevsky, 1879).

[107] **liberation and freedom for modern human beings**: It should be evident from the context that the 'freedom' referred to here does not imply the absence of external constraints on individual action (which would align more with what Fromm describes as 'freedom from' in (Fromm, 1941)), but rather to the

inner freedom of thought and volition based on the autonomous individual agency – regardless of the external constraints. As one example of what is meant here, one can think of Viktor Frankl's situation, who, even as a prisoner in a Nazi concentration and extermination camp, retained the ability to exercise individual agency and freedom in his search for meaning. This capacity allowed him to rise above the experience of pain, face suffering with dignity, and extend care to others (Frankl, 1946). Meaning cannot be supplied from outside; it must be arrived at by the free individual self – inner freedom is necessary for a quest for meaning. Another way to think about inner freedom — and the stable inner platform it provides for the one who attains it — is to ponder it in Nietzsche's maxim "They who have a *why* to live for, can bear almost any *how*" (this is one possible translation of "Hat man sein warum? des Lebens, so verträgt man sich fast mit jedem wie?" (Nietzsche, 1889)).

[108] **cognitive illusions**: this term was introduced by Nobel laureate economist and psychologist, Daniel Kahneman, in close collaboration with Amos Tversky, see e.g. (Kahneman, 2011).

[109] **thinking is … shrouded in mystery for modern science**: Cognitive science has made considerable strides in understanding various aspects of thinking, but it is important to acknowledge that our scientific understanding is very much incomplete in this domain. We don't even have a single, universally accepted definition of what thinking is. Most cognitive scientists seem to be firmly planted in the materialist/physicalist/reductionist paradigm and firmly believe that — to cite one instance — the mind must be "a system of organs of computation designed by natural selection"; however, such statements are indeed often accompanied with acknowledgments that the topic should be approached with "a note of humility" because "we don't understand how the mind works" and are in a state of "thoroughgoing perplexity about the enigmas of consciousness, self, will, and knowledge" (quotes are from (Pinker, 2009), this work is just one representative example of the sentiment in the field). Similarly, Noam Chomsky — who is considered one of the founders of the field of cognitive science and often called "the father of modern linguistics" — stated that "as soon as questions of will, or decision, or reason, or choice of action, when those questions arise, human science is at a loss, it has nothing to say about them as far as I can see, these questions

remain in the obscurity in which they were in classical antiquity" (Chomsky & Magee, 1978).

[110] **"blooming, buzzing confusion"**: This often utilized phrase was coined by the American psychologist William James and used in his works *The Principles of Psychology* (James, 1890) and *Some Problems of Philosophy* (James et al., 1911).

[111] **sensory impulses provided to our minds [are] organized and interpreted to us by means of thinking**: an apt description of the experience of this process is given in Steven Pinker's introspection of the quick moment when thinking organizes and interprets the "blooming, buzzing confusion" of our sensory input, where he terms it "a satisfying rush of insight" (Pinker, 2009). One could add that there is indeed something very satisfying, even liberating, when the light of thinking reveals the hidden relationships within the confusion of the observed phenomena (I will go out on a limb and state that, in some ways, this is maybe not unlike to what Plato's *Demiurge*, or *Nous*, does while ordering the chaos according to the eternal ideas (Plato, 1989 [c. 360s BC], *Timaeus*)).

[112] **descriptions akin to "satisfying rush of insight" and "a distinctive joy" are used by cognitive scientists to characterize the moment when thinking reveals meaningful connections**: The "satisfying rush of insight" phrase is from (Pinker, 2009). In (Gopnik, Meltzoff, & Kuhl, 2001) we find a phrase expressing both sides of this experience, as a developing child clearly experiences it when a meaningful connection with the environment cannot be made "a deeply disturbing dissatisfaction when you can't make sense of things" and "a distinctive joy when you can."

[113] **thinking ... reveals the otherwise hidden connections and meanings to us**:

At this point, it might be useful to clarify some of this work's epistemological stances regarding knowledge acquisition. This is not primarily a philosophical treatise, and thus this endnote represents a succinct attempt to accomplish it.

Many thinkers attuned to the modern Western worldview subscribe to the notion that the ultimate reality is fundamentally unknowable to human beings. This position has entrenched itself in the 18th century, chiefly relying on the writings of Hume and

Kant. Some adherents of this position are aligned with Hume's extreme empiricist views, which posit that the mind is merely a bundle of disjointed perceptions, thereby denying objective reality to our knowledge (as an aside, such a viewpoint also seems to dismiss (overlook?) the human experience of self as a continuous entity.) Many, probably even most adherents of this position, in essence align with Kant's proposition that we can never truly grasp the *thing-in-itself*, a concept introduced in his *Critique of Pure Reason* (Kant, 1787). According to this perspective, our understanding is limited to observed *phenomena* and their manifestations as they are given to us via our senses and cognitive faculties. We remain barred from accessing the underlying reality that exists independent of our perception – referred to as the thing-in-itself (also termed *Ding an sich* or *noumenon*.) Kant postulates that direct knowledge of the thing-in-itself remains elusive due to our knowledge being invariably filtered through our senses and our individualized cognitive apparatus. Each individual's senses are distinct, leading to inherently subjective interpretations. However, despite this subjectivity, humanity's consistent ability to accurately comprehend the world, understand each other, perform complex mathematical operations, and build advanced technologies and civilizations tells us that there is a big gap to bridge between the subjective sensory data and objective reality that we comprehend. To explain how we bridge this gap, Kant had to invent some sort of connecting link in our cognitive apparatus, so he postulated the existence of *a priori* structures within the human mind – an innate and universal framework, serving as the foundation for comprehending universal concepts like time, space, causality, and mathematical relationships. These a priori structures were supposed to act as interpretative lenses of sorts, shaping our understanding of the world. As a result, our mental constructs might not fully and exactly mirror external reality, preventing us from accessing the true thing-in-itself. The origins and development of such an intricate cognitive apparatus remain enigmatic. Modern cognitive scientists generally accept the innateness of cognitive abilities, but the genesis and evolution of this remarkable capacity remain largely speculative. Kant's theory aligns well with the positions of many modern cognitive scientists with a materialist/physicalist orientation, who typically equate the mind with the brain, viewing it thus as a distinct and isolated entity from the external world. This modern perspective postulates a stark separation between our internal mental experiences and the external reality, with our physical senses serving as the sole bridge between them. As a result, our mental representations are deemed inherently subjective, we are supposed to consider them distorted images of reality and are cautioned against attributing them with universal significance. Echoing Kant, many cognitive scientists assert that humans can grasp only the manifestations or appearances of things, while their true essence remains perpetually beyond our direct comprehension and intimate experience. This stance is deeply entrenched in contemporary epistemology.

However, this work seeks (humbly, if you could believe me) to elucidate that this entrenched position is less a product of scientific inquiry and more an outcome of deeply ingrained beliefs and biases. It also aims to revive and shed light on a timeless insight, one that has been unjustly overshadowed in recent discourse, introduced to philosophy by Plato, that *thinking mind has the capacity to intimately reunite us with the "external" world to which we intrinsically belong and with the ideas permeating it* – this is a profound meaning of what Plato termed *dialectic* (see e.g. in Plato, 2013b [c. 370s BC], *Republic*, 532a-535a)). It is our human mind's capacity to reason that has the potential to open the gate of Plato's *world of ideas* (also referred to as the world of *forms*) for us (see e.g. in Plato, 2013b [c. 370s BC], *Republic*, 475e-480a, ~508e, 510a-511e, 514a-519b, 596a-597e). To Plato, dialectic was not merely a rhetorical device or an instrument of philosophical discussions, but an *inner exercise of a reasoning mind* that could lead one toward the ultimate object of knowledge and to the source of foundational ideas of *The Good* and *Justice*. Though such a perspective might seem distant, or even alien, to contemporary epistemological debates, it is becoming increasingly critical to revisit and understand its depth – this is where we can find the keys to the kingdom. It is only through the rigorous application of dialectic, by training and disciplining of the individual human mind in a quest for knowledge about ourselves and about the world, that one can ascend, moving from the realm of illusions and mere opinions to the sanctuary of the highest knowledge (*noesis*), where ideas are directly and intimately apprehended. Plato doesn't speak about the world of ideas as if it were a hypothetic speculative contraption, he speaks of it as one who has already visited it and got specific insights through that process, and as one whose mind experienced its profound heights

307

and depths. Plato understands that all human beings can claim their citizenship of it if they are willing to undergo a rigorous process of training and disciplining of their minds. As already indicated before, the purpose of Socratic method explored in his works is to set his readers on such a path, enabling them to come closer to — in Plato's words — the deeper "knowledge of the subjects to which I devote myself" and about which "I have composed no work … for there is no way of putting it in words like other studies" because "acquaintance with it must come rather after a long period of attendance on instruction in the subject itself, and communion therewith, when suddenly, like a blaze kindled by a leaping spark, it is generated in the soul and at once becomes self-sustaining" (Plato, 1989, 1996; [orig. 353 BC], *Epistle VII*, 341c-d).

To many of us who are steeped in the modern Western worldview, Plato's perspective may seem foreign. Seduced by the materialist/physicalist paradigm cultivated over the past two centuries, we view ourselves as isolated from the rest of the world, separate and alone, transient particles aloof in cosmic dust. We thus live in what Plato termed "cave", in his well-known *Allegory of the cave*. Our gaze is fixated to the appearances and fleeting shadows on the cave wall that we call the physical world, and we are afraid to turn around and start moving towards the source of true light, but rather cling to a fervent belief that this is the only reality available to us, even if we claim that it is incomprehensible to us (Plato, 2013b [c. 370s BC], *Republic VII*, 514a–520a).

[114] **unbridgeable gap between our abstract, complex, highly structured knowledge of the world, and the concrete, limited, and confused information provided by our senses**: (Gopnik, 2003).

[115] *computational theory of mind* **and** *connectionism*: There is a debate about this in cognitive science; for an overview see (Rescorla, 2020) and (Buckner & Garson, 2019); also for example (Fodor, 2015, 2008, 1994), (Pinker, 2009), (Chomsky, 2000), (Churchland P.M., 2012), (Churchland P.M., 1995), (Antony & Hornstein, 2003).

[116] **some aspects of** *connectionism* **… are at work in modern AI technology, [but] we shouldn't refer to any of it as** *thinking*: It should be recognized that modern AI (for example, Large Language Models, LLMs such as ChatGPT, which are based on *deep neural networks* and utilize *reinforcement learning* aided by

human beings) can persuasively mimic intelligent behavior, such as "understanding" and generation of language and identification of patterns. However, we need to keep in mind that AI is a machine, a tool. AI is complex, but still limited to deterministically transforming given input data into output data (based on the numeric *parameters* (or *weights*) assigned to its neural nodes and their connections.) For example, if the randomness value of a given LLM AI machinery, often called *temperature*, is set to zero, the AI system always generates exactly the same output for a given input – in principle, it operates deterministically, just like a thermostat. And if the numerical values of its parameters are transferred to a different (compatible) platform, this new platform will behave identically – it will also generate exactly the same output (thus we can't really talk about different "agencies" or "personalities" of LLMs.) Machines, without the aid of human minds, are limited in the sense that they cannot "decide to say things that are new – but not random" (Chomsky & Magee, 1978) and also cannot express ideas "in ways appropriate to situations but not caused by them" (Chomsky, 2016). This is why LLM AI machines must also be *trained* — extensively — via human reinforcement feedback (controlled or performed by human beings, using judgments made by human minds) if they are expected to produce outputs that are recognized as contextually and socially appropriate. It is important to notice that — *unless we mix in our prejudices and wishful thinking* — the mimicked intelligence of AI is experienced by human beings as machine-like, detached and cold, because it lacks other qualities essential to human beings, including true understanding and empathy. This is not an unimportant aspect, and it will be revisited in later material.

[117] **traumatic experiences that compromise our *epistemic trust*:** This is meant in the sense of basic epistemic trust, in trust one places in the knowledge, intentions, and communications of others. This is not unlike what is described in the theory of *mentalization* and in the mentalizing approach to psychotherapy, see e.g. (Bateman & Fonagy, 2019) and (Sharp & Bevington, 2022).

[118] **our minds are so "effective at hallucinating that we [only] believe [that] we see the world objectively":** (Barrett, 2020)

[119] **thinking is "uniform" across human species":** Cognitive science recognizes that the human cognitive system is "essentially

uniform in a community, and in fact roughly uniform for species" (Chomsky & Magee, 1978) and that "the peoples of the world share an astonishingly detailed universal psychology" and "humans everywhere on the planet see, talk, and think about objects and people in the same basic way. The difference between Einstein and a high school dropout is trivial compared to the difference between the high school dropout … and a chimpanzee" (Pinker, 2009).

[120] **the ability for language is innate**: Starting in the 1950s, Noam Chomsky revolutionized the field of linguistics with the theory that the *human ability for language is innate*. His work, which burst onto the scene with (Chomsky, 1959), marked a radical departure from behaviorist views that dominated psychology at the time (behaviorists like B.F. Skinner argued that language acquisition could be explained entirely through environmental stimuli and responses, essentially claiming that children learn language through imitation and reinforcement; many in the field observe that this particular work published by Chomsky in 1959 effectively dethroned behaviorism as a discipline.) The innateness theory has had its critics from various fields, but no convincing alternatives to this theory have been offered. Chomsky introduced the concept of *Universal Grammar*, an innate set of linguistic principles shared by all humans. Universal Grammar explains why children can learn any human language relatively quickly and why languages around the world, despite their surface differences, share many underlying similarities. One of Chomsky's arguments for innateness is the *poverty of the stimulus* argument. He points out that the linguistic input available to young children is often incomplete, unstructured, and even ungrammatical, yet children rapidly acquire complex grammatical structures that they haven't explicitly been taught. See e.g. (Chomsky, 2002, 2007, 2015a, 2015b). This has implications on the innateness of thinking too, as Chomsky well understands: "language is not … a system of communication. It is a system for expressing thought" even if "it can of course be used for communication, as can anything people do" (Chomsky et al., 2002). Alison Gopnik points to an interesting fact that even though "there are a range of empirical phenomena, particularly developmental phenomena, that could be adduced to support the innateness hypothesis" Chomsky's arguments for "innateness don't come from studying the development of language and thought … Chomsky's most important argument … is the same argument that

Socrates [as given to us in Plato's dialogues] originally formulated in the *Meno*; it has come to be called the poverty of the stimulus argument. The learning mechanisms we know about are too weak to derive the kind of knowledge we have from the kinds of information we get from the outside world." Gopnik further characterizes Chomsky's theory by recognizing that "representations and rules are not inferred or derived from the input. This rationalist answer was, of course, a radical, indeed revolutionary, departure from the empiricist assumptions of earlier psychology, particularly behaviorism. It has also been very widely influential" (Gopnik, 2003). Gopnik and her collaborators on the *"theory theory"* of child development accept aspects of the innateness and state that "infants are born with initial innate theories [abstract coherent systems of entities and rules]" and "even newborns already know a great deal about people and objects and language" and infants use this capacity to learn and hypothesize imaginatively about the world, even babies "have powerful learning mechanisms that allow them to spontaneously revise, reshape, and restructure their knowledge," enabling them to build and revise the theories they hold, each of them considering the world like a "scientist in the crib" (Gopnik, 2003), (Gopnik, Meltzoff, & Kuhl, 2001).

[121] **In his dialogue *Phaedrus*, Plato presents the famous *Chariot Allegory*:** (Plato, 2022 [orig. c. 370s BC], *Phaedrus*, 246a-254e).

[122] **"reason is no match for passion":** This is the often used paraphrase of a statement Hume made in his work *A Treatise of Human Nature*. The exact quote can be found in Book II, Part III, Section III (Of the Influencing Motives of the Will): "Reason is, and ought only to be the slave of the passions, and can never pretend to any other office than to serve and obey them." (Hume, 1739).

[123] **"I" is "not even master in its own home":** See (Freud, 1920, lecture XVIII). From the perspective of Freud's psychoanalytic theory, the mind is divided into three main parts: the *id* (our basic, unconscious, primitive, unrestrained, instinctual drives and desires; the *id* follows the pleasure principle, seeks immediate gratification and pain avoidance), the *superego* (internalized societal expectations / norms / rules / beliefs / values; *superego* has conscious and unconscious aspects, and most commonly surfaces in feelings of guilt or pride), and the *ego*

(rational, conscious; deals with external reality). Freud believes that *ego* is the closest to what we commonly consider "I" or "self," and he views *ego* as a mediator among the forces of the unrestrained *id*, the expectation imposing *superego*, and the limitations of the external world; *ego* strives — and struggles — to navigate among these competing forces. See e.g. (Freud, 1920, 1930, 1933).

[124] **"our intellect is a feeble and dependent thing, a playing and tool of our instincts and affects"**: Freud's statement expressed in a letter to Frederic Van Eeden, S.E. Vol. 14, p. 301(Freud, 1964). It is worth noting that, starting in the 1950s, psychoanalysts began to recognize the importance of interpersonal relationships for the effectiveness of psychotherapy. As a result, psychoanalysis has been shifting away from Freud's instinct theories and toward more relational paradigms, such as object relations, self psychology, attachment theory, and intersubjective approaches. These all fall under the broad umbrella of psychodynamic psychotherapy today. This aspect will be revisited in later material.

[125] **statement by Immanuel Kant that "Out of the crooked timber of humanity no straight thing was ever made."**: this is a paraphrase from Kant's 1784 essay *Idea for a Universal History with a Cosmopolitan Purpose* (6th thesis).

[126] **that our altruistic behavior is just a veneer we put over our animalistic passions and drives**: The belief that human altruistic behavior can only be a veneer covering up our otherwise selfish nature is rather prevalent, and it represents a real feat of demagogy. Thus, it is a real pleasure reading how skillfully Frans de Waal counters this myth in his book *Our Inner Ape*, in subsection "A VENEER OF CIVILIZATION" (de Waal, 2006, p. 18). The whole *Our Inner Ape* is an inspiring read.

[127] **"better angels of our nature"**: The meaning of the phrase "our better angels" is well captured in Charles Dickens's novel Barnaby Rudge (Dickens, 1841). "The Better Angels of Our Nature" is a phrase used by Abraham Lincoln in his first inaugural address in 1861, expressing a hope that passion would give way to reason, and thus help unite a divided nation. In Steven Pinker's 2011 book *The Better Angels of Our Nature*, the phrase has also been used as a metaphor for four human motivations — Empathy, Self-

312

control, Moral sense, Reason — he believes can "orient [us] away from violence and towards cooperation and altruism."

[128] **essential prerequisite for the existence of a healthy individual and thus of a healthy society**: (Plato, 1996 [c. 370s BC], *Republic*), … see also https://plato.stanford.edu/entries/justice-virtue/ and also https://plato.stanford.edu/entries/plato-ethics/ and recorded lectures from the two excellent introductory university philosophy courses: *Justice* (Harvard) and *Philosophy and the Science of Human Nature* (Yale Open Courses), available via (Sandel, 2010) and (Gendler, 2011).

[129] **"What's the right thing to do?"**: This is the title of the very popular *Justice* course given by Michael Sandel from Harvard University (Sandel, 2010), it is also available online (at https://www.harvardonline.harvard.edu/course/justice or https://youtu.be/kBdfcR-8hEY?si=OhFlQ5FsEisRFyDJ). Related material can also be found under Yale Open Courses: *Philosophy and the Science of Human Nature* given by Tamar Gendler, at https://oyc.yale.edu/philosophy/phil-181, (Gendler, 2011). Both are excellent introductory university philosophy courses.

[130] **we must put "more emphasis on contemplation as a way of being" and we should ultimately not settle for anything less than being "floored by the universe as it reveals its hidden code" to us**: (LaFrance, 2023b).

[131] **"generate in the soul" a state akin to "a blaze kindled by a leaping spark"**: See (Plato, 1989, 1996; [orig. 353 BC], *Epistle VII*, 341c-d).

[132] *we don't do* **philosophy, at best** *we just talk* **about it**: Pierre Hadot famously said that there are no more philosophers, only professors of philosophy. For a sample of Hadot's work see (Hadot, 2004, 1995, 1993).

[133] **Ring of Gyges story, posed to Socrates as a challenge**: See (Plato, 2013a [orig. c. 370s BC], Republic II, 359a-360d).

[134] *only a deed out of love can truly be a moral deed*: There are cognitive scientists and philosophers, who despite their materialist proclamations, show a remarkable openness to the idea of moral (or spiritual) intuitions. At least when they consider the presence of children in our lives when we care: as already mentioned in the foreword of this book, a case in point is Alison Gopnik, a

renowned developmental psychologist and philosopher of mind, who gives us an inspiring passage in her work *The Philosophical Baby* — demoting all moral systems we currently have, and placing them below *loving moral intuitions*, not unlike the St. Augustine's *ama et fac quod vis* (love, and do what you will) — like this: "These *moral intuitions* about childrearing aren't captured in most philosophical traditions. The classic philosophical moral views—utilitarian or Kantian, libertarian or socialist—are rooted in intuitions about good and harm, autonomy and reciprocity, individuality and universality. Each individual person deserves to pursue happiness and avert harm, and by cooperating reciprocally we can maximize the good of everyone—the basic idea of the social contract. But individualist, universalist, and contractual moral systems just don't seem to capture our intuitions about raising kids. On the other hand, *this combination of particularity and selflessness is much like the love and concern that are part of our spiritual intuitions. We capture it in stories of saints and bodhisattvas and tzaddikim. They are supposed to feel that combination of singular, transparent, particular affection and selfless concern for everybody.* No real human can do that. And, of course, there are many ways to approach that ideal and to care for others—ways that don't involve children. *Still, caring for children is an awfully fast and efficient way to experience at least a little saintliness.*" (emphasis mine), from (Gopnik, 2009, p. 242). My only comment is that some real humans might have to commit to the path above. And soon. At any rate, as Gopnik says, loving care for a child might be an experience just one step away from it, as it has an unmatched transformational power for inner development. This is an important point. I will attempt to show later that any care, for anybody, has that quality, even if children bring with them a unique help of a spiritual kind, which — if lovingly embraced — can bring tons of joy and make it much easier. This idea of the transformational power of caring is connected in later material with (among other things) some insights from the work of Selma Fraiberg, who pioneered *Infant Parent Psychotherapy* (today known as *Child Parent Psychotherapy*) and of John Bowlby, whose insights resulted in the *attachment theory*. The same idea is foundational for the later material explaining the need for a strong push for a globally accepted paradigm of *economy of care*, which could be viewed — as I will try to present — as an indispensable intervention in the economic sphere, ushering in the humane economics that can bring us forward.

Anyway, there is more in *The Philosophical Baby* that is relevant here, because true scientists ask questions about the things they observe: "This is part of the deeper question that haunts all scientists who think about spirituality. Human beings have characteristic emotions of awe and wonder, moral worth and aesthetic profundity. They have a sense of meaning and purpose, and an intuition that there is something larger than themselves. But do these emotions and intuitions capture something real about the world?" and "I don't know about the spiritual intuitions that accompany mystical experiences or religious ceremonies. But I do think that the sense of significance that accompanies the experience of raising children isn't just an evolutionarily determined illusion ... Children really do put us in touch with *important, real,* and *universal aspects of the human condition.* ... Children can also tell us, more than anything else, about the *spiritual intuitions that we might call love.*" (emphasis mine), from (Gopnik, 2009, p. 235-240). Wow. Shiver me timbers.

[135] **"love should be inseparable from justice"**: (Murdoch, 1970, p.88)

[136] **philosophers recognized this and called such a virtue arete**: *Arete* is usually translated as "virtue" or "excellence," and represents one of the central themes deliberated in Plato's dialogues and at the Academy he founded around 387 BC. Extensive treatment of *arete* can be found in *Republic, Phaedrus,* and *Meno* (Plato, 1996 [c. 380-370s BC]). Plato's works teach that enabling *arete* to flourish in one's inner life results in the development of a *just* individuality, which is a prerequisite for harmony that defines a *just* society.

[137] **This aspect has been cogently captured in Philip Goff's book *Galileo's Error.*** (Goff, 2019).

[138] **in his 1623 work *The Assayer***: This work is Galileo's exposition (in a dialogue form) of the new scientific method; see in (Galilei, 1623), an abridged version can be found at https://web.stanford.edu/~jsabol/certainty/readings/Galileo-Assayer.pdf.

[139] **to focus only on those observable phenomena that "could be captured in the purely quantitative language of mathematics"**: (Goff, 2019, p.23).

140 leaving the phenomena of mind "outside of its domain of inquiry and placing them in the conscious mind. This was a great success, as it allowed *what remained* to be captured in the quantitative language of mathematics.": emphasis mine, see (Goff, 2019, p.27-28).

141 Nobel laureate Sir Paul Nurse has stated regarding our prospects for finding satisfactory answers about the phenomena of the mind, "I do not think we can rely only on the tools of the traditional natural sciences to get there": See (Nurse, 2021).

142 Nobel laureate Sir Paul Nurse stated about our prospects for finding satisfactory answers about the phenomena of the mind: "I do not think we can rely only on the tools of the traditional natural sciences to get there," Thomas Nagel views the "dominant scientific naturalism" as "incapable of providing an adequate account" about it, Philip Goff and Galen Strawson both call for a new "revolutionary" way of thinking necessary to tackle the problems of mind research.: Additional details can be found in the introductory chapter discussion, under the subsection *Fervent Beliefs and Other Roadblocks: The Promise of Science and Are We Living Up to It?* and related endnotes (these ideas are shortly summarized here again to aid the flow of the argument.)

143 René Descartes famously pronounced in the 17th century: "I think, therefore I am" ("cogito, ergo sum") – I can doubt almost everything, but since I can think, I am — at the very minimum — sure that I exist. The inner experience of thinking is intimately connected with human agency – with the very individual self that does the activity of thinking.: Attempts to discredit this statement of Descartes by saying that any other activity can also prove the existence of thinking subject are missing the point. For example, "I walk, therefore I exist" is not experienced directly by anyone; only if I *think* about my walking do I *know* that I am walking, and thus can *know* that I exist. The inner experience of thinking — as a direct and intimate activity of my own agency — is what ultimately demonstrates to me that I exist, that I am. For this consideration it doesn't even matter whether my thinking is deceived by wrong facts or by some trick or illusion – even if, due to wrong initial facts, I arrive at incorrect conclusions

and can't be sure about the content of my thinking, I still know that it is me doing it, that I exist. It is also worth noting that some infant researchers have concluded that Descartes's statement can't be correct because an infant's cognitive abilities (*thinking*) are manifested only after the process of *affect regulation* (experienced *emotions* and their *mentalization* in the mind) through *attachment relationships* with primary caregivers occur. In other words, emotional life and relationships are the true cradle where thinking is born, and only after this process can we truly observe the infant's self, see e.g. (Fonagy et al., 2005). This is obviously a very important discovery, with many implications for human individual and social development, and we will devote our full attention to it in a dedicated chapter. Nevertheless, this fact does not change the truthfulness of Descartes' *cogito, ergo sum* statement – even if an infant's mind only gradually arrives at the developmental point where they can manifest cognitive ability, it is solely this ability to think that enables them to experience the existence of their own agency, their own individual self.

[144] *"survival of the fittest"*: this phrase was coined not by Darwin or Wallace, but by Herbert Spencer in the 19th century.

[145] *The Age of Empathy*, **a book by primatologist Frans de Waal**: (de Waal, 2009).

[146] **"many animals survive not by eliminating each other or keeping everything for themselves, but by cooperating and sharing"**: (de Waal, 2009, p. 6).

[147] **"we now know from sequencing the entire DNA of species (their genomes) that … chimps and humans are nearly 99 percent identical at the DNA level"**: from *Endless Forms Most Beautiful* (Carroll S.B., 2005).

[148] **much of it was always a mere assumption, and not based on empirical facts**: Within the still-prevalent neo-Darwinian school of thought, little attention has been given to investigating how (or why) gene mutations (variations) occur. It was simply assumed that changes in evolutionary development are caused solely by random changes in gene DNA that are passed to offspring (by now, scientists have identified other pathways.) Scientists in the field of evolutionary developmental biology (evo-devo) have achieved significant advancements by tracking DNA mutations in species. With the availability of fast DNA sequencing

since the 2000s, they have been able to pinpoint the evolutionary developmental paths for many species in numerous cases. (Among its other achievements, evo-devo science arrived at a completely unexpected (startling?) finding that very different animals have very similar developmental genes (a.k.a. toolkit genes.) Different organisms are indeed relying on and utilizing a somewhat universal toolkit.) This is in many ways a great achievement of evo-devo science; however, it still doesn't tell us much about the underlying causes of variations. It has generally been assumed that variations must be happening via random-chance events at a molecular level. This assumption is not a result of scientific research, it is rooted in beliefs of a certain worldview. This in itself does not make it incorrect, but in keeping with the scientific method, it would be more appropriate to treat it as an untested hypothesis rather than presenting it as an established fact to the public. Moreover, the current neo-Darwinian paradigm has failed to provide convincing answers to the important question about how major changes, i.e. new species, are created. Evo-devo and related disciplines have inherited this colossal problem. As expressed in evolutionary biologist Arthur Wallace's book *Understanding Evo-Devo*: "challenge for evo-devo is to achieve a much better understanding than we have at present of how evolutionary novelties … and [new] body plans … arise. … It is all very well having case studies that can describe in detail how the sizes and shapes of bones change in the evolution of horses or humans. But if we can't explain how those bones evolved in the first place from an animal that lacked them, our science is that much the poorer. Evo-devo hasn't yet produced a satisfactory answer to such questions" (Wallace, 2023, p. 166).

[149] **The new understanding of evolution — as *a process mainly driven by the active agency of organisms with intention and purpose*, as opposed to random-chance events — has been establishing itself as a scientific reality**: The early origins of ideas challenging the neo-Darwinian gene-centric model (and its drastic simplifications of the process of evolution), can probably be traced back to mid-twentieth century when Conrad Waddington introduced the concept of *epigenetics*. Already in 1986, Karl Popper delivered a lecture openly calling for "A new interpretation of Darwinism" and argued "that living organisms are active agents" and that it is "not random mutations that should be the point of departure of an evolutionary explanation" (Jablonka, 2017). In

2014, a group of scientists published an article *Does evolutionary theory need a rethink?* in the leading journal *Nature* (Laland et al., 2014), debating ideas of the new paradigm in evolution theory. Today we have many eminent scientists who have published experimental results that clearly stand against "the assertion that small random mutations are the main source of new and useful variations" (as described on the website of *The Third Way*, an organization formed to promote the evolutionary debate: https://www.thethirdwayofevolution.com/). A very good and informative overview of scientific discussions in this field (including some unsavory backlash from the traditionalist wing) is given in the Guardian article *Do we need a new theory of evolution?* (Buranyi, 2022). For a sample of works in this area see for example recently published *Evolution on Purpose*, with over 20 contributing authors (Corning et al., 2023); also *Evolutionary Causation* (Uller & Laland, 2019), *Understanding Living Systems* (Noble & Noble, 2023), *Evolution in Four Dimensions* (Jablonka, Lamb, & Zeligowski, 2014), and *Organisms, Agency, and Evolution* (Walsh, 2015). The debate between Denis Noble and Richard Dawkins on this topic is also illuminating (video available on *Institute of Art and Ideas (iai)* website: https://iai.tv/video/the-gene-machine, see also https://iai.tv/video/why-dawkins-is-wrong-denis-noble). Instead of using the old framework of *Modern Evolution Synthesis* (a.k.a. MS, or neo-Darwinian gene-centric model), many authors are now contributing toward the *Extended Evolutionary Synthesis (EES)* scientific framework, which seeks to offer a more holistic view of how species evolve over time.

[150] **influenced by the purposeful, goal-oriented behavior of an organism, rather than solely by rare, random-chance events**: Here is one illustrative example of organism plasticity from (Buranyi, 2022): "Emily Standen is a scientist at the University of Ottawa, who studies Polypterus senegalus, AKA the Senegal bichir, a fish that not only has gills but also primitive lungs. Regular polypterus can breathe air at the surface, but they are "much more content" living underwater, she says. But when Standen took Polypterus that had spent their first few weeks of life in water, and subsequently raised them on land, their bodies began to change immediately. The bones in their fins elongated and became sharper, able to pull them along dry land with the help of wider joint sockets and larger muscles. Their necks softened. Their primordial

319

lungs expanded and their other organs shifted to accommodate them. Their entire appearance transformed. "They resembled the transition species you see in the fossil record, partway between sea and land," Standen told me. According to the traditional theory of evolution, this kind of change takes millions of years. But, says Armin Moczek, an extended synthesis proponent, the Senegal bichir "is adapting to land in a single generation. ... [This] plasticity doesn't invalidate the idea of gradual change through selection of small changes, but it offers another evolutionary system with its own logic working in concert."

Such insights are also supported by experiments confirming mutation bias (genetic mutations are not random, they show higher frequency in certain regions or directions), see e.g. a recent article about the mutation bias in the journal *Nature* (Monroe et al., 2022). See also (Noble, 2022) and (Levin, 2023b).

[151] **In his book *The Music of Life*:** (Noble, 2008).

[152] **The associations between the genes and certain organismal traits can also be overridden by the organism if needed**: one example is given in the 2022 debate between Denis Noble and Richard Dawkins (https://iai.tv/video/the-gene-machine). See also an informative *Genetics Pedagogies Project* on the University of Leeds website at https://geneticspedagogies.leeds.ac.uk/ (yes, please go ahead, and send this link to a biology teacher in your circle, if they haven't heard about it yet.)

[153] **"selfish gene"**: see (Dawkins, 1976), see also *Origins and Demise of Selfish Gene Theory* (Noble & Noble, 2022).

[154] **"blind watchmaker"**: see (Dawkins, 1986), see also considerations in (Noble & Noble, 2017).

[155] **"evolutionary biologists feel uncomfortable recognizing organismal agency"**: (Uller & Laland, 2019, p. 135).

[156] **"neither predetermined, nor random"**: (Uller & Laland, 2019, p. 131).

[157] **New ideas take time to get accepted, we tend to cling to old habits all too easily**: Another reason why the new science of evolution may be gaining public attention rather slowly could be because the dominant culture in scientific debates around it is characterized by measured discourse rather than bold assertions. As Nobel laureate Paul Nurse stated, "we biologists often shy away

from talking about great ideas and grand theories. In this respect we are rather different from physicists. We sometimes give the impression that we are more comfortable immersing ourselves in details, catalogues and descriptions" (Nurse, 2021). It would be to our benefit to listen closely to what all dedicated scientists are sharing.

[158] **speculative *just-so stories*:** see discussions in (Gottlieb, 2012) and (Smith, 2016) for example. Noam Chomsky, while discussing evolutionary psychology, said: "You find that people cooperate, you say, 'Yeah, that contributes to their genes' perpetuating.' You find that they fight, you say, 'Sure, that's obvious, because it means that their genes perpetuate and not somebody else's. In fact, just about anything you find, you can make up some story for it." (Horgan, 2000, p. 179).

[159] **as Richard Dawkins put it, "survival machines—robot vehicles that are blindly programmed to preserve the selfish molecules known as genes":** See (Dawkins, 1976); compare this and related statements with new paradigms in science starting to emerge, see e.g. (Bongard & Levin, 2021).

[160] **we are free to choose which parts of our nature we want to identify with, nourish, and promote:** This meaning is embodied in the well-known native American story about the young boy talking to his grandfather:
An old Cherokee is teaching his grandson about life. "A fight is going on inside me," he said to the boy. "It is a terrible fight, and it is between two wolves. One is evil – he is anger, envy, sorrow, regret, greed, arrogance, self-pity, guilt, resentment, inferiority, lies, false pride, superiority, and ego." He continued, "The other is good – he is joy, peace, love, hope, serenity, humility, kindness, benevolence, empathy, generosity, truth, compassion, and faith. The same fight is going on inside you – and inside every other person, too." The grandson thought about it for a minute and then asked his grandfather, "Which wolf will win?" The old Cherokee simply replied, "The one you feed."

[161] **it may not be prudent to give it the most central place in the worldviews our culture espouses:** Only proven scientific discoveries should be presented as a fact. All unproven assumptions should be declared as such and considered mere opinions. This is important because we indeed consider science as a

beacon of truth, and we trust in it. This trust of human beings gives science its true value. This is why we let it influence our deepest positions and commitments. We all do. Paul Nurse, who writes very candidly about his inner experiences related to honest acceptance of scientific facts, exemplifies this well: "Learning about evolution also had a rather dramatic impact on the course of my life…. Thus began my gradual descent from religious belief to atheism, or to be more precise, sceptical agnosticism. I saw that different religions can have very different beliefs, and that those different creeds could be inconsistent with each other. Science gave me a route to a more rational understanding of the world." (Nurse, 2020, p. 52).

162 **"we modern human beings have an astonishingly recent origin, and a sudden one. In evolutionary terms, we acquired our extraordinary symbolic reasoning capacities virtually overnight"**: (Tattersall, 2022, p. 148).

163 **"how all this emerges from the wet chemistry of our brains provides us with an extraordinarily challenging set of questions"**: (Nurse, 2020, p. 140).

164 **Paola Arlotta stated that "we really don't understand, even how they can emerge from an actual real brain, and therefore we cannot measure or study…"**: (Arlotta & Fridman, 2019).

165 **"no current theory of consciousness is scientific"**: (Hoel, 2023).

166 **"Language does indeed pose a severe challenge for evolutionary explanation."**: (Berwick & Chomsky, 2016, p. 3).

167 **Our science would serve us better if it were more humble in its attempts to proclaim that we have certainty in this domain**: Statements similar to "our organs of computation [i.e. mind] are a product of natural selection" which is "the only nonmiraculous natural process we know of that can manufacture well-functioning machines" (Pinker, 2009, p. 37) can sometimes be found in professional and popular scientific literature, presented not as opinions, but as facts. But, scientifically speaking, we don't know enough to claim them as facts. They cannot be scientific statements, and thus can only be considered expressions of faith in a particular worldview or belief system (materialist/physicalist in this case). At best, we can consider them assumptions.

[168] **"…more than 100 billion neurons … the brain must grow at the rate of about 250,000 nerve cells per minute (and form more than one million new neural connections every second)"**: See (Ackerman, 1992) and materials from the *Center on the Developing Child at Harvard University*, e.g. (Brain Architecture. (n.d.)).

[169] **the notion that all cells in a developing organism receive purposeful, top-down signals based on some centralized developmental blueprint is hard to escape**: An assumption that we can explain complex biological phenomena "without a blueprint," i.e. without an overarching architecture is harbored by many scientists. The idea of a blueprint, or architecture, evokes the idea of an agency that designed it, and physicalist science is simply frightened by the idea of agency of any kind. Research at the low level of chemical processes, either random, or with some interactions from neighborly cells, are often preferred explanations in biology it seems. There is nothing scientific about such preferences of course, they are just a reflection of physicalist bias. For example, Robert Sapolsky states that "if you can explain something of breathtaking complexity, adaptiveness, and even beauty without invoking a blueprint, you don't have to invoke a blueprint maker either" (Sapolsky, 2023, p. 239), while skipping over the obvious fact – we actually can't explain such things without a blueprint, even if we have no idea what does that mean in terms of an agency of "blueprint maker." Experiments in developmental electricity are revealing that there is indeed a blueprint of sorts. We should go where empiric evidence leads us.

[170] **"How all of this spatial order develops is one of the more challenging questions in biology…"**: (Nurse, 2020, p. 99).

[171] **"Nobody knows what the entire code of development is … it's really mind-blowing"**: (Arlotta & Fridman, 2019).

[172] *Epigenetics* **studies changes in gene activity that don't involve alterations to the underlying DNA sequence**: See for example (Jablonka & Lamb, 1999), (Jablonka, Lamb & Zeligowski, 2014), (Noble, 2008), (Laland, 2017).

[173] *Developmental bioelectricity* **(often referred to as** *bioelectricity networks* **or simply as** *bioelectricity***) is a remarkable discovery**: The concept of the morphogenetic field,

representing a top-down cellular ordering principle, that governs the development of an organism, was introduced in the early 20th-century work of biologist Alexander Gurwitsch. However, it is only with the discovery of developmental bioelectricity (alongside technologies like voltage-sensitive fluorescent dye) in the early 2000s that this concept could enter the mainstream of science. One of the bioelectricity pioneers is Michael Levin, who, together with collaborators from his Tufts and Harvard labs, has published extensive scientific research on this topic. He was interviewed by TED in 2020, and a very informative video is available at (Levin, 2020). For an overview see (Levin, 2023a), (Pezzulo & Levin, 2016), (Levin, 2014), see also (Levin, 2023b), and video presentations (Levin, 2023c), (Levin, 2023d).

[174] **Genes do not seem to specify the complex features of bodily anatomy nor how it unfolds from a single cell into a whole organism**: See e.g. (Levin, 2023b, 2023c).

[175] **Experiments are fascinating, majority of them were published and documented by Michael Levin and the team from his Tufts and Harvard labs**: See the previous endnote about the developmental bioelectricity, for a quick look, see videos at (Levin, 2020), and (Levin, 2023c).

[176] **"Lamarck is back"**: from the 2022 debate between Denis Noble and Richard Dawkins (https://iai.tv/video/the-gene-machine).

[177] **a considerable amount of scientific works that endorse this sentiment have been published**: For example, see the edited volume *Transformations of Lamarckism: From Subtle Fluids to Molecular Biology*, containing 41 contributions, by a distinguished group of historians, biologists, and philosophers (Gissis et al., (2011).

[178] **"Lamarck and his ideas were ridiculed and discredited. In a strange twist of fate, Lamarck may have the last laugh"**: From *An Introduction to Zoology* (Springer & Holley, 2013).

[179] **experiments are demonstrating that the inter-organism bioelectricity information exchange is also taking place**: We will return to this, but just to mention it here in passing, the fact that intelligent inter-organism communication can be observed in these experiments evokes the idea from another branch of science, that of *The Mother Tree* paradigm. The Mother Tree concept was developed by Suzanne Simard from the University of British

Columbia. Her groundbreaking research uncovered that trees in a forest communicate and interact with each other. They are interconnected through underground fungal networks (mycorrhizal networks), dubbed the *"Wood Wide Web"*. These networks enable the trees to exchange nutrients, water, and information (via chemical signals). The largest, oldest trees in a forest were observed to act as central hubs, and these "Mother Trees" play a crucial role in supporting younger trees and maintaining forest health, particularly in managing resources and enhancing resilience against disturbances. Research observations are captivating. For example, if one tree is attacked by insects, it can release certain chemicals that can be picked up by neighboring trees. These neighboring trees might then increase their production of chemical compounds that deter these insects or even attract predators of the insects. This work has been influential, challenging traditional views of trees as solitary entities and highlighting the complex organismal relationships within forests. See e.g. TED talk (Simard, 2016), book (Simard, 2021), *Nature* paper (Simard et al., 1997). (It is noteworthy that a related imagination has been poignantly captured in the first movie *Avatar* (2009)).

[180] **"from all we have learnt about the structure of living matter, we must be prepared to find it working in a manner that cannot be reduced to the ordinary laws of physics…":** (Schrödinger, 1944, p. 76-80).

[181] **Experiments with planarian flatworms:** These species fully regenerate, even if cut into hundreds of pieces, each piece fully regenerates from head to tail, see (Levin, 2023c).

[182] **We can only wonder how all that works when nature itself scrambles the bioelectric pattern in order to create it anew, like in the case of butterfly development. During the two-week chrysalis stage, the caterpillar undergoes a remarkable transformation, completely reorganizing its body into the shape of a butterfly (while intriguingly retaining information/memories from its caterpillar stage):** See (Blackistone et al., 2015), (Blackistone et al., 2008), (Levin, 2023d).

[183] **"the *information is likely stored outside of the brain* and it [likely] has to be imprinted onto the new brain as it develops":** (Levin, 2023c).

[184] **Everything science claims about the origins of life is "highly speculative":** (Nurse, 2020, p. 139).

[185] **"perhaps surprisingly, there is no standard definition of life, although scientists have wrestled with this question across the ages":** (Nurse, 2020, p. 1).

[186] **"everything that is alive on the planet is either a cell or made from a collection of cells":** (Nurse, 2020, p. 5).

[187] **…we will see nature "delightful and entrancing":** Feynman reminds us again… (Feynman, 1964).

[188] **human beings need *productive work, loving relationships,* and a *sense of meaning* for their mental health:** This is a fact widely agreed upon across all mental health disciplines. For some thoughts in this direction: (Rogers, 1995), (Maslow, 1987), (Frankl, 1946), (Fromm, 1956, 1947, 1955, 1976).

[189] **Psychiatrist Viktor Frankl added "meaning" to these essentials:** (Frankl, 1946).

[190] **Intimate attachments to other human beings are…:** From John Bowlby's *Attachment and Loss, Vol. 3: Loss: Sadness and Depression* (Bowlby, 1980, p. 442).

[191] **While there is an important place for solitude … in human life…:** See *Solitude: A Return to the Self* by psychiatrist and psychoanalyst Anthony Storr (1988).

[192] **and for the ability to be alone:** See *The Capacity to be Alone* by pediatrician and psychoanalyst Donald Winnicott (1965a).

[193] **we actively undermine these relational values by prioritizing raw individual self-interest over relationships and care…:** Through this we have adopted a way of life that makes us lonely, anxious, and inept at living in a community with other people, and we also let experiences of stress roam freely in our environments, with devastating consequences for our health. See (Johnson & Gomez, 2023), also a powerful portrayal given in the 2008 documentary *Stress, Portrait of a Killer*, featuring experiments done by Robert Sapolsky and several other researchers (Heminway et al., 2008). Important perspectives can also be found in (Waldinger & Schulz, 2023a, 2023b) and TED talks (Waldinger, 2015, 2022), describing what the longest study on human happiness found as the key to a good life (hint: it's all about deep relationships). Many thinkers address this topic, see e.g., *Bowling*

Alone (Putnam, 2020), *Coming Apart* (Murray, 2013), *The Big Sort: Why the Clustering of Like-Minded American is Tearing Us Apart* (Bishop, 2009), *iGen* (Twenge, 2018). In his Atlantic article *How America Got Mean* (Brooks D., 2023a) and in his 2023 book *How to Know a Person: The Art of Seeing Others Deeply and Being Deeply Seen*, David Brooks reminds us that we forgot "how to treat others with kindness and consideration" and that "there is one skill that lies at the heart of any healthy person, family, school, community organization, or society: the ability to see someone else deeply and make them feel seen—to accurately know another person, to let them feel valued, heard, and understood," and reminders we need, as this is already starting to feel as a forgotten wisdom. However, it doesn't seem that reminders themselves are enough to move us toward a transformative action.

[194] ***The Body Keeps The Score***: (van der Kolk, 2014).

[195] **in their recent book *Deaths of Despair***: (Case & Deaton, 2021).

[196] **as Case & Deaton tell us, already back in 1963, Kenneth Arrow implored that "the laissez-faire solution for medicine is intolerable"**: (Case & Deaton, 2021, p. 248).

[197] **it can be argued that most such endeavors — i.e. attempts to build utopian communes — failed in big part due to assumptions that human nature is noble by birth, and does not need to be transformed**: Literature on the topic of utopias is a field unto itself... One comprehensive and engaging exploration of American utopian movements can be found in Chris Jennings's *Paradise Now: The Story of American Utopianism* (Jennings, 2016), for a comprehensive overview of the concept of utopia in social and political thought see also Ruth Levitas's *The Concept of Utopia* (Levitas, 1990).
In this context, it is interesting to note that the community of Shakers (treated at length in Jennings's *Paradise Now*) is one of the longest-lived communities based on utopian ideals, and their core striving revolves exactly around the transformation (and thus liberation) of human nature – in words of their founding figure Ann Lee: "Are you free as you are? Are you in any degree bound by your appetites, your passions, your self-will? Are you at all in bondage to the opinion of your neighbors, to the customs and notions of society, however harmful or absurd? These do not

trammel the true shaker." Shakers were also known for their economic discipline and innovation; ethics behind the quality of their products and their work life is well captured in the words of Thomas Morton: "The peculiar grace of a shaker chair is due to the fact that it was made by someone capable of believing that an angel might come and sit on it." The Shaker movement was founded in 1774 when Ann Lee (Mother Ann) led a small group of followers from England to New York. Despite the decline in membership, the Shaker community at Sabbathday Lake (in Maine) has persisted. A heartfelt portrayal of Shakers is given in Ken Burns's 1985 documentary *The Shakers*.

[198] **The Age of Reason was ushered in through the humanist impulse of the Renaissance, a major part of which was the "rebirth" of Platonic and Neoplatonic philosophy. It was at the onset of the Renaissance that the new Platonic Academy was re-founded in Florence (with the support of the Medici family), and led by Neoplatonist and humanist philosopher Marsilio Ficino ... and that Pico della Mirandola published the *Oration on the Dignity of Man*, considered one of the great manifestos of humanism**: It is important to note that humanism of the Renaissance was also influenced by Christian theology, particularly by the New Testament and its message of love. Pico's *Oration* sought to harmonize the rediscovery of classical antiquity with the Christian worldview. It integrates Christian theology with its humanist perspective, presenting humans as possessing divine potential.

[199] **We can see humanist ideals well represented from the Renaissance on, they resonate in many cultural currents, even if they dress in different philosophies, like the Enlightenment Humanism, Transcendentalism, Existentialism, Secular Humanism, and Critical theory**: *Enlightenment Humanism*: The Enlightenment period in the 17th and 18th centuries continued and expanded upon Renaissance humanist ideals. It emphasized reason, rational inquiry, individual liberty, and the questioning of traditional authority. Enlightenment thinkers like Voltaire, Rousseau, John Locke, and Immanuel Kant advocated for education, reason, and democratic principles, reflecting a belief in the potential and dignity of individuals. Contrary to the opinion popular within neoliberal economics, Adam Smith is also one of the great proponents of humanism, which is most visible in his 1759 work *Theory of Moral*

Sentiments (this view is widely supported by economists and historians, see e.g. (Heilbroner, 1953), (Rothschild, 2002), (Sen, 1988), (Stiglitz, 2003), and (Digby, 2023)). It should be noted that — in a departure from Platonic and Neoplatonic philosophy — many Enlightenment philosophers were also empiricists, believing that knowledge comes primarily from sensory experience and observation rather than innate ideas or pure reason.

Transcendentalism. Emerging in the 19th century in the United States, Transcendentalism was a philosophical and literary movement that emphasized the inherent goodness of people and nature. It incorporated the idea that an ideal spiritual state (state of heightened spiritual awareness or enlightenment) transcends the physical and empirical and is only realized through the individual's intuition, rather than through the doctrines of established religions or traditional philosophy. Figures like Ralph Waldo Emerson and Henry David Thoreau championed individual intuition and conscience, a clear reflection of humanist ideals. *Existentialism.* In the late 19th and 20th centuries, Existentialism arose as a philosophical movement for the exploration of human existence, its meaning, and its freedoms. Philosophers like Jean-Paul Sartre and Albert Camus explored the meaning of human existence in a seemingly indifferent universe, focusing on human potential for self-realization. A diverse group of philosophers can be considered existentialists, some of them are: Søren Kierkegaard, Friedrich Nietzsche, Jean-Paul Sartre, Albert Camus, Martin Heidegger, Simone de Beauvoir, Fyodor Dostoevsky, Franz Kafka, Karl Jaspers. While Existentialism and Platonic/Neoplatonic thought can diverge significantly in their metaphysical and spiritual considerations, both philosophies share deeply humanist concerns regarding the understanding of the human self and the search for meaning and truth. *Secular Humanism.* In the 20th century, Secular Humanism emerged, emphasizing human reason, ethics, and justice. It emphasizes individual dignity and the importance of individual reasoning, autonomy, and moral decision-making. It asserts that individuals have the capacity to understand the world through reason and empirical observation. It also recognizes the interconnectedness of human beings and stresses the importance of collective action for societal progress. It promotes a sense of social responsibility and the pursuit of social justice, recognizing that the well-being of individuals is inextricably linked to the well-being of the broader community. Similar to Existentialism, Secular Humanism and Platonic/Neoplatonic thought diverge significantly in their metaphysical and spiritual considerations, but they share humanist ethical concerns. Among other contributors to Secular Humanism, Bertrand Russell and Paul Kurtz are two notable figures. *Modern Liberalism*: Modern liberal thought, evolving from the Enlightenment, continued to emphasize individual rights, equality, democracy, and the importance of a just society. It champions human welfare, freedom, and progress. John Rawls and John Stuart Mill are considered among the key figures. *Critical Theory*: Associated with the Frankfurt School, Critical Theory in the mid-20th century critiqued the structures of modern societies, aiming to liberate individuals from the conditions that enslave them. It has its roots in humanist principles, even if it is generally secular and not grounded in metaphysical or spiritual ideas. Critical Theory focuses on issues of power, oppression, and emancipation. Some key figures associated with it are Max Horkheimer, Theodor Adorno, Herbert Marcuse, Jürgen Habermas, and Erich Fromm. Frankfurt School was also strongly influenced by Max Weber, and by the theories of Karl Marx and Sigmund Freud.

[200] **In Machiavelli's words: "This may be said of men generally: they are ungrateful, fickle, feigners and dissemblers, avoiders of danger, eager for gain" and thus we "must be prepared to act immorally" because "circumstances do not permit living a completely virtuous life"**: (Machiavelli, 1523, chapters XVII and XV).

[201] **the day when we will stand on the ruins of civilization may not be too far away**: This sentiment has already been echoed in many dystopian stories, novels, and movies in recent decades. Just to name a few poignant narratives: *Watchmen* graphic novel by Alan Moore, Dave Gibbons and John Higgins, *Nineteen Eighty-Four* by George Orwell, *Brave New World* by Aldous Huxley, *The Road* by Cormac McCarthy, *Fahrenheit 451* by Ray Bradbury, *A Clockwork Orange* by Anthony Burgess, *Lord of the Flies* by William Golding, *The Hunger Games* series by Suzanne Collins, *Station Eleven* by Emily St. John Mandel, *Do Androids Dream of Electric Sheep?* by Philip K. Dick. Some of them inspired, or are made into movies, and several other films have also been created in this genre: *Blade Runner*, *The Matrix*, *Snowpiercer*, *Mad Max*, *WALL-E*, and many others.

[202] **even a humanist like Adam Smith can be coopted by demagogues and interpreted one-sidedly as a supporter of this kind of philosophy**: It has been established that Adam Smith was motivated by compassion and a desire to introduce an economic paradigm that could lift many people out of poverty. His use of the term "self-interest," and especially that of the "invisible hand," was taken out of its natural context for the purpose of justifying a neoliberal economic mindset. This view is widely supported by economists and historians, see e.g. (Heilbroner, 1953), (Rothschild, 2002), (Sen, 1988), (Stiglitz, 2003), and (Digby, 2023). An excerpt from his *The Theory of Moral Sentiments*, in which he considers the threads of empathy among human beings, makes that obvious: "How selfish soever man may be supposed, there are evidently some principles in his nature, which interest him in the fortune of others, and render their happiness necessary to him, though he derives nothing from it, except the pleasure of seeing it." (Smith, 1759).

[203] **The philosophy of postmodernism...** : The 1971 debate between Michel Foucault and Noam Chomsky is very informative in this respect. This is a seminal discussion that pits Foucault's poststructuralist views against Chomsky's linguistics and rationalist stance. During their exchange, they notably diverge on topics related to human nature, ethics, and knowledge. The ethical contrasts in the "power vs. justice" discussion are particularly noteworthy. Available at
https://youtu.be/3wfNl2L0Gf8?si=BFUOCFfRNNWH_3d6 (Dutch, French, and English are used, enable CC for subtitles in English).

[204] **significant shift towards neoliberal economics in the West happened, bringing with it the ethical narrative that has "exalted some of the most distasteful of human qualities into the position of the highest virtues."**: John Maynard Keynes used these words in his 1930 essay *Economic Possibilities for Our Grandchildren* (Keynes, 2015). In it, Keynes also casts his sights into the future, (which — we may dare to hope — might be approaching us, if we decide to choose it willingly) and he dares to predict that our self-interested preoccupation with money and power must be shed off for the humanity to move forward: "the love of money as a possession ... will be recognized for what it is, a somewhat disgusting morbidity, one of those semi-criminal, semi-

pathological propensities which one hands over with a shudder to the specialists in mental disease."

205 **despite the fact that [neoliberal economics] is undergoing its own evolution**: Some economists consider neoliberal economics to be an already broken paradigm. Be it as it may, its underlying sentiment of raw self-interest is still a powerful dehumanizing force. And as already mentioned, considerations about a potential replacement are sobering; in the words of economist Brad DeLong, we can expect that it will likely be "mixed with surviving Neoliberal remnants, ethno-nationalist populism, authoritarian state surveillance capitalism, or out-and-our neo-fascism" (DeLong, 2022b). See also *Slouching Towards Utopia: An Economic History of the Twentieth Century* (DeLong, 2022a) and *The Rise and Fall of the Neoliberal Order* (Gerstle, 2022).

206 **Neoliberal policies' … underlying sentiment**: A poignant portrayal can be found in *Davos Man: How the Billionaires Devoured the World* (Goodman, 2022), which exposes the hidden impact of the global billionaire class on the widening inequality and anti-democratic nationalism. .

207 **… without evidence, as demonstrated in the preceding material of this and previous chapter**: See in the first chapter, under the section *Fervent Beliefs and Other Roadblocks: The Promise of Science and Are We Living Up to It?*, and in the second chapter, under sections: *Evolution, and its Pernicious Misunderstanding as "Survival of the Fittest"*, and *Evolutionary Molecular Biology on the Frontiers of Science*.

208 **No agency, no purpose, and no meaning play any role in this view, they could only be illusions**: See related content in the first chapter, under the section *Fervent Beliefs and Other Roadblocks: The Promise of Science and Are We Living Up to It?* Discussion, and the associated endnote, about attempts of scientists with physicalist worldview to "simply wish away and eliminate all phenomena directly attributed to the mind by dismissing them as 'illusions' " is of interest here.

209 **… from a student saying "Dear Professor …, What advice do you have for someone who has taken ideas in your books and science to heart, and sees himself as a collection of atoms? A machine with a limited scope of intelligence, sprung out of selfish genes, inhabiting spacetime?"**: (Pinker, 2018, p. 4).

[210] **the approaching existential dread (or the grip of loneliness or depression)**: For some additional thoughts from the mental health perspective, see (Austen Riggs Center, 2023).

[211] **"evidence-based" (an abused buzzword)**: The term "evidence-based" is widely abused in medicine and medical insurance. This is very pronounced in mental health and psychotherapy. Medical insurance companies use it to justify a limited number of mental health treatment sessions (often resulting in poor outcomes) and a simple short-term scripted/manualized treatment process. Defenders of short-term scripted/manualized psychological treatments (also companies providing AI therapy chatbots) often use the term "evidence-based" as a buzzword for marketing purposes, sometimes even referring to such short-term therapies as a "gold standard." Yes, because they are scripted, they are also much easier to standardize and research empirically. But this is all very misleading. While the scripted/manualized treatments obviously have their place as one of the important tools in mental health, they should not be viewed as a remedy for all mental health problems, because that's not what they are. The so-called "evidence-based" psychotherapy treatments in fact do not show any practically relevant superiority to other forms of psychotherapy. See for example, the analysis in the paper by Jonathan Shedler (clinical professor at UCSF), *Where Is the Evidence for "Evidence-Based" Therapy?* (Shedler, 2018): "Empirical research actually shows that 'evidence-based' therapies are ineffective for most patients most of the time … The term evidence-based therapy has become a de facto code word for manualized therapy – most often brief, highly scripted forms of cognitive behavior therapy. It is widely asserted that 'evidence-based' therapies are scientifically proven and superior to other forms of psychotherapy. Empirical research does not support these claims. Empirical research shows that 'evidence-based' therapies are weak treatments. Their benefits are trivial, few patients get well, and even the trivial benefits do not last." See also (Shedler, 2010), (Lilliengren, 2023, 2017), (Plakun, 2023), (Fonagy, 2015), (Luyten et al., 2017), a Guardian article (Burkeman, 2016), and a video recording from *The Limbus Critical Psychotherapy Conference* (Shedler, 2015).

These misleading notions around "evidence-based" psychotherapies are also affecting the public mindset and endangering the support for effective psychodynamic therapeutic approaches. For example, in the US, there is a decrease in the number of programs that offer psychodynamic coursework, see e.g. (Levendosky et al., 2023).

In their 2020 book *The Illusion of Evidence-Based Medicine: Exposing the Crisis of Credibility in Clinical Research*, Jon Jureidini and Leemon B. McHenry (Jureidini & McHenry, 2020), expose the corruption of medicine on many levels; see also video report (McHenry & Brier 2021). Aseem Malhotra's video lecture *Evidence Based Medicine Has Been Hijacked* (Malhotra, 2022) also shows why the term "evidence-based" is tainted.

[212] **... every 11 minutes a human being commits suicide in the US, every 2.5 seconds someone seriously considers it; and the suicide rates reached an all-time high in 2022 when nearly 50,000 killed themselves**: "Suicide rates increased approximately 36% between 2000–2021. Suicide was responsible for 48,183 deaths in 2021, which is about one death every 11 minutes. The number of people who think about or attempt suicide is even higher. In 2021, an estimated 12.3 million American adults seriously thought about suicide, 3.5 million planned a suicide attempt, and 1.7 million attempted suicide." (CDC, 2023), see also (Weiss, 2023), (Reich, 2023), and (Wernau, 2023).

[213] **even the survivors suffer, for example, as of 2023, the percentage of US adults who report having been diagnosed with depression at some point in their lifetime has reached 29%, and among women alone, the percentage is 37%**: See e.g. (Witters, 2023).

[214] **The vast majority of corporations in our economic system feel fully justified to set themselves up to extract maximum profit for the owners of capital as the first order of business**: see e.g. a poignant narrative in (Varoufakis, 2020).

[215] **big corporations do not shy from exposing people to suffering or death if they can get away with it**: Case in point: big pharmaceutical companies take advantage of relaxed regulation and willingly pressure humans in developing countries to become "lab rats" (for drug development trials), and when things go wrong and people (including babies and children) suffer or die, their families commonly receive no explanation, compensation or justice; see two video reports: (Real Stories, 2017) and (Journeyman Pictures, 2016). Also, a report on some aspects of how big pharma

gets dangerous drugs approved: (VICE News, 2021) and about what doctors don't know about the drugs they prescribe (Goldacre, 2012).

[216] **Nordic countries are shining examples of how to promote humanist values in society while maintaining a vibrant life and economy:** The humanist cultural narrative has found a strong foothold in Nordic countries. The *Nordic Model* successfully combines free market capitalism with a comprehensive welfare state, high levels of social equality, collective responsibility, and civic participation. All Nordic countries provide universal free healthcare, free education, a pension system, a sponsored culture, and robust modern infrastructure. They are well known for their high quality of life, outstanding educational outcomes (e.g. the Finnish educational system has been called a miracle, and much of it can be understood from *Finnish Lessons 3.0* (Sahlberg, 2021), also (Hancock, 2011)), strong civil liberties, commitment to individual human development, high levels of trust in their elected governments, virtually non-existent corruption, and healthy competitive economy. Of course, the Nordic Model is not without its challenges, and there are areas of vigorous debate, with integration policies being only one of them, this must be acknowledged. It is also true that Nordic countries are relatively small (however, note that their combined population is comparable to that of Canada or California) and still comparatively homogenous. But neither their size nor their demographics should be used as an excuse not to learn about how effectively and humanely they manage their societies. Even if their size and relative homogeneity make it easier to implement their model — their humanist lessons are valid universally, and in principle there is no rational reason why the key tenets from their cultural narrative could not be pursued or applied in a wider context and in other countries too. This topic is extensive and cannot be fully explored here, but fortunately there is a wealth of easily accessible material about the *Nordic Model.* A must read (or listen) is *The Nordic Theory of Everything: In Search of a Better Life* (Partanen, 2017), also *Viking Economics* (Lakey, 2016), many important aspects shine through in Michael Moore's 2015 documentary *Where To Invade Next.* There is much more…, and Wikipedia entries for *Nordic Countries* and the *Nordic Model* are also a very good start.

[217] Throughout the history of science, we have never really been able to research in depth the phenomena mentioned in these statements. This was already demonstrated in the preceding material in this and in the previous chapter: See in the first chapter, under the section *Fervent Beliefs and Other Roadblocks: The Promise of Science and Are We Living Up to It?*, and in the second chapter, under sections: *Evolution, and its Pernicious Misunderstanding as "Survival of the Fittest"*, and *Evolutionary Molecular Biology on the Frontiers of Science.*

[218] Schrödinger: "the material universe and consciousness are made out of the same stuff", Louis de Broglie: "I regard consciousness and matter as different aspects of one and the same thing", and Max Planck: "I regard consciousness as fundamental ... I regard matter as derivative from consciousness. We cannot get behind consciousness. Everything that we talk about, everything that we regard as existing, postulates consciousness.": See (Strawson, 2019) and (The Observer, 1931).

[219] As shown in the material earlier in this chapter, experiments performed in recent decades, in the fields of developmental bioelectricity and epigenetics convincingly demonstrate that living beings develop as purposeful active agents, and not primarily (possibly not at all) via random-chance mutations: See in the second chapter, under sections: *Evolution, and its Pernicious Misunderstanding as "Survival of the Fittest"* and *Evolutionary Molecular Biology on the Frontiers of Science.*

[220] *theory of mind*: Also known as *ToM* in psychology and cognitive science, it refers to the ability to attribute mental states (thoughts, emotions, intents, desires, beliefs, knowledge, etc.) to oneself and others, and understand that others have beliefs, desires, and intentions different from one's own.

[221] the whole discipline of philosophy of science has been created in search of answers: See e.g. (Hepburn & Andersen, 2021) and (Hansson, 2021). Several prominent thinkers wrote about it. Only a few pointers are given here in order to illustrate the nature of discussion in the field of philosophy of science: Karl Popper's *The Logic of Scientific Discovery* (Popper, 1959; originally published in German in 1934), Thomas Kuhn's *The Structure of Scientific Revolutions* (Kuhn & Hacking, 2012; first edition published

in 1962), and Paul Feyerabend's *Against Method* (Feyerabend & Hacking, 2010; first edition published in 1975) capture the core of the ongoing discussions; an interesting take on the Kuhn vs. Popper debate is captured in *Kuhn vs. Popper: The Struggle for the Soul of Science* (Fuller, 2004).

222 **"philosophy of science is just about as useful to scientists as ornithology is to birds"**: In (Weinberg, 1987).

223 **emergence of a "new paradigm" in science — a term coined by philosopher of science Thomas Kuhn**: In (Kuhn & Hacking, 2012).

224 **Human beings utilize *reason***: The term *reason* is used somewhat loosely in modern science and philosophy, often interchangeably with *cognition* or *intellect*. The way it is used here aims at a more comprehensive meaning and is more closely aligned with its usage in Classical antiquity, particularly in Platonic philosophy. The term is multifaceted, originating from the Latin "ratio"/"reri" (to consider, think, reckon), which was commonly used to encapsulate aspects of the Greek *"logos"* (word, meaning, foundational principle, rationality, thought.) In Platonic philosophy, reason can be thought of as the highest human faculty, essential for understanding the true nature of reality and steering one's life toward the foundational idea of *The Good*. The cultivation and exercise of reason lead to a life of wisdom and virtue, which are prerequisites for a healthy (mentally and physically) life of individuals and of society as a whole.

(As an aside, in the context of this section's material, we choose to set aside the topic of epistemological limitations as expressed, for example, in Hume's empiricism or in Kant's transcendental idealism. Following the Platonic method of dialectic, we assume that human reason has the potential to attain knowledge of reality. A more detailed treatment of this topic can be found in the first chapter, under the section *Free Will? Individual Freedom and Ethics*. Additionally, this work's epistemological stance, including comparisons of Hume's empiricism, Kant's transcendental idealism, and Plato's understanding of dialectic in the context of knowledge acquisition, is further elaborated in endnote #113, related to that section.)

225 **in their book *The Scientist in the Crib***: (Gopnik, Meltzoff, & Kuhl, 2001).

[226] **in order to learn babies "formulate theories, make and test predictions, seek explanations, do experiments, and revise what they know in the light of new evidence...":** (Gopnik, Meltzoff, & Kuhl, 2001, p.161).

[227] **...metaphorical presentation as a *charioteer* in Plato's dialogue *Phaedrus*:** In Plato's *Phaedrus*, the human soul is depicted via an allegory of a charioteer guiding horses. The charioteer symbolizes the central reasoning part of the soul (*logistikon*), which, when healthy and developed, has access to the faculty (*nous*) that grasps eternal truths. The reasoning part is tasked with organizing and guiding the soul's journey. One horse symbolizes the "spirited" part of the soul (*thumos*), through which powerful noble impulses — like enthusiasm and courage in the face of injustice or adversity — enter the soul. The other horse represents the "appetitive" part of the soul (*epithumetikon*), and this is where passions, desires, and basic instincts live. Both spirited and appetitive parts of the soul must be organized by reason. This allegory portrays the conflict and struggle within the soul in its search to attain balance and harmony among its parts. Plato's *Republic* extends this concept, by explaining how the organization and proper guidance of these parts contribute to the formation of a just individual and, through that process, of a just society. This process is also portrayed as fundamental for the mental and physical health of individuals, and by extension, the health of society. (Plato, 2022 [orig. c. 370s BC], *Phaedrus*, 246a-254e), (Plato, 2013a [orig. c. 370s BC], *Republic IV*, 435c-445e), (Plato, 2013b [orig. c. 370s BC], *IX*, 580d-588a). In a wider context, a very similar allegory appears in the ancient Hindu text *Katha Upanishad*, e.g. in I.3.3-5:

> Know the Self [*Atman*] as lord of the chariot,
> The body as the chariot itself,
> The discriminating intellect [*Buddhi = inner awakened wisdom*] as
> The charioteer, and the mind [*Manas*] as reins.
> The senses, say the wise, are the horses;
> Selfish desires are the roads they travel.
> When the Self is confused with the body,
> Mind, and senses, they point out, he seems
> To enjoy pleasure and suffer sorrow.
> When a person lacks discrimination
> And his mind is undisciplined, the senses
> Run hither and thither like wild horses.

Katha Upanishad I.3.3-5, (Easwaran, 2007) or https://www.wisdomlib.org/hinduism/book/katha-upanishad-shankara-bhashya/d/doc145206.html.

A related sentiment — about the necessity to control the intrusive (appetitive) aspects of our minds — is also a recurring theme in Hindu scripture *Bhagavad Gita,* notably throughout chapter II. There are many translations of the Bhagavad Gita, see e.g. (Sargeant, 2009) and (Mitchell S., 2000), also https://vedabase.io/en/library/bg/2/60/.

This sentiment is also present in Buddhism, which will be the topic of a dedicated chapter in this book.

[228] **Philosophy literally means** *love of wisdom* **or rather** *intimate and affectionate receptivity for wisdom*: We are told that Pythagoras, at the dawn of philosophy in the 6th century BC, was among the first to call himself a "philosopher" or "lover of wisdom." In his book about Pythagoras, *When the Dog Speaks, the Philosopher Listens*, Nigel McGilchrist (2022, p. 104) parses the *philo-sophia* for us with great subtlety and nuance, pointing out that the original meaning of *philos* is pointing to the idea of *intimacy* and *affectionate respect*, with a *welcoming* and *receptive* attitude. Following its original intent, *philo-sophia* represents an *intimate and affectionate receptivity for wisdom*, rather than intellectual acquisition and dissecting of knowledge. (A note about *love* being an *intimate and affectionate welcoming* is a lesson by itself.)

As the Platonic thought holds significant importance in this book, it's worth noting that Platonism has deep roots in Pythagoreanism. Neither Pythagoras nor the early members of his school and mystical community left behind written documents as their teachings were closely guarded secrets and members took vows of silence. However, indirect sources have suggested a close kinship between Pythagorean thought and Platonic core ideas (which came about a century later.) Highlighting this connection, Bertrand Russell commented in his *A History of Western Philosophy* on Pythagoras's immense influence, stating that Pythagoras "was intellectually one of the most important men that ever lived" and that he doesn't know of anybody "who has been as influential as [Pythagoras] was in the sphere of thought. I say this because what appears as Platonism is, when analysed, found to be in essence Pythagoreanism." Russell also notes few details known to us about the Pythagorean mystical community, in which "men and women were admitted on equal terms; property was held in common, and there was a common way of life. Even scientific and mathematical discoveries were deemed collective." (Russell B., 1946).

[229] **we started to branch off from age-old worldviews**: This statement doesn't seek to diminish the value of stories and systems of thought preceding the ancient Greek philosophy, as they contributed immensely to building early civilizations and the cultural life of humanity. They crystallized in narratives like (to name a few) the Egyptian Myth of Isis and Osiris, The Epic of Gilgamesh from Mesopotamia, in Vedas and Upanishads from India, in Persian stories about Zoroaster and Ahura Mazda, in the philosophy of Confucius in China, in Nordic Mythology, in the Finnish Epic Kalevala, in the Greek mythology, and in many original myths and legends of native cultures planetwide.

[230] **Several pointers to technical AI resources are provided in the endnotes**: A good number of introductory books are available, we'll list just a few: Melanie Mitchell's *Artificial Intelligence: A Guide for Thinking Humans* (Mitchell M., 2020), Stephen Wolfram's *What is ChatGPT Doing... and Why Does It Work?* (Wolfram, 2023a), Max Tegmark's *Life 3.0: Being Human in the Age of Artificial Intelligence* (Tegmark, 2018). An interesting way to think about ChatGPT can be found in *Watch an A.I. Learn to Write by Reading* (Bhatia, 2023). Many video presentations are also available, here is a sample: *Deep Learning* by Grant Sanderson consists of four short videos (Sanderson, 2017), *AI Essentials* playlist from IBM Technology (IBM, 2023), and a Lex Friedman MIT lecture (Fridman, 2019). For readers with some programming background, who are looking for hands-on knowledge, or just more technically detailed and comprehensive material, *Artificial Intelligence: A Modern Approach* (Russell S. J. & Norvig, 2021), *Deep Learning* (Goodfellow et al., 2016), *Deep Learning* (LeCun et al., 2015), and *Artificial intelligence: Foundations of computational agents* (Poole & Mackworth, 2023) provide a wealth of information. Both (Géron, 2023) and (Raschka et al., 2022) are detailed practical guides (beware, practical guides can quickly become outdated in this field), with real-world examples, for those who want to work on implementing AI using Python programming language.

[231] **Several pointers to the material about the history of AI are also provided in the endnotes**:

See *A Brief History of Artificial Intelligence: What It Is, Where We Are, and Where We Are Going* (Wooldridge, 2021), already mentioned Melanie Mitchell's *Artificial Intelligence: A Guide for Thinking Humans* (Mitchell M., 2020), and *Artificial Intelligence: A Modern Approach (4th Ed.)* (Russell S. J. & Norvig, 2021). Interviews with Demis Hassabis, he of the DeepMind, AlphaGo, and AlphaFold fame (Hassabis & Fridman, 2022), (Klein, 2023b), Ilya Sutskever, chief scientist during ChatGPT and DALL-E development at OpenAI (Sutskever & Fridman, 2020), Ian Goodfellow who introduced Generative Adversarial Networks (GANs) (Goodfellow & Fridman, 2019), Greg Brockman, co-founder of OpenAI (Brockman & Fridman, 2019), and Geoffrey Hinton, considered a "godfather of artificial intelligence" (Hinton & Silva-Braga, 2023) are all very informative.

[232] **human minds are not passive mechanisms or illusory contraptions**: See considerations in the first chapter, under section *Fervent Beliefs and Other Roadblocks: The Promise of Science and Are We Living Up to It?*, and in the second chapter, under sections: *Evolution, and its Pernicious Misunderstanding as "Survival of the Fittest"*, and *Evolutionary Molecular Biology on the Frontiers of Science*.

[233] **US President Franklin D. Roosevelt understood the importance of the new media well: from 1933 until 1944, he delivered more than 30 "fireside chats," a series of evening radio addresses, consistently listened to by tens of millions of people, which were influential in transforming the American worldview from one of despair to one of hope during the Great Depression and World War II**: see the excellent seven-part documentary *The Roosevelts: An Intimate History*, directed and produced in 2014 by Ken Burns.

[234] **At roughly the same moment in history, it took just five weeks … to tilt the political votes in favor of the Nazis in the 1933 election, which enabled them to fully consolidate power**: see *Radio and the Rise of The Nazis in Prewar Germany* (Adena et al., 2013).

[235] ***Social networking platforms* (and related human-attention-focused platforms) have been at the forefront of this process**: *Social networking platforms* is the umbrella term encompassing many online platforms for connecting and sharing content among people. Some of the more prevalent are Facebook

(probably the most widely used and influential, with billions of users), Instagram, TikTok, YouTube, WeChat, ShareChat, X/Twitter, Sina Weibo, Douyin, VKontakte, LINE, Naver, Daum, and more, many more. The term human-attention-focused platforms is used here to capture a broad range of online venues or forums focused primarily on capturing user attention and using it as the primary factor when tailoring their content. Among other organizations, this category includes several news outlets and conspiracy theory information dissemination websites. These platforms tailor their content based on user sentiment and ratings (balanced use of facts and honesty are typically not a priority), which create feedback loops that further amplify the original sentiments, regardless of their validity, and thus foster the creation and maintenance of informational echo chambers.

[236] **This and many other related aspects are captured in the economist Yanis Varoufakis's 2023 book Technofeudalism**: (Varoufakis, 2023b), see also (Varoufakis, 2018).

[237] **we cannot always consider social networking platforms as harmless and benign agents in human societies**: See e.g. (LaFrance, 2020b, 2021) and (Varoufakis, 2023b), also (FTC, 2019).

[238] **in *open societies* that seek to foster and protect individual human rights and provide safety**: The concept of open society is understood here largely as presented in Karl Popper's *The Open Society and Its Enemies*, (Popper, 1945). The main characteristics of open societies are strong protections of individual rights, tolerance of diverse viewpoints, responsive and accountable government, and the rule of law. Open societies are open to change and criticism, they allow free exchange of ideas, and provide ways for challenging and reforming their institutions. (As an aside here: Karl Poper's *The Open Society and Its Enemies* has been criticized for oversimplifying and misinterpreting Plato's ideas (mainly from the *Republic*), which is arguably a fair assessment, even if this flaw doesn't really diminish any of the key characterizations of the concept of open society in Popper's work.)

[239] **there are many good resources out there**: A good place to start research on the impact of social networks is the *Center for Humane Technology* (https://www.humanetech.com/).

[240] ***Social Dilemma***: Several critics have labeled *Social Dilemma* as too dramatized and sensationalistic, however that doesn't take away the validity of its core message.

[241] **LLM … software is designed to represent several hundred billion *parameters* or more**: An LLM (Large Language Model, such as ChatGPT from OpenAI) consists of a software representation of a "deep neural network" (terms are inspired by the assumed analogy with neurons in the brain anatomy) running on a hardware platform that utilizes vast computational resources. Connections between the "neural nodes" in the network are characterized by *parameters* that represent the strengths of these connections, also referred to as *weights*. These parameters are what the LLM *learns* during the trial-and-error *training* process, and they fully capture the entirety of the LLM. (Transferring numerical values of these parameters to a different, compatible, platform can fully recreate the trained LLM, so that the same input deterministically generates the same output on the new platform (provided that the randomness value, often called *temperature*, is set to zero)). LLMs can have hundreds of billions of parameters, or more. This information is commonly kept as a closely guarded secret by companies developing LLMs, but it is known, for example, that OpenAI's GPT-3 has 175 billion parameters. More detailed (but still high-level) descriptions can be found e.g. in (Wolfram, 2023a) and (Mitchell M., 2020).

[242] **Most modern AI systems are based on deep neural network architectures**: Deep neural networks have multiple layers of neural nodes (terms are inspired by the assumed analogy with neurons in the brain anatomy): in addition to the input and output layers of nodes, they also have multiple "hidden layers." For example, GPT-3 has 96 transformer layers of nodes and 175 billion parameters representing *weights* between node connections (the exact number of nodes has not been disclosed.) Deep neural network research was pioneered by Geoffrey Hinton from the University of Toronto in the 1980s. The term "transformer layer" in the context of Large Language Models (LLMs like GPT-3) refers to the specific type of network architecture, based on the *transformer* model introduced in the 2017 paper "Attention is All You Need" (Vaswani et al., 2017) by former Google researchers. The transformer network architecture utilizes a technique of *attention*, which allows each node to focus on different parts of the input

data (e.g. tokens, or words in a sentence), thus enabling it to analyze the entire context more effectively.

[243] **One of the first widely recognized milestones in AI based on deep neural networks**: Important milestones in AI research based on deep neural networks occurred even before the widely publicized success of AlphaGo in 2016. Geoffrey Hinton, from the University of Toronto, pioneered this research since the 1980s. This approach — that deep neural networks can learn by changing the strength of their neural connections — was long considered a dead end by most computer science researchers. Its first commercial application emerged in speech recognition software in 2012. However, it was the groundbreaking image recognition program designed by Hinton's graduate students, Alex Krizhevsky and Ilya Sutskever, which won the *ImageNet* 2012 competition (ImageNet project was established by computer scientist Fei-Fei Li, see (Levy, 2023b)), that shifted focus toward deep neural networks. For some background see the 2023 interview with Hinton (Hinton, G. & Silva-Braga, B. (2023), as well as (Gershgorn, 2018) and (AI Frontiers, 2018).

[244] **when AlphaGo (developed by Google DeepMind) achieved a victory in the complex strategy board game Go by defeating world champion Lee Sedol**: In 2016, Lee Sedol was a reigning Go champion with 18 international titles, he has been playing Go professionally since he was 12 years old. See the award-winning documentary *AlphaGo Movie* (Kohs, 2016); also (Hern, 2016), (Silver et al., 2016), (Hassabis & Fridman, 2022), and (Metz, 2016).

[245] *AlphaGo Zero*, **which utilized only self-play, "based solely on reinforcement learning, without human data, guidance or domain knowledge beyond game rules"**: see (Silver et al., 2017).

[246] **latest iteration released by DeepMind was AlphaZero, which can play not only Go, but also chess and shogi**: see (Silver et al., 2018).

[247] **AlphaFold, a system that was able to predict protein folding (the process by which proteins achieve their functional shapes from a specific sequence of amino acids), with important implications for biomedical applications including drug discovery**: see (Jumper et al., 2021), (Callaway,

2020), (Hassabis & Fridman, 2022), (Collins, 2021), (Perrigo, 2022a), (Perrigo, 2022b), and (Toews, 2021).

[248] **at the time of this writing, the LLM field is very competitive and crowded, with several models still vying for dominance**: Among them are: *GPT-4* (from OpenAI), *PaLM, LaMDA* (Google), *Chinchilla* (DeepMind), *Llama* (Meta), *Claude* (Anthropic), *Inflection* (Inflection), *Grok* (xAI), Ernie (Baidu), and several others. In addition to LLMs, some companies are involved in other aspects within the wider field of Natural Language Processing (NLP); for example, Amazon — through its cloud computing division (AWS) — offers a range of AI, machine learning, speech recognition, and NLP services (e.g. *Comprehend, SageMaker, Lex.*)

[249] **AI can synthesize speech that sounds like a specific individual, living or deceased**: see e.g. article *Using A.I. to Talk to the Dead* (Carballo, 2023).

[250] **Image generation experienced a revolution with the introduction of** *Generative Adversarial Network* **(GAN) models**: GANs were introduced by Ian Goodfellow and his colleagues (Goodfellow et al., 2014). GAN is an AI model implemented as a system of two deep neural networks competing in a zero-sum contest: *generator* of new instances (e.g. images), and *discriminator*, which evaluates these instances against a real dataset. The discriminator effectively trains the generator via a feedback loop, so that over time, the generator improves its generation of new images, and the discriminator gets better at distinguishing real images from fake ones. Big datasets of images (created and labeled by humans) are used for this process. For example, *BigGAN* (now part of DeepMind) was trained on the *ImageNet* dataset containing over 14 million high-resolution images with labels for over 20,000 categories. For a high-level discussion about GANs, see the interview with Ian Goodfellow at (Goodfellow & Fridman, 2019).

[251] **"impossible to know what's true by having so many fakes out there..."**: Geoffret Hinton, dubbed the "godfather of AI," in (Amanpour and Co., 2023b). See also the 2019 documentary *The Great Hack* about the *Facebook–Cambridge Analytica* malversations. See also (Thompson, 2023).

[252] **"transparency should be a core tenet in the new human exchange of ideas—people ought to disclose whenever an**

artificial intelligence is present or has been used in communication.": See *The Coming Humanist Renaissance* (LaFrance, 2023b).

[253] **child sexual abuse material and nonconsensual pornography, like revenge-porn or image-based sexual abuse, are being created and proliferated, exposing the underbelly of modern technology and its misuse**: see e.g. (Lapowsky, 2023), (Hsu, 2023), (Kelleher, 2023), (Hurst, 2023), (Tenbarge, 2023), (Thiel, 2023), (Monge, 2022), (End Cyber Abuse, n.d), (Hilly & Allmann, 2015), (National Domestic Violence Hotline, n.d.), (Flitter & Cowley, 2023), ("Deepfake pornography", 2023), and ("Revenge porn", 2023). The trailer for the 2023 documentary *Another Body* (which, in an interesting twist, protects protagonists by using "face-veil" deepfake technology) can be found here: https://youtu.be/Cs3Wlf9BcEI?si=A3PbEu3BEq9clfPP. Sexual harassment can also happen in the virtual environment like metaverse, see e.g (CNN video, 2023).

[254] **It is welcome news that this discourse is starting to enter the mainstream**: See e.g. the National Bureau of Economic Research Conference Report *The Economics of Artificial Intelligence, An Agenda* (Agrawal et al., 2019). At the time of this writing AI is almost omnipresent in the news cycle. See, for example, the interviews with Google executives, where Sundar Pichai, Google CEO, said that he doesn't think that modern society is prepared for the challenge of AI because "the pace at which we can think and adapt as societal institutions, compared to the pace at which the technology's evolving, there seems to be a mismatch. On the other hand, compared to any other technology, I've seen more people worried about it earlier in its life cycle. So I feel optimistic. The number of people, you know, who have started worrying about the implications, and hence the conversations are starting in a serious way as well." (Pichai & Pelley, 2023, April/July). OpenAI's *GPT-4 System Card* is also very informative (OpenAI Papers, 2023). *AI Dilemma* created by the *Center for Humane Technology* has already been seen by millions of people (Harris & Raskin, 2023).

[255] **our ignorance in this domain is how some version of a dystopian society becomes humanity's reality**: as already mentioned in the previous chapter, many dystopian stories, novels, and movies in recent decades serve as reminders of this possibility. Again, here are a few poignant narratives: *Watchmen* graphic novel

by Alan Moore, Dave Gibbons and John Higgins, *Nineteen Eighty-Four* by George Orwell, *Brave New World* by Aldous Huxley, *The Road* by Cormac McCarthy, *Fahrenheit 451* by Ray Bradbury, *A Clockwork Orange* by Anthony Burgess, *Lord of the Flies* by William Golding, *The Hunger Games* series by Suzanne Collins, *Station Eleven* by Emily St. John Mandel, *Do Androids Dream of Electric Sheep?* by Philip K. Dick. Some of them inspired, or are made into movies, and several other films have also been created in this genre: *Blade Runner*, *The Matrix*, *Snowpiercer*, *Mad Max*, *WALL-E*, and many others.

[256] **elaborate fabrications**: see e.g. *The Prophecies of Q* (LaFrance, 2020a), also (Verma, 2023), (LaFrance, 2020b, 2021), (Donovan et al., 2022), and (Born, 2023).

[257] **Open societies and their democratic institutions**: See note #241 about the open societies.

[258] **effective government regulation**: Both European and American proposed AI legislations are trying to keep up with the fast AI developments, see (EU AI Act, 2023) and (The White House, 2023).

[259] *AI detection* **applications**: Many are available, for example, *originality*, *copyleaks*, and *gptzero* are some of the widely used at the time of this writing.

[260] **"most effective tool is to increase media literacy among average readers"**: See (Verma, 2023), See also (Warzel, 2023a, 2023b).

[261] ***"You Can't Be Neutral on a Moving Train"***: (Zinn, 2018).

[262] **use of deepfakes for image-based sexual abuse has already demonstrated its vicious effects. This danger has also exposed a lack of societal determination — sometimes even reluctance — to regulate and curb them**: see e.g. (Maddocks, 2023), (Killion, 2022).

[263] **Another often-discussed danger is that of *AI autonomous weapons* and the *creation of human targets***: For examples of the real-life utilization of AI for large-scale human target creation and assassination, see e.g. (Golodryga & Abraham, 2024) and (Davies et al., 2023).

[264] **Sophisticated AI tools are increasingly being integrated into the security/surveillance systems of many**

countries, companies, and organizations: For some
perspectives on this topic, see (Russell S. J., 2019), (NPR, 2023),
(Lee & Chin-Rothmann, 2023), (Reese, 2022), (Mozur & Satariano,
2023), (Metz, 2019), (Smerconish, 2023b), and (Santow, 2020).
Some obvious dystopian scenarios — that must be prevented
through regulation — include predictive policing (think the 2002
movie *Minority Report*) and AI supported rating system for the
"social score or trustworthiness" of individuals (think 2016 series
Black Mirror, III/Nosedive).

²⁶⁵ **The danger of privacy invasion at the workplace (in
companies and some government agencies) is particularly
worrisome**: Much has been written about the invasion of privacy
at the workplace and the increased presence of the so called
"bossware" (a.k.a. "tattleware" or "workspace analytics")
surveillance applications. A comprehensive list of applications as of
June,2020 can be found in (Cyphers & Gullo, 2020). See also
(Carnegie, 2023), (SSIR, 2023), (Scherer & Brown, 2021),
(Klosowski, 2022, 2021), (Waddell, 2017), (Skopeliti, 2023),
(Corbyn, 2022), (Crispin, 2021), (Kantor et al., 2022), (Blackman,
2020), (Satariano, 2020).

²⁶⁶ **Our civilization stands on the Enlightenment values
we must preserve, "reason, human autonomy, and the
respectful exchange of ideas" and for this reason "privacy is
key to preserving our humanity."**: See (LaFrance, 2023).

²⁶⁷ **but not only is bossware ineffective ("activity is not
productivity")**: See e.g. (CNBC, 2020).

²⁶⁸ **And they basically use the same kind of software that is
illegally used for stalking people**: See e.g. (Wells & Klosowski,
2020).

²⁶⁹ **Much has been written about this lately, for example in
a recent Wired article titled *The Creepy Rise of Bossware***: See
(Carnegie, 2023).

²⁷⁰ **Widespread harms of bossware were discussed during
the 2023 Stanford Social Innovation Review panel, *Bossware Is
Coming for You: Worker Surveillance Technology Is Everywhere***:
See (SSIR, 2023).

²⁷¹ **Danger #5: *Danger of AI uniting with self-interested
neoliberal economics (or its remnants)***: As already mentioned,
neoliberal economics is undergoing its own evolution, and some

economists consider it an already broken paradigm, see e.g. (DeLong, 2022b), (Gerstle, 2022), and (Varoufakis, 2023b). Be it as it may, its underlying sentiment of raw self-interest is still a powerful dehumanizing force. And considerations about a potential replacement are sobering; in the words of economist Brad DeLong, we can expect that it will likely be "mixed with surviving Neoliberal remnants, ethno-nationalist populism, authoritarian state surveillance capitalism, or out-and-out neo-fascism" (DeLong, 2022b). See also *Slouching Towards Utopia: An Economic History of the Twentieth Century* (DeLong, 2022a) and *The Rise and Fall of the Neoliberal Order* (Gerstle, 2022).

[272] **"In a decent society that would be great, it would mean everything got more productive, and everyone was better off, but the danger is that it'll make the rich richer and the poor poorer [and] that's not AI's fault.":** These are the words of Geoffrey Hinton, dubbed the "godfather of AI" (Amanpour and Co., 2023b).

[273] **a known fact to all students of history and much has been written about it:** E.g. see *The Rise and Fall of the Neoliberal Order* (Gerstle, 2022), *Slouching Towards Utopia: An Economic History of the Twentieth Century* (DeLong, 2022a), *A People's History of the United States* (Zinn, 2015), and (Agrawal et al., 2019); see also (Morozov, 2023).

[274] **economics of Milton Friedman:** Even if Nobel laureate economist Milton Friedman's work and popular presentations (e.g. his book and the ten-part series *Free to Choose* broadcast in 1980 on public television) gave market-based neoliberal economics its preeminent expert backing, it is often forgotten that Friedman understood very well that society needs to provide a guaranteed minimum income level for all in order to directly address poverty. He advocated for a form of *Universal Basic Income*, which he termed *Negative Income Tax* or *NIT*. However, it was never enacted; the related legislative proposal was debated in the US Congress in 1970, passed in the House of Representatives, but not in the Senate, and thus never became law.

[275] **deeply seated force in humanity, the one we mentioned as surviving the liberating impulses of the Renaissance and Age of Reason, and which also made itself manifest in works like Machiavelli's *The Prince* and Mandeville's *Fable of the***

Bees: See discussion in the second chapter, under the section *Existential Despair and Physicalist Worldview of Modern Science.*

[276] **At the time of this writing, in the US, one of the richest countries in the world, more than 13 million children face hunger, and more than 40 million people live in poverty**: See US Census Bureau report (Bureau U. C., 2023b) at https://www.census.gov/library/stories/2023/12/poverty-rate-varies-by-age-groups.html and Feeding America reports at (Feeding America, (n.d.)).

[277] **the wealth owned by the top 1% in the wealth bracket equals $46 trillion, which is more than tenfold the amount owned by the bottom 50% of people. Notably, just 735 billionaires possess more wealth than the bottom half of the US population**: See the US Federal Reserve report *Distribution of Household Wealth in the U.S. since 1989* (The Fed, 2023) at https://www.federalreserve.gov/releases/z1/dataviz/dfa/distribute/table/ and also (Jayshi, 2023).

[278] **when Warren Buffet quipped that "there's class warfare, all right, but it's my class, the rich class, that's making war, and we're winning."**: (Stein, 2006).

[279] **willingly created a world that looks like this**: See e.g. (Varoufakis, 2020).

[280] **Plato and Aristotle called it "appetite" and prescribed inner work within an ethical framework to battle it**: See for example Plato's *Republic, Phaedrus*, and *Symposium*. Aristotle's *Nicomachean Ethics* is another masterpiece about the ethical battles within.

[281] **"dictatorship of the proletariat"**: see *The Communist Manifesto* and *Critique of the Gotha Program* (Marx, 1844, 1875).

[282] **unprecedented levels of inequality we have reached**: A short treatment of inequality, including a list of references to some very insightful material, can be found in note #9. It should suffice here to mention a single fact, which can stand alone as a powerful example, the title of the research article tells it all: *"The Top 1% of Americans Have Taken $50 Trillion From the Bottom 90% — And That's Made the U.S. Less Secure"* (Hanauer, & Rolf, 2020), (Price & Edwards, 2020).

[283] **If the power of AI unites with the mindset of neoliberal economics, it is all but guaranteed that many ways will be found to use it to extract even more resources from the working majority (or to simply discard many people as unneeded)**: A case in point is the utilization of AI by conglomerates like Amazon in their drive to shrink workplaces along their supply chain where AI predicts a higher probability of unionization, see (Varoufakis, 2023a).

[284] **The fact that the neoliberal order itself is undergoing its own evolution and possibly approaching its own demise (this process started after the neoliberal mindset caused the devastating 2008 economic crisis worldwide)**: *The Rise and Fall of the Neoliberal Order* (Gerstle, 2022) represents an engaging and detailed analysis of this process. 2015 movie *The Big Short* and the 2011 movie *Margin Call* stand as two portrayals of how the ignorance and the corruption of our ethical values brought about the 2008 economic crisis, and so does the book *13 Bankers* (Johnson & Kwak, 2010), which also demonstrates how despite "its key role in creating the ruinous financial crisis of 2008, the American banking industry has grown bigger, more profitable, and more resistant to regulation than ever. Anchored by six megabanks whose assets amount to more than 60 percent of the country's gross domestic product, this oligarchy proved it could first hold the global economy hostage and then use its political muscle to fight off meaningful reform" (from the book review).

[285] **If the power of AI unites with the mindset of neoliberal economics (or worse, with its "remnants, mixed with ethno-nationalist populism, authoritarian state surveillance capitalism, or out-and-out neo-fascism" as some predict)**: See (Gerstle, 2023, p. 267) and (DeLong, 2022b).

[286] **Margaret Thatcher famously said "Who is society? There is no such thing! There are individual men and women."**: see in (Thatcher & Keay, 1987).

[287] **paraphrasing neoliberal icon Friedrich Hayek: "The market giveth, the market taketh away: blessed be the name of the market."**: (DeLong, 2022a).

[288] **walled off and with virtually no shared experiences**: For some perspectives on this topic, see e.g. *The Big Sort: Why the*

Clustering of Like-Minded American is Tearing Us Apart (Bishop, 2009) and *Coming Apart: The State of White America* (Murray, 2013).

[289] **"I didn't believe that anyone lived like that" said Eleanor Roosevelt when she visited children in a poor neighborhood for the first time**: An intimate portrayal of this experience can be found in the seven-part documentary *The Roosevelts: An Intimate History*, directed and produced in 2014 by Ken Burns.

[290] **"AI will save the world"**: see (Andreessen, 2023).

[291] **Economists Anton Korinek and Joseph E. Stiglitz remind us…**: see (Agrawal et al., 2019, p, 386-387).

[292] **it is indeed impossible "to have a strong democracy on top of a rotting social fabric"**: David Brooks's statement from (Brooks & Smerconish, 2023).

[293] **We need to finally heed the message Charles Dickens imparted to us 180 years ago**: *A Christmas Carol* was published in 1843.

[294] *economy of care*: This term is not new, it has been considered in work of Nancy Folbre, Ai-jen Poo, and others. See e.g. (Folbre, 2001), (Poo, 2015), and interview with Ai-jen Poo on The Ezra Klein Show (Poo & Klein, 2021).

[295] **ethical impulses most people feel for their children**: Developmental psychologist Alison Gopnik is among the thinkers who recognize the superiority of ethics grounded in loving moral intuitions, which we can most easily experience in our relationships towards children: "These moral intuitions about childrearing aren't captured in most philosophical traditions … [they] just don't seem to capture our intuitions about raising kids. On the other hand, this combination of particularity and selflessness is much like the love and concern that are part of our spiritual intuitions. We capture it in stories of saints and bodhisattvas and tzaddikim. They are supposed to feel that combination of singular, transparent, particular affection and selfless concern for everybody. … And, of course, there are many ways to approach that ideal and to care for others—ways that don't involve children. Still, caring for children is an awfully fast and efficient way to experience at least a little saintliness." (Gopnik, 2009, p. 242). See also note #134.

[296] **Loving parents don't expect their small children to "earn their keep," they also don't think that their children are getting "something for nothing."**: The unfounded, but still common, *just so* stories about how parents do this either as "evolutionary adjustment," or in the "service of selfish genes" are based on mere speculations (in other words, they are made up) and completely missing the point. Please refer to the second chapter, under sections: *Evolution, and its Pernicious Misunderstanding as "Survival of the Fittest"*, and *Evolutionary Molecular Biology on the Frontiers of Science* where we discuss the scientifically outdated notions about evolution being a non-purposeful process initiated by random chance molecular mutation and natural selection. Scientific facts, based on many experiments, point to active purposeful agents as drivers of evolution – they have been for decades, even if the fervent beliefs of many in the scientific establishment are slow to incorporate and openly talk about these facts.

[297] **"… what is the moral basis for denying all children the same advantage?"**: See the essay *The Universal Right to Capital Income* by Yanis Varoufakis (2016). A similar position is also presented in a humanely written economics for everyone, *Talking to my daughter about the economy or, how capitalism works - and how it fails* (Varoufakis, 2019) in which, in addition to explaining economics in a language that is both exact and easy to understand, Varoufakis exposes "the inability of market-driven policies to address the rapidly declining health of the planet his daughter's generation stands to inherit" (from book review).

[298] **It is argued here that humanity is facing a host of incoming cataclysmic challenges, AI technology being just one of them**: see note #9.

[299] **"there is tremendous power in defining ideals"**: From *The Coming Humanist Renaissance* (LaFrance, 2023b).

[300] **even if we are not quite sure how to get there**: In terms of resource and wealth distribution, several different ideas — like the *Universal Basic Income, Universal Basic Dividend,* and *Universal Right to Capital Income* — have already been pondered (see e.g. Varoufakis, 2016, 2018, 2020), which demonstrates that there could be ways to do this reasonably and humanely. All we need is the will to do it. Such concepts are not new. We find them, for example,

already in Thomas Paine's *Agrarian Justice* (1797) in which he
suggested that all owners of property within a community should
pay a community rent and thus support a national fund, which
could provide each citizen a sum of money at age 21 and a yearly
amount after age 50 (as an aside here, it should be noted that
Thomas Paine is an unheralded genius, whose works *Common Sense*,
The American Crisis, and *Rights of Man* provided a decisive intellectual
and motivational fire for the American and French Revolutions in
the 18th century). Then there is Bertrand Russell's *Roads to Freedom*
(1918) in which he advocates for a basic income as a defense
mechanism against the coercive power of employers and the state,
thus promoting individual freedom. Milton Friedman, he of the
"neoliberal economics godfather" fame, in his *Capitalism and
Freedom* proposes the *Negative Income Tax* as a guaranteed minimum
income level as a means to combat poverty (Friedman & Friedman,
1962).

[301] **"we would need a new mindset, one that understands
wealth as something we all share and that prioritizes keeping
each and every family financially secure, regardless of their
participation in the job market … Americans valorize work.
We tolerate inequality and poverty. The problem is not the
robots, then. The problem is us."**: see (Lowrey, 2023).

[302] **Goldman Sachs report estimates that AI technology
might be able to automate around 25% of labor tasks in
advanced economies**: Business surveys show that a small impact
on jobs is expected in the next 1-3 years, and a large impact in the
next 3-10 years, see (Goldman Sachs Intelligence, 2023).

[303] **Articles, books, and movies have been created about
various aspects of relationships with AI**: Meghan O'Gieblyn's
book *God, Human, Animal, Machine: Technology, Metaphor, and the
Search for Meaning* (2021) offers some thoughtful forays into the
topic of intersection between human minds and machines. Many
articles and news clips address the topic too, e.g. (Wilkinson &
Frost, 2022), (Chayka, 2023), (Wang, 2023), (Gopnik, 2023a),
(Liang, 2023), (Griffith, 2023), (Krueger, 2017), (Kuyda & Fridman,
2020), (Mahmood, 2022), (Metz, 2020), (Turkle, (n.d.)), (Turkle,
2023), (Vittert, 2023), (Smerconish, 2023a). Movies and series too,
e.g.: *her* (2013), *Ex Machina* (2014), *I'm Your Man* (2021), *West World*
(1973, 2016-2022), short film *Rachels Don't Run* (2021).

[304] **Industry offering AI "companions" (like Replika and Pi for example):** For one portrayal of the relationship between a person and a Replika AI companion see (Brooks E. & Rosin, 2023) and (Brooks E., 2023).

[305] **Even if their efficacy is limited, mental health AI chatbots (like *Woebot* and *Youper*) have been at least tried by tens of thousands of people in need of mental health treatment:** Much has been written about this topic, some of the resources are: (Bram, 2022), (Khullar, 2023), (Farrow, 2021), (Brown, 2021), (Knight, 2017), (Chatterjee & Sengupta, 2022), (Ashcroft & Ashcroft, 2023), (Kaveladze & Schueller, 2023), (Bickmore & O'Leary, 2023), (Kuhlmeier et al., 2022), (Zagorski, 2022).

[306] **Intimate attachments to other human beings are…:** From John Bowlby's *Attachment and Loss, Vol. 3: Loss: Sadness and Depression* (Bowlby, 1980, p. 442).

[307] **Any "conversation with an artificial intelligence is one-sided—an illusion of connection":** See *The Coming Humanist Renaissance* (LaFrance, 2023b).

[308] **"brotherhood and inter-dependence of mankind," to borrow the words from Frederic Douglass:** See (Douglass, 1859, p. 5).

[309] **it can't create completely new and original content with a unique perspective:** One might wonder whether the famous "move 37," which AlphaGo played in 2016 when it, for the first time, defeated the reigning Go champion, qualifies as a "completely new and original content with a unique perspective" (see e.g. story in (Metz, 2016)). Move 37, fascinating as it is because no humans thought of it before AlphaGo utilized it during the game, was still generated within a limited framework. AlphaGo could, based on its "training" and millions of games it played, discover a move that no human discovered before, but limited by its training framework, it couldn't extrapolate and create a radically new concept, not contained within its training framework. Neither AlphaGo, nor any other AI model known to us could, based on the data it was trained on, invent a new discipline for example. That would require a departure from the already existing knowledge paradigms.

[310] **culture is roughly everything we do and monkeys don't**: This quote is attributed to anthropologist FitzRoy Richard Somerset.

[311] ***The Ape and the Sushi Master***. (de Waal, 2001).

[312] **"a self-rolling wheel, a first movement"**: See (Nietzsche, 1885), *The Three Metamorphoses* ("ein aus sich rollendes Rad, eine erste Bewegung").

[313] **"unmovable mover"**: Literally "that which moves without being moved" (Aristotle, 1998 [orig. c. 350 BC], *Metaphysics*, XII).

[314] **In higher education, STEM (Science, Technology, Engineering, and Mathematics) educational fields are becoming disproportionally inflated and humanities are experiencing a sort of exodus**: For several perspectives on this topic see e.g. *The End of the English Major* (Heller, 2023), *The Humanities Have Sown the Seeds of Their Own Destruction* (Harper, 2023), and *Don't Kill 'Frankenstein' With Real Frankensteins at Large* (Dowd, 2023).

[315] **"Literature is the human activity that takes the fullest and most precise account of variousness, possibility, complexity, and difficulty"**: From (Trilling, 1950).

[316] **while we should "outsource busywork to machines," we must refrain from "outsourcing our humanity to this technology, ... we should resist overreliance on tools that dull the wisdom of our own aesthetics and intellect." The AI "of the near future will supercharge our empirical abilities, but it may also dampen our curiosity. We are at risk of becoming so enamored of the synthetic worlds ... that we cease to peer into the unknown with any degree of true wonder or originality."**: From *The Coming Humanist Renaissance* (LaFrance, 2023b).

[317] **The AI *alignment* problem, which revolves around the fact that AI may perform tasks in a way that is not aligned with the intentions of human beings who deployed it...**: For several perspectives related to the *alignment* problem see e.g. (Russell S. J., 2019), (Christian, 2022), (Rosin, 2023).

[318] **popular example is paperclip maximizer, where an AI, "designed to manage production in a factory, is given the final goal of maximizing the manufacture of paperclips, and**

proceeds by converting first the Earth and then increasingly large chunks of the observable universe into paperclips.": See (Bostrom, 2014, p. 150).

[319] **AI systems demonstrate increasing levels of raw intelligence, but they don't have common sense, they don't reason, they are *idiot savants* in many respects**: A little thought experiment may be appropriate here. If we go out on a limb and invoke a remote analogy with human minds, the kind of intelligence AI is demonstrating seems akin to what neuroscientist Iain McGilchrist termed *emissary* (aspect of our minds utilizing mainly the left brain hemisphere), and is different from the entity of the *master* (using mainly the right brain hemisphere, the master is where context and meanings reside.) In McGilchrist's terminology, the emissary (left hemisphere) is "better at carrying out procedures than understanding their meaning" and is thus appointed by the master (right hemisphere) to carry out only very specific tasks (see (McGilchrist I., 2019, 2021), the citation is from (McGilchrist I., 2021, p. 336)). In this context, it is interesting to reflect on one feature associated with the brain's left hemisphere. Experiments involving patients with a severed corpus callosum (nerve fibers connecting the left and right brain hemispheres) demonstrate a curious aspect of processing associated with the left hemisphere. When a problem is presented to them in such a way that its processing must happen via the left hemisphere — and the left hemisphere cannot find a solution due to the absence of a wider context — they will completely fabricate an answer that may sound coherent and persuasive, without any regard to its factual accuracy. This phenomenon is often referred to as *confabulation*, or *left-brain interpreter*, see e.g. (Gazzaniga & Alda, 2011). One might ponder in this light the propensity of LLMs to *hallucinate*. Of course, this analogy can only go so far, and it is used here only as an attempt to tease out an insight about what is lacking in the current AI.

[320] **is only science fiction at this point**: for several perspectives on this topic see also: (Marcus & Davies, 2019), (Hutson, 2023), (Andersen, 2023), (Metz, 2023d), (Bubeck et al., 2023), (Metz, 2023e), (Metz, Weise, Grant & Isaac, 2023), and (Metz, 2023a). Also (Holt, 2023) about what some consider a "promising" technology (*Active Inference AI*, which seeks to "mimic the way biological intelligence works," based on the *Free Energy Principle*, a theory developed by neuroscientist Karl J. Friston) that

might deliver the AGI, or even ASI (Artificial Super Intelligence) as some believe, while relying on the questionable fact that "mind is what the brain does" (and nothing else.)

Gary Marcus and Ernest Davies summarize the AGI challenge in one sentence: "Getting to that level—general-purpose artificial intelligence with the flexibility of human intelligence—isn't some small step from where we are now; instead it will require an immense amount of foundational progress—not just more of the same sort of thing that's been accomplished in the last few years, but, as we will show, something entirely different" (Marcus & Davies, 2019). Indeed, we can't simply assume that because AI's "artificial neurons" are "similar enough" to biological neurons we can simply scale their number (and the number of parameters characterizing their connections), and the AGI with agency will simply "emerge." There are too many beliefs and assumptions packed in such thoughts. We know next to nothing what the intelligent agency is and how it is created.

[321] **carelessly inflicting adverse traumatic experiences on other humans**: children are most often the target – see Adverse Childhood Experiences study (The Original ACE Study, (n.d.)), (Felitti et al., 1998), (Adverse childhood experiences, 2023), (Center on the Developing Child at Harvard University: What Are ACEs?, (n.d.)).

[322] **Yann Lecun: "...*those systems are incredibly stupid...*"**: see (Greene et al., 2023), emphasis mine.

[323] **it is truly remarkable that infants somehow have the innate capacity to use reason (common sense) and rapidly learn from very limited data**: see also (Gopnik et al., 2001), (Gopnik, 2023b).

[324] **this can be only a hypothetical belief and nothing more**: For some additional thoughts about AGI, see (Rogers, 2023), (Metz, 2023d); see also note #320.

[325] **the notion that human agency, reason, purposeful intentions, and sentience are just "emerging" from the processes in the human brain is not based on anything we know, it is just a belief, a mere assumption**: See discussion in the first chapter, under the section *Fervent Beliefs and Other Roadblocks: The Promise of Science and Are We Living Up to It?*, and also in the second chapter, under sections: *Evolution, and its Pernicious*

Misunderstanding as "Survival of the Fittest", and Evolutionary Molecular Biology on the Frontiers of Science.

[326] **Not having a wider context and common sense is indeed a serious constraint. This is the main reason why we cannot allow AI to conduct many important tasks today**: An example of this can be gleaned from the 2023 interview with Gary Marcus in which he highlighted the example of Google's self-driving cars requiring additional training because they were not able to understand that it was acceptable to drive over piles of leaves on the road (such a situation was not in their training set), and also how in April 2022, when a Tesla car was "summoned" during an airplane trade show, it collided with a standing jet, as it's training set didn't contain jets. (Goldman Sachs Global Macro Research, 2023).

[327] **LLMs can generate content that is incorrect, completely made up, or even nonsensical; in other words, they can *hallucinate* unpredictably**: see e.g. (Smith, 2023), (Metz, 2023g), and (Weiser, 2023).

[328] **there is always a reminder under the ChatGPT prompt box: "ChatGPT can make mistakes. Consider checking important information."**: this is the text of the warning as of November 2023.

[329] **...constructing its output one word at a time, an LLM doesn't "know" what the next word is going to be – every time the next word in a sentence needs to be determined, the complete text constructed up to that point is fed into the input, and the probabilities are calculated for the subsequent word to generate; the word with the highest score comes next, and the whole process is repeated**: a visual illustration of this process can be found in (Collins, 2023).

[330] **"Large language models have no idea of the underlying reality that language describes. ..."**: see in (Smith, 2023)

[331] **there is so much more to our inner and outer worlds than language can describe**: As an aside here: this observation is indeed challenging the often-cited proposition that "The limits of my language mean the limits of my world" (Wittgenstein, 1922, prop. 5.6).
(And as an aside to the aside, even Wittgenstein himself seems to

have embraced such challenge, as he ends his Tractatus with the following: "My propositions are elucidatory in this way : he who understands me finally recognizes them as senseless, when he has climbed out through them, on them, over them. (He must so to speak throw away the ladder, after he has climbed up on it.) He must surmount these propositions ; then he sees the word rightly. Whereof one cannot speak, thereof one must be silent." (Wittgenstein, 1922, prop. 6.54 & 7)).

[332] **reinforcement learning with human feedback**: It should be noted however, that reinforcement learning via human feedback involves humans, and such work can be very traumatic and can affect mental health of participants significantly (especially moderators who screen the content for AI training). For several perspectives, see for example (Shaw, 2022), (Alba, 2023), (Bharucha et al., 2024), (Steiger et al, 2021), (Ahmad, 2019), and (Arsht & Etcovitch, 2018).

[333] **AI bias is a well-recognized problem:** see for example *The Ethics of Artificial Intelligence* (Bostrom, & Yudkowsky, 2014), *AI can be sexist and racist—It's time to make it fair* (Zou & Schiebinger, 2018), *Man is to computer programmer as woman is to homemaker?* (Bolukbasi et al., 2016), *Machine Bias* (Angwin et al., 2016), *A.I. Bias Caused 80% Of Black Mortgage Applicants To Be Denied* (Hale, 2021), *Amazon scraps secret AI recruiting tool that showed bias against women* (Dastin, 2018), *The Secret Ingredient of ChatGPT Is Human Advice* (Metz, 2023f), and *Algorithmic bias detection and mitigation* (Lee et al., 2019).

[334] **A lot has been said and written about the AI interpretability problem**: here is a sample: (Wolfram, 2023b), (Xiang, 2022), (Linardatos et al., 2023), (Lanier, 2023), (Porcedda, 2023), (Lipton, 2018), (Adadi & Berrada, 2018), (Haque et al., 2023), (Nyrup, 2023), (Gilpin et al., 2018), (Bender et al., 2021), (Wolfram & Fridman, 2023a), and (Wolfram & Fridman, 2023b). An interested aspect of this topic came up during the interview with Sundar Pichai, Google CEO: "… Some AI systems are teaching themselves skills that they weren't expected to have. How this happens is not well understood. For example, one Google AI program adapted, on its own, after it was prompted in the language of Bangladesh, which it was not trained to know. We discovered that with very few amounts of prompting in Bengali you can now translate all of Bengali, so now all of a sudden, we now have a

research effort where we're now trying to get to a thousand languages. ... There is an aspect of this which we call all of us in the field call it as a black box. You know you don't fully understand, and you can't quite tell why it said this or why it got wrong. We have some ideas and our ability to understand this gets better over time but that's where the state of the art is." (60 minutes, 2023b).

[335] **"tool, not a creature"**: Sam Altman often uses this phrase when talking about OpenAI's deep neural network AI. Former President Obama echoed that sentiment by saying: "the way I think about AI is as a tool, not a buddy" (Obama, 2023).

[336] **randomness value (a.k.a.** *temperature***)**: In LLMs, the *temperature* setting controls the level of randomness in the generated text. Higher *temperature* values increase the likelihood that the LLM will choose less probable (more random) words from the subset of statistically likely options for the next word in the output. If the *temperature* is set to zero, the next word is always the one with the highest statistical score. This parameter controls the balance between randomness and deterministic predictability in the LLM's responses.

[337] **It is precisely because we can't explain their behavior in a deterministic fashion, that ideas about AI being a "creature" of sorts — a "being" with "sentience" and its own "purposes" — start appearing natural to us and start to creep into AI discourse, as they already have:** Well publicized story about a Google engineer stating this, see (Levy, 2023a) and (Lemoine, 2023), is just one of many, see also (Metz, 2022). It can indeed be hard not to associate agency to AI behavior that appears very intelligent to us.

[338] **"Is there a future where the massive proliferation of robots ushers in a new era of human flourishing, not human marginalization? Where AI-driven research helps us safely harness the power of nuclear fusion in time to help avert the worst consequences of climate change? It's only natural to peer into the dark unknown and ask what could possibly go wrong. It's equally necessary—and more essentially human— to do so and envision what could possibly go right.":** From the Atlantic article *Technology Makes Us More Human* (Hoffman R., 2023a).

[339] **"Will the best in human nature please stand up"**: From *Superintelligence: Paths, Dangers, Strategies* (Bostrom, 2014, p. 319).

[340] **emphasis on *beauty*, *goodness* and *truth* traces back to both the Bhagavad Gita and Plato**: (Tegmark, 2018, p.269-270).

[341] **"today we need a cultural and philosophical revolution, … we need a human renaissance in the age of intelligent machines"**: See *The Coming Humanist Renaissance* (LaFrance, 2023b).

[342] **we will almost certainly experience the 21st-century Renaissance**: Many people in the AI community do have hopes that it is possible to create a world where AI will help everyone to be better off, as exemplified by Satya Nadella, Microsoft CEO, who said: "That means 8 billion people have abundance. That's a fantastic world to live in" (Nadella & Levy, 2023).

[343] **portrayed in movies *Blade Runner* and *Mad Max* or in literary works like Watchmen, *Brave New World* or *Nineteen Eighty-Four***: As already mentioned in the previous chapter, many dystopian stories, novels, and movies in recent decades are a powerful expressions of this sentiment. Just to name a few poignant narratives: *Watchmen* graphic novel by Alan Moore, Dave Gibbons and John Higgins, *Nineteen Eighty-Four* by George Orwell, *Brave New World* by Aldous Huxley, *The Road* by Cormac McCarthy, *Fahrenheit 451* by Ray Bradbury, *A Clockwork Orange* by Anthony Burgess, *Lord of the Flies* by William Golding, *The Hunger Games* series by Suzanne Collins, *Station Eleven* by Emily St. John Mandel, *Do Androids Dream of Electric Sheep?* by Philip K. Dick. Some of them inspired, or are made into movies, and several other films have also been created in this genre: *Blade Runner*, *The Matrix*, *Snowpiercer*, *Mad Max*, *WALL-E*, and many others.

[344] **AI can improve diagnostic accuracy**: This has already been happening in the field of radiology/imaging, see (Cowen, 2023), (Barreiro-Ares et al., 2023), also (Google DeepMind, 2022c). Google has recently developed LLM for the medical domain referred to as MED PaLM, see (Google, 2023a) and (Singhal, 2023).

[345] **… aid in drug discovery**: See e.g. (Gallagher, 2023), (Ren et al., 2023), (Google DeepMind, 2022a).

[346] **AI can easily crunch vast amounts of medical data and help with early disease detection and better treatment plans**: See e.g. (Moor et al., 2023); see also the incoming National Bureau

of Economic Research Conference Report *The Economics of Artificial Intelligence: Health Care Challenges* (Agrawal et al., 2024).

[347] **universal free healthcare for all**: Not only is this possible, but it has also been achieved (with various degrees of success) in many developed countries; see Michael Moore's documentaries *Sicko* (2007) and *Where to Invade Next* (2015) for examples.

[348] **free high-quality education with nearly equal access for all**: Again, for examples of developed countries that have accomplished the goal of providing universal free high-quality education for all, see the 2015 Michael Moore documentary *Where to Invade Next*. Sections about education in Finland and Slovenia are especially insightful.

[349] **AI model for faster and more accurate global weather forecasting**: See for example Google DeepMind's GraphCast model (Lam et al., 2023).

[350] **research project on plastic-eating enzymes that could help with pollution**: See (Google DeepMind, 2022b).

[351] **high hopes that AI will help scientists achieve a commercially viable fusion process**: See (Mullen, 2023), and also IAEA Coordinated Research Projects: AI for Accelerating Fusion R&D (IAEA, 2022).

[352] **grow (as a society) past the exploitative mindset of neoliberal economics (or its successor)**: As already mentioned, neoliberal economics is undergoing its own evolution, and some economists consider it an already broken paradigm. Be it as it may, its underlying sentiment of raw self-interest is still a powerful dehumanizing force. And considerations about a potential replacement are sobering; in the words of economist Brad DeLong, we can expect that it will likely be "mixed with surviving Neoliberal remnants, ethno-nationalist populism, authoritarian state surveillance capitalism, or out-and-our neo-fascism" (DeLong, 2022b). See also *Slouching Towards Utopia: An Economic History of the Twentieth Century* (DeLong, 2022a) and *The Rise and Fall of the Neoliberal Order* (Gerstle, 2022).

[353] **with equality and fraternity as guiding principles of humanity**: This sentiment is aligned with the ideals of *freedom*, *equality*, and *fraternity*, whose roots go back to the Age of Enlightenment. These principles powerfully emerged onto the cultural stage during the French Revolution in the 18th century (as

Liberté, Égalité, Fraternité) and have since seared themselves as guiding ideals of humanity. (Note that the concept of *fraternity* is meant in its widest significance, where it seeks to embrace meanings of brotherhood, sisterhood, and all solidarity in general.)

[354] **efforts to reverse the global bee colony collapse (bees and other insects are dying in large numbers globally and we don't know why)**: See (Google, 2019a).

[355] **If we don't end up in some form of a dystopian authoritarian society, AI will benefit us all with advances in public safety and security**: Both American and European proposed AI legislations seek to guard against this, see (EU AI Act, 2023) and (The White House, 2023).

[356] **There is a single point ...**: „es gibt einen Punkt, einen einzigen Punkt in der weiten unermeßlichen Natur- und Geisteswelt, welcher jeder Wissenschaft und daher auch jeder kausalen Betrachtung nicht nur praktisch, sondern auch logisch genommen unzugänglich ist und für immer unzugänglich bleiben wird: dieser Punkt ist das eigene Ich. — Ein winziger Punkt, wie ich sagte, im Weltenbereich, und doch wiederum eine ganze Welt, die Welt, die unser gesamtes Fühlen, Wollen und Denken umfaßt" (Planck, 1923, p.45).

[357] **Some Western philosophers and scientists espouse this belief and cloak it in scientific language. It boldly proclaims that "the human self is an illusion"**: See also note #34.

[358] **belief that the "human self is an illusion," espoused by some Western philosophers and scientists, should not be confused with the notion of "non-self" (anattā/anātman) in Buddhism, as they represent different concepts, even though there were philosophical attempts to consolidate them in the past**: See an insightful treatment of this topic in *Analytical Buddhism: The Two-tiered Illusion of Self* (Albahari, 2006).

[359] **Buddha himself declined to comment on the notion that the "individual self" simply does not exist ... On the other hand, the individual, still "bounded," and not fully liberated self is simply referred to as "non-self" (anattā/anātman)**: In Cula-Malunkyovada Sutta (The Shorter Instructions to Malunkya, MN63), Buddha states that the questions about the nature of the universe, the existence of the self, and life after death are "undeclared" by him; he considered them

unimportant for the spiritual progress and "not fundamental to the holy life," monks were supposed to focus unwaveringly on the path leading to "disenchantment, dispassion, cessation, calming, direct knowledge, self-awakening, Unbinding." In Acintita Sutta (Unconjecturable, AN4.77), Buddha speaks about topics that are "unconjecturable", and their pondering can only lead to frustration, i.e "madness & vexation." In Anuradha Sutta (To Anuradha, SN22.86), Buddha, in a style of Socratic discourse demonstrates that speculations on the existence of the self are not beneficial for the path dedicated to the cessation of suffering "it is only suffering that I describe, and the cessation of suffering." In the Anatta-lakkhana Sutta (The Discourse on the Not-self Characteristic, SN22.59), Buddha talks about the "self" and "non-self", and in this sutta we see that what Buddha considers "self" (attā/ātman) is unbounded, free to take any form, and it does not lend itself to affliction or disease: "[Physical] form, monks, is **not self**. If form were the **self**, this form would not lend itself to dis-ease. It would be possible [to say] with regard to form, 'Let this form be thus. Let this form not be thus.' But precisely because form is **not self**, form lends itself to dis-ease. And it is not possible [to say] with regard to form, 'Let this form be thus. Let this form not be thus' and consequently "every form is to be seen as it actually is with right discernment as: 'This is not mine. This is **not my self**. This is **not what I am**'." See also a detailed discussion of this topic in *An Introduction to Buddhism* (Harvey, 2013) and *Analytical Buddhism* (Albahari, 2006) for example. Another point of view related to the interpretation of anattā/anātman as the "nonexistence of self" or "entity that does not exist" is reflected in the question Aldous Huxley poses in *The Perennial Philosophy* (1945, p. 9): "why the Tathagata and the Bodhisattvas display an infinite charity towards beings that do not really exist?"
(Note: all suttas referenced here can be found on the Access to Insight website at www.accesstoinsight.org/tipitaka).

[360] **sometimes it is even claimed — most often unjustifiably — that these disciplines are not "evidence-based"**: See note #214 for details regarding the greatly misleading notions around the so-called "evidence-based" psychotherapies.

[361] **"The best minds of my generation are thinking about how to make people click ads. That sucks."**: See (Vance, 2011).

[362] *Forty-Four Juvenile Thieves: Their Characters and Home-Life*: (Bowlby, 1944).

[363] **Starting with his contributions in the 1950s (which continued into the 1980s)**: Most notably *Attachment and Loss* trilogy: (Bowlby, 1969), (Bowlby, 1972), and (Bowlby, 1980).

[364] **Attachment theory increasingly gained prominence, due in part to its further development and empirical validation accomplished by Mary Ainsworth**: Among other contributions, Ainsworth and her colleagues developed the *Strange Situation* empirical test (Ainsworth et al., 1978), "a 20-minute laboratory test where the child is exposed to two 'miniscule separations' of a maximum of 3 minutes each. Mary Ainsworth and her colleagues found that the majority of middle-class one-year-old children respond to the mother with proximity seeking and relief at reunion (securely attached infants) but about 25 percent respond with subtle signs of indifference (anxious avoidantly attached infants) and a further 15 percent respond with proximity seeking but little relief at reunion (anxious resistantly attached infants) ... [and it was] recognized that separation (physical absence of the mother) was not the key to understanding the infant's response to the Strange Situation. It was the infant's appraisal or evaluation of the mother's departure in the context of her expected behavior that accounts for the infant's response ... it is not the mother's absence but rather her apparently arbitrary behavior that accounts for the child's distress and the relief occasioned by her return." (Fonagy, 2001, p. 11).

[365] **"attachment theory views the sense of self as essentially relational"**: From *Self-agency in Psychotherapy* (Knox, 2011).

[366] **Adult Attachment Interview ... has demonstrated that it can reliably predict the infant's attachment style based on the caregiver's AAI narrative, even before the birth of the infant**: (Hesse, 1999).

[367] **"the parent's capacity to adopt the intentional stance towards a not-yet-intentional infant..."**: (Fonagy, 2001, p. 27).

[368] **Sharon Olds's poem *Bathing the Newborn***: In *The Dead and the Living: Poems* (Olds, 1984).

[369] **Attachment bonds also have their significance in relationships beyond infancy. An affectional bond becomes**

an attachment bond whenever the individual seeks security or comfort from the relationship: See (Ainsworth, 1989) and (Fonagy, 2001).

370 **There is plenty of literature on attachment, a small sample is listed in the endnotes:** There are several popular books on attachment theory and parenting, here is a small sample: (Nicholson & Parker, 2013), (Sears & Sears, 2001), (Eijgenraam, 2017), and (Newton, 2008). For more detailed information, the *Handbook of Attachment: Theory, Research, and Clinical Applications* (Cassidy & Shaver, 2018) is considered a reference handbook on attachment. A comprehensive presentation of attachment theory in the context of mentalization and child psychotherapy can be found in *Enhancing Attachment and Reflective Parenting in Clinical Practice* (Slade et al., 2023). Peter Fonagy's book *Attachment Theory and Psychoanalysis* (2001) and Morris N. Eagle's book *Attachment and Psychoanalysis: Theory, Research, and Clinical Implications* (Eagle, 2013) provide an in-depth overview and integration of the fields of attachment and psychoanalysis.

371 **four distinct stages of early self formation: "1) the sense of *emergent self* (0–2 months) involves the process of the self coming into being and forming initial connections; 2) the sense of *core self* and the domain of core relatedness (2–6 months) are based on the single organizing subjective perspective and a coherent physical self; 3) the sense of *subjective self* and the domain of intersubjective relatedness (7–15 months) emerge with the discovery of subjective mental states beyond physical events; and 4) the sense of *verbal self* forms after 15 months.":** See (Fonagy, 2001, p. 117-118).

372 **"some notion of consciousness" must be present very early on:** See (Stern, 2000).

373 **he describes human relationships as "the stuff of all human connectedness, intimacy, and trust throughout development, and sees the ability to engage in them as essential to mental health.":** See (Fonagy, 2001, p. 118).

374 **Stern's books *The Interpersonal World of the Infant, Diary of a Baby,* and *The Present Moment in Psychotherapy and Everyday Life*:** (Stern, 1985 & 2000), (Stern, 1998), and (Stern, 2004).

375 **theory of mind**: In this chapter, we use the term "theory of mind" in its wider sense, as it is used in philosophy and science. This should be differentiated from the "theory of mind" or "ToM" as used in psychology and cognitive science, where it refers to the ability to attribute mental states — like thoughts, emotions, intents, desires, beliefs, knowledge, etc — to oneself and others, and to understand that others have beliefs, desires, and intentions different from one's own.

376 **Many consider [psychoanalysis] to be "the most disciplined and dedicated method ever devised for the study of human subjectivity"**: See (Mitchell S. A., 2000, p. x).

377 **What was known as Freudian psychoanalysis transitioned into what is often called psychodynamic psychotherapy today. Both its theory of mind and therapeutic practice incorporated many aspects from relational models like attachment theory, object relations, intersubjectivity, and self-psychology**: See e.g. *Relational Concepts in Psychoanalysis: An Integration* (Mitchell S. A., 1988). Peter Fonagy writes in 2001: "Only in the last decade and a half, as the psychoanalytic mainstream appeared to almost have evaporated in the United States, have the contributions of the interpersonalist tradition have come to be acknowledged. The idea of mutual participation in the transference has become part of the general psychoanalytic ethos. The ideal psychoanalyst ceased to be a neutral observer but rather the patient's collaborator engaged in a continuous negotiation about truth and reality—the conversation with the other person being the only way of escaping preconception." (Fonagy, 2001, p. 125)

378 **"The *self* is alive and well, and living in relational psychoanalysis ... it continues to occupy a central role ...[and it] has survived the premature reports of its demise."**: (Reis, 2005).

379 **Self psychology, a theory introduced by Heinz Kohut in the 1970s**: See e.g. (Kohut, 1971, 1977).

380 **It is Kohut's work that "broke the iron grip of ego psychology by forcing psychoanalysts to think in less mechanistic terms, in terms of selfhood rather than psychological function"**: (Fonagy, 2001, p. 108).

381 **Kohut considers the human self to be the "center of individual's psychological universe, ... the center of initiative**

and the recipient of impressions," and the locus of all relationships: See (Kohut 1977).

[382] Self is not a mere representation but is itself the active agent: See (Greenberg & Mitchell S.A., 1983).

[383] "we cannot, by introspection or empathy, penetrate to the self per se... the self is not a concept of an abstract science": See (Kohut 1977, p. 310-311)

[384] theories of Ronald Fairbairn: See (Fairbairn, 1954).

[385] similar to the interpersonal school of psychoanalysis and the theories of Ronald Fairbairn and Donald Winnicott, both central figures in the development of the object relations theory: See also (Greenberg & Mitchell S.A., 1983).

[386] self psychology considers parental attunement and the ability to empathize with their children as essential for their development: See also (Baker & Baker, 1987).

[387] Empathy has to do with the "recognition of the other" ...: See also (Kohut et al., 1984).

[388] "In Kohut's view of mature relationships there is a predominance of mutuality in exchanges of empathy and self-object function, while the distinctive ambitions, goals, and ideals of each partner are afforded recognition by the other. The major goal of psychoanalysis ... is to open up mutual paths of empathy between self and other, and empathy undeniably involves recognition of the one toward whom it flows": See (Teicholz, 2001, p. 28).

[389] The relationship itself is the goal and the true substance of the interaction: Fairbairn was among the first to place relationality at the center of motivation, see e.g. (Fairbairn 1954).

[390] Donald Winnicott's concept of *potential space*: See e.g. *Playing and Reality* (Winnicott, 1971a) and *The Matrix of the Mind* (Ogden, 1993), and, including the wider field of topics on Winnicott, *The Winnicott Tradition: Lines of Development-Evolution of Theory and Practice over the Decades* (Spelman & Thomson-Salo, 2015).

[391] In his 1993 work *The Matrix of the Mind*: (Ogden, 1993).

[392] [*Potential space*] is the "Spielraum" of the human self: From *Negotiating Potential Space: Illusion, Play, Metaphor, and the Subjunctive* (Pizer, 1996).

[393] **Ogden uses the term dialectic:** Dialectic is used here in its generic meaning, representing two poles and a mediating process (relationship, tension, unification) between them. It is only indirectly related to the term dialectic as used in Platonic doctrine, and as described in the second part of this work. The more profound meaning of dialectic, as outlined in Platonic doctrine, represents a mediating process — accomplished by the intimate activity and efforts of human reason — aimed at the spiritual ascent of the human self. Through it, the individual human self can ascend from 1) experiencing reality in an isolating, limiting ("bounded" in Buddha's words), crude, dark, and static world in the allegorical cave of the "physical" world, to 2) experiencing the reality of the world of foundational ideas in the unbounded dynamic world of the universal mind. By means of Platonic dialectic, the human self can fully comprehend and commune, as it were, with foundational ideas (like those of truth, beauty, and goodness) in the fullness of their dynamic existence.

[394] **"The dialectical process is centrally involved in the creation of subjectivity…":** From (Ogden, 1993).

[395] **"Fantasy cut adrift from reality becomes irrelevant and threatening. Reality cut adrift from fantasy becomes vapid and empty…":** (Mitchell S. A., 2000).

[396] **In potential space… Perception renders fantasy relatively safe; fantasy renders perception relatively meaningful":** (Mitchell S. A., 2000).

[397] **Further exploration and application of phenomena related to potential space in psychotherapy extend beyond the scope of this work, and some additional references are provided in the endnotes:** More leads can be explored in (Ogden, 1997, 2001). It is generally the field of relational psychoanalysis and certain areas of developmental psychology (focusing on relational development and attachment) that study mental phenomena by utilizing this framework.

[398] **Intersubjectivity can be defined as the interrelating of two or more selves or subjectivities. It can also be conceptualized as a shared psychological space (or field) where the relating selves co-exist and co-experience):** Terms *intersubjective field* (e.g. Frie & Reis, 2001) and *intersubjective matrix* (e.g. Stern, 2004) are also in use.

[399] One way to approach the modern idea of intersubjectivity is to grasp it through the concept of the *present moment* as introduced by Daniel N. Stern: (Stern, 2004)

[400] this statement does not seek to devalue emotion, which is a power in its own right, see e.g. the compendium *The Healing Power of Emotion*: Edited by Diana Fosha, Daniel J. Siegel, and Marion F. Solomon; *The Healing Power of Emotion: Affective Neuroscience, Development & Clinical Practice* (Fosha et al., 2009)

[401] This has been understood since at least the time of Adam Smith, who identified empathy as crucial for moral judgment: See *The Theory of Moral Sentiments* (Smith, 1759).

[402] Even David Hume acknowledged that there exists "some spark of friendship for human kind" and impelled that it must "direct the determinations of our mind": In *An Enquiry Concerning the Principles of Morals* (Hume, 1751).

[403] Psychologist Paul Bloom even states that he is "against empathy," in favor of "rational compassion.": In *Against Empathy* (Bloom, 2016).

[404] Steven Pinker (grudgingly) appreciates empathy just enough to give it a high rank as one of the four "better angels of human nature" (the other three being self-control, moral sense, and reason): (Pinker, 2011).

[405] the intersubjective-relational theories were at the forefront of the "relational turn," the paradigmatic shift in psychoanalysis, which placed human relationality at the center of the field: See e.g. (Mitchell S. A., 1988), (Fonagy , 2001), (Grotstein, 1999).

[406] a notable example is what can be termed *interpersonal neurobiology...* : This is exemplified by works like Daniel Siegel's *The Developing Mind* (Siegel, 2012), *From Neurons to Neighborhoods: The Science of Early Child Development* (National Research Council (U.S.) & Institute of Medicine, 2000), and Allan Shore's *The Science of The Art of Psychotherapy* and *Affect Regulation and the Origin of the Self.*.

[407] "intersubjectivity concerns the ability to share in another's lived experience": (Stern, 2005).

[408] In his work *The Present Moment in Psychotherapy and Everyday Life*, Daniel Stern considers psychotherapy in terms

of intersubjectivity, which he considers a "major motivational system essential for human survival – akin to attachment or sex": (Stern, 2004, p. xvi)

[409] "the concept of an isolated individual mind is a theoretical fiction": (Stolorow & Atwood, 1991).

[410] "if we developed in a forest on our own, without human contact ... we would have consciousness, but he wouldn't be aware of that consciousness, we wouldn't be able to reflect on it, we wouldn't be able to reflect on ourselves or on others": (Fonagy, 2016a).

[411] "Why is the centrality of the relational so easy to miss...": (Mitchell S. A., 2000, p. x-xii)

[412] In the words of Ralph Waldo Emerson: "There is one mind common to all individual men...": (Emerson, 1841; *Essays, First Series, History*)

[413] "In short, our mental life is cocreated...": (Stern, 2004).

[414] theory that explicates the links between processes of affect regulation, mentalization, and development of the self: See e.g. (Fonagy et al., 2005) which is the source for quotations in this section; see also (Fonagy, 2001) and (Fonagy et al., 2007).

[415] Allan Shore focused on the same process from the neurobiological perspective: See e.g. *Affect Regulation and the Origin of the Self* (Shore, 1994)

[416] *Mentalization-based therapy* (MBT), developed by Anthony Bateman and Peter Fonagy, is closely related to this framework, and has proven its clinical effectiveness in multiple studies, ...: See e.g. *Handbook of Mentalizing in Mental Health Practice* (Bateman & Fonagy, 2019), *Mentalizing in Psychotherapy* (Sharp & Bevington, 2022), also (Drozek et al., 2023), (Malda-Castillo et al., 2019), and (Bateman & Fonagy, 2004).

[417] to develop and embed mental representations: In mentalization theory, they are also referred to as *second-order representations* or *symbolic representations*, sometimes also called "language for thoughts and feelings." Such representations are created to represent the *primary subjective states* (i.e. *primary psychological states*), such as feelings of joy, anger, annoyance, etc, in human minds. They enable us to, for example, know that we are angry if we are angry. If a person could experience only the primary

subjective states, without the ability to represent them symbolically in "language for thoughts and feelings," such experiences would be too direct and immediate, and there would be no possibility to modulate and regulate them, and no possibility to rationally comprehend or consider them.

[418] ***Still Face Experiment***: See video presentation at https://youtu.be/vmE3NfB_HhE?si=GLX9RXddmnHFlJqM (UMass Boston, 2010), and also (Tronick, 2007), (Tronick et al., 1978), (Goldman, 2010), and (Tronick et al., 1975).

[419] **often referred to as *reflective parenting* and it requires that a parent exercises their "capacity to reflect on or mentalize the child's experience" as it unfolds, "to envision or imagine the child's thoughts, feelings, desires, and intentions"**: This is described in great detail in *Enhancing Attachment and Reflective Parenting in Clinical Practice* (Slade et al., 2023). See also a short video (Fonagy, 2016b).

[420] **An example of healthy and attuned support for a crying infant's affect regulation would be to hold them and convey a soothing message**: The recommendation often given to parents, to let their infant "cry it out" to avoid "spoiling" them and to help them grow "stronger" or "tougher," is misinformed and scientifically outdated. Instead, parents can nurture their child's capacity for affect regulation and mentalization in a healthy way, by holding them and conveying the message with the meaning similar to "your pain matters to me, I am here for you, and I will help you," which the child can represent and internalize as part of their sense of self. On the other hand, if a parent consistently ignores a crying infant until they cease to cry, the child may internalize the belief similar to "I should ignore my pain, repress my feelings, or otherwise I am not wanted." In general, a child whose unfolding sense of self is supported in a healthier way, will stop crying and become "stronger" sooner (not unlike a young seedling plant that is well protected early on, rather than being immediately exposed to harsh conditions). For those interested in learning more about nurturing parenting approaches, a wealth of information is available, including literature on attachment parenting (see note #373 as a starting point.)

[421] **Donald Winnicott described the attitude of a caregiver with the term *good enough mothering*:** See e.g. *The Maturational*

Processes and the Facilitating Environment (Winnicott, 1965b), *Playing and Reality* (Winnicott, 1971a); also work by Beatrice Beebe, Frank Lachmann, Phyllis Cohen and collaborators, for example *The Mother-Infant Interaction Picture Book: Origins of Attachment* (Beebe et al., 2016) and *The Origins of Attachment* (Beebe & Lachmann, 2014), among others.

[422] **holding environment:** See *The Maturational Processes and the Facilitating Environment* (Winnicott, 1965b).

[423] **It is crucial during the first seven years of a child's life, and it is truly fundamental during the first three years of a child's life:** In the words of Gabor Mate, "the first seven years are crucial … the first three years are the nub of it, if you don't get the first three years right, you will be practicing remedy of parenting for decades." Numerous disciplines that study child development unanimously support the finding that the years 0-3 are fundamental in human development. There are many parenting resources on this topic, see e.g. *ZERO to THREE* at https://www.zerotothree.org/ and *Center on the Developing Child at Harvard University* at https://developingchild.harvard.edu/science/key-concepts/.

[424] **"experience of affect is the bud from which eventually mentalization can grow, but only in the context of at least one continuing, safe attachment relationship. The parent who cannot think about the child's mental experience deprives him of a core self-structure that he needs to build a viable sense of himself":** See (Fonagy, 2005).

[425] **In the candid words of Peter Fonagy, this happens when "I do not see the world from her point of view. At all. All I see is my perspective and my perception of her … this just doesn't lead to anywhere good…":** (Fonagy, 2017a).

[426] **Based on the insights from the mentalization theory…:** See (Fonagy, 2018).

[427] **René Spitz, in the 1940s did a striking study where he compared mortality rates of the kids who were brought up in prison with their mothers and those who were on their own in hospitals, and irrespective of physical illness, death rates in hospitals was 37%, and in prison all children thrived:** See (Spitz, 1945, 1946), and (Lang et al., 2020).

[428] **"mentalization is not something that exists within an individual…"**: See (Fonagy, 2017b).

[429] **"mentalization is not something that exists within an individual…"**: See (Fonagy, 2017b).

[430] **Wolfram's *Parzival***: There are several English translations, see e.g (von Eschenbach & Hatto, 1980).

[431] **Freud termed them *superego***: See also note #123.

[432] **as Alison Gopnik calls it, "a little saintliness"**: See note #134 (the quote is from Gopnik, 2009, p. 242)).

[433] **"loving, pure in heart, humble in spirit"**: A repeating motive from Aldoux Huxley's *The Perennial Philosophy* (1969) in which he reviews many disciplines associated with the cultivation of intimate processes of the human mind, including their meditative and contemplative practices, and other methods. His overview includes Zen Buddhism, Hinduism, Taoism, Christian mysticism, and Islam Sufi traditions.

[434] **The term mind science is not widely used**: As a side note, from a philological or linguistic perspective, the German term *Geisteswissenschaft* — literally translating to "spirit science" — bears a close resemblance to the term *mind science*. Historically, it has indeed been used to encompass broader concepts of spirit and mind. However, in more recent times, the scope of this term was reduced, and it now mainly represents the disciplines commonly recognized as "humanities" or "social sciences."

[435] **i.e. whether it can earn the label "evidence-based"**: See also note #214.

[436] **they must be well trained, experienced**: Many countries presently have strict requirements for the licensing of clinicians. In most cases, clinicians must complete graduate-level training and accumulate a significant number of supervised clinical hours before they can practice independently. Even then, many clinicians both seek and offer supervising relationships, participate in processing groups where clinical material is discussed among professionals, and pursue continuing education.

[437] **another way to think about the role of mind science is to think of it as a qualitative study of dynamic phenomena of higher order, compared to "hard science's" study of lower order phenomena in the physical body**: We have similar

higher/lower level relationships between domains in other disciplines too. For example, for computer scientists and electronic engineers developing a new computer processor, the right level to focus on would be electronic circuitry, and they spend most of their time considering and talking about wires, capacitors, resistors, transistors, and the like. They might utilize low-level programming via machine code or assembly language as well. On the other hand, for computer scientists and software engineers developing a new software application that is intended to run on that new processor, the science looks rather different, they use higher-level abstractions and talk about things like software architecture, algorithms, data patterns, objects with their attributes and methods, and the like. They use high-level programming languages like Python, C, or Go to implement software applications. At their level, they cannot consider lower-level phenomena like wires and transistors. Yes, it would be theoretically possible in principle, but rather foolish to try to fix a bug in a software application by quickly manipulating wires in the low-level hardware circuitry. Similarly, in the science of mind outlined in the main text, even if we assumed that the "mind is what the brain does," as Marvin Minsky proposed, (which we obviously don't assume in this work, even if we acknowledge the role of the brain) we can't focus on low-level phenomena like action potentials in neurons in the brain, cell metabolism, chemical pathways, and the like, if we are intent on understanding human self and agency and affecting changes in patterns of thought, feelings, and behavior. For this reason, it is now obvious why, for example, the outdated concept of "depression is just a chemical imbalance in the brain" is useless; stating this is akin to stating that a software application doesn't work properly because of an imbalance of electrons in the wires around the processor. Technically speaking, such a statement is true, but it is nonetheless useless. All this does not mean that we should be uniformed and ignorant of physical phenomena when considering the phenomena unfolding in the human mind (in a similar way that a software engineer cannot be ignorant of the limits of the computer hardware they use.)

[438] **Ghosts in the Nursery**: See (Fraiberg et al., 1975), and also *Looking Back to Light the Path Forward: Ghosts In the Nursery Revisited* (Slade, 2023).

[439] **Arietta Slade states that "Fraiberg's work was revolutionary":** (Slade et al., 2023).

[440] **Alicia Lieberman says "from Selma Fraiberg I learned about healing":** (Lieberman, 2018).

[441] **Peter Fonagy calls it "paradigmatic":** (Fonagy, 2001).

[442] *Child-Parent Psychotherapy (CPP)*: Child-Parent Psychotherapy, or CPP, today covers ages 0-5, it is described in works such as the 2008 book by Alicia F. Lieberman and Patricia Van Horn *Psychotherapy with Infants and Young Children: Repairing the Effects of Stress and Trauma on Early Attachment* (Lieberman & Van Horn, 2008).

[443] *Minding the Baby* **(MTB) approach:** Minding the Baby approach is described in the 2023 book Arietta Slade, Lois S. Sadler, Tanika Eaves, and Denise L. Webb, *Enhancing Attachment and Reflective Parenting in Clinical Practice* (Slade et al, 2023).

[444] **The objectivity and rigor necessary in this domain — rooted in a therapist's mind — can only be achieved by many years of thorough and conscientious training:** See also note #439.

[445] **metaphor of "ghosts":** It can be argued that the concept/metaphor of "ghosts" — and its treatment as unconscious and unrepresented/unsymbolized areas of powerful affect in human minds — is among the most important paradigms in mental health. This is recognized in the field; for example, Arietta Slade considers the passage describing "ghosts" in Fraiberg's paper *Ghosts in the Nursery*, as "arguably the most significant in the entire infant mental health literature" (Slade et al., 2023).

[446] **"In every nursery there are ghosts…":** From (Fraiberg et al., 1975).

[447] *holding environment*: See *The Maturational Processes and the Facilitating Environment* (Winnicott, 1965b).

[448] **Detailed descriptions and examples can be found in the literature:** See e.g. *Enhancing Attachment and Reflective Parenting in Clinical Practice* (Slade et al., 2023), *Psychotherapy with Infants and Young Children* (Lieberman & Van Horn, 2008), and of course the original description in the paper *Ghosts in the Nursery* (Fraiberg et al., 1975).

[449] **"The evidence from diverse studies and schools of psychology converges and has led to this consensus: the**

human capacity to love and to make enduring partnerships in love is formed in infancy ... When a baby has been deprived of a mother or a mother substitute through adversity or disaster or the indifference of his society, we have found that the later capacity of that child to commit himself to love, to partners in love, and to the human community will be diminished or depleted: From *Every Child's Birthright: In Defense of Mothering.* (Fraiberg, 1978).

[450] ...especially pronounced in the US, where support for parental leave and child care for age 0-3 is almost non-existent: See (Chzhen et al., 2019), (Francis et al., 2021), (Ferrante, 2019), and (Vu, 2023). Also Michael Moore's 2015 documentary *Where To Invade Next.*

[451] at the time of this writing, more than 13 million children face hunger in the US: See e.g. (Luscombe, 2023) and (Bureau U. C., 2023a, 2023b).

[452] Nordic countries: For more information about support for parenting and education in Nordic countries, see note #219.

[453] "infrastructure of care": This term is not new, it has been considered in the work of Nancy Folbre, Ai-jen Poo, and others. See e.g. (Folbre, 2001), (Poo, 2015), and interview with Ai-jen Poo on *The Ezra Klein Show* (Poo & Klein, 2021).

[454] "care penalty": The term used by economist and philosopher Nancy Folbre in her 2001 book *The Invisible Heart: Economics and Family Values* (Folbre, 2001).

Made in the USA
Monee, IL
07 February 2024

53092718R00246